RECENT ADVANCES IN GALLATE RESEARCH

CHEMISTRY RESEARCH
AND APPLICATIONS

Additional books in this series can be found on Nova's website
under the Series tab.

Additional e-books in this series can be found on Nova's website
under the e-book tab.

CHEMISTRY RESEARCH AND APPLICATIONS

RECENT ADVANCES IN GALLATE RESEARCH

AMANDA L. KINSEY
EDITOR

New York

For permission to use material from this book please contact us:
Telephone 631-231-7269; Fax 631-231-8175
Web Site: http://www.novapublishers.com

NOTICE TO THE READER

The Publisher has taken reasonable care in the preparation of this book, but makes no expressed or implied warranty of any kind and assumes no responsibility for any errors or omissions. No liability is assumed for incidental or consequential damages in connection with or arising out of information contained in this book. The Publisher shall not be liable for any special, consequential, or exemplary damages resulting, in whole or in part, from the readers' use of, or reliance upon, this material. Any parts of this book based on government reports are so indicated and copyright is claimed for those parts to the extent applicable to compilations of such works.

Independent verification should be sought for any data, advice or recommendations contained in this book. In addition, no responsibility is assumed by the publisher for any injury and/or damage to persons or property arising from any methods, products, instructions, ideas or otherwise contained in this publication.

This publication is designed to provide accurate and authoritative information with regard to the subject matter covered herein. It is sold with the clear understanding that the Publisher is not engaged in rendering legal or any other professional services. If legal or any other expert assistance is required, the services of a competent person should be sought. FROM A DECLARATION OF PARTICIPANTS JOINTLY ADOPTED BY A COMMITTEE OF THE AMERICAN BAR ASSOCIATION AND A COMMITTEE OF PUBLISHERS.

Additional color graphics may be available in the e-book version of this book.

Library of Congress Cataloging-in-Publication Data

ISBN: 978-1-63117-071-3

Published by Nova Science Publishers, Inc. † *New York*

Contents

Preface

Drug resistance continues to be a major problem in the effective treatment of many diseases. Resistance to chemotherapy, whether intrinsic or extrinsic, is the result of at least three well defined mechanisms: prevention of the interaction of drug with the target decreased intracellular concentration of the drug due to an increased efflux or a decreased influx, and enzymatic modification or destruction of the drug. With the advancement in technology, the molecular mechanisms of drug resistance have been unravelling at a rapid rate. This book is a timely review of such advances in drug resistance research. The nine chapters of this book, written by a group of clinicians and scientists, elegantly summarises recent advances in our understanding of this important clinical problem with emphasis on cisplatin, fibroblasts, natural compounds, erythropoiesis-stimulating agents, prostate cancer and kidney cancer. This book will be an important contribution to science, and an invaluable tool for researchers who are interested in drug resistance.

Chapter I – Flavonoids represent the most common and widely distributed group of plant phenolics, and can be further divided into classes including mainly flavones, flavonols, flavan-3-ols, anthocyanins, flavanones and isoflavones. Flavan-3-ols are the most structurally complex subclass of flavonoids, ranging from the simple monomers (+) catechin and its isomers (-)-epicatechin, which can be hydroxylated to form gallocatechins (gallocatechin and epigallocatechin) and also undergo esterification with gallic acid (epicatechin-3-O-gallate and epigallocatechin-3-O-gallate), through to complex structures including the oligomeric and polymeric proanthocyanidins, which are also known as condensed tannins. Flavan-3-ols and their derivatives are a class of phenolic compounds found in green tea leaves, chocolate, grape and grape seeds, having several healthy properties. Epidemiological studies suggest that long term consumption of diets rich in nongallated and gallated flavan-3-ols offers protection against development of cancers, cardiovascular disease, diabetes, osteoporosis and neurodegenerative diseases. Therefore, the objective of the present review is to provide a perspective on the health benefits associated with food consumption rich in nongallated and gallated flavan-3-ols through critical analysis of the available literature on the chemistry, bioavailability and biological potential of these bioactive compounds and the current level of scientific evidence for these health benefits.

Chapter II – The unfolded protein response (UPR) is an evolutionarily conserved mechanism that activates both pro-apoptotic and survival pathways to allow eukaryotic cells to adapt to endoplasmic reticulum (ER) stress. A major UPR protective response is the induction of the ER chaperone protein GRP78/BIP, which is required for the proper folding and assembly of membrane and secretory proteins. GRP78 is up-regulated under stress conditions, such as glucose deprivation, hypoxia, or the presence of toxic agents. Overexpression of GRP78 is prominent in a wide variety of tumors and protects tumor cells against ER stress as well as a range of cancer therapeutic agents. (-)-Epigallocatechin-3-gallate (EGCG), the major component of green tea, has been found to directly interact with GRP78 at the ATP-binding site of protein and regulates its function by competing with ATP binding, resulting in the inhibition of ATPase activity. EGCG binding results in the conversion of GRP78 from its active monomer to the inactive form. Some studies have reported that EGCG has anticancer effects on various tumors, however, the exact molecular mechanism of this kind of activity is not well understood. Improving the knowledge about the implications of EGCG/GRP78 interaction in cancer cells could throw light on EGCG antitumor properties and provide a new rationale for its therapeutic use.

Chapter III – Oxidative stress resulting from increased reactive oxygen species (ROS) can overwhelm cellular antioxidant defenses and cause significant damage to macromolecules such as proteins, lipids, DNA and RNA, resulting in compromised cellular function. Oxidative damage is a critical determinant for several disease pathologies. It exacerbates inflammatory responses, and damages amongst others, the respiratory, neurological and the cardiovascular systems, which, cumulatively then affect age-related physiological changes. Further, oxidative damage is the leading cause of cancer in aging. In tumor cells, altered redox balance and ROS-mediated signaling pathways trigger cellular proliferation in the context of dysregulated cell replication genes. Hence, the argument for stemming oxidative damage to our cells is indisputable. Nature's potent antioxidants, polyphenols, are biologically active plant-based molecules that can aid in the restoration of cellular redox potential due to their ability to accept and release electrons. Also, polyphenols indirectly reduce the burden of oxidative stress by altering cellular signaling pathways. The urgency to reduce oxidative stress-induced disease pathologies, and thereby their psychological and socioeconomic consequences, has accelerated research on developing polyphenols as natural therapeutic agents. Additionally, acquired drug resistance and toxicity to chemotherapeutic agents has necessitated the development of novel therapeutic strategies to selectively target cancer cells. This review will provide a summary of the research advancements suggesting that gallate polyphenols such as methyl gallate and EGCG may be responsible for improved outcomes in cardiovascular function, toxicity associated with carcinogenesis, and cognitive decline in aging, amongst other health benefits.

Chapter IV – Gallic acid is a phenolic acid also known as 3,4,5-trihydroxybenzoic acid. It is found free in plants but also as salts and esters. The last kind of compounds is named gallates. They are widespread in nature and are consumed as part of the human diet in significant amounts. Gallates show an interesting biological profile and they have significant antiinflammatory activity in preclinical assays. This review summarizes the current knowledge on the effects of gallic acid and gallates on inflammation, with a focus on the mechanisms involved. In this sense, different molecular and cellular targets and radical scavenging properties are also analyzed. On the other hand since few clinical trials have described the relevance of gallates in human diseases related to inflammatory process, the need for further controlled intervention trials will be discussed.

Chapter V – Lanthanum gallate doped with strontium or simultaneously with strontium and magnesium, the latter entering the sites of gallium in perovskite structure, opened a wide series of oxygen ionic conductors promising for energy saving technologies in the so called Solid Oxide Fuel Cells (SOFC). However, introduction of bivalent elements into lanthanum gallate, which creates vacancies in the oxygen sublattice and thus triggers the oxygen conductivity of the material, makes it rather instable to decomposition, especially at high temperatures. This circumstance made the scientists to search for some additions stabilizing perovskite structure. Such stabilizers were found to be transition elements substituting for gallium. Taking into account the fact that doped lanthanum galates are rather diluted solid solutions we carried out a thorough study of magnetic susceptibility of a wide range of solid solutions by magnetic dilution method. This method allows the state of magnetic atoms and the exchange interactions in the structure to be determined. We varied the transition elements (Cr, Mn, Fe, Co, Ni), the ratio M:Sr(Mg), changed Sr for Ca and Ba as the doping elements, and compared the results with the magnetic dilution of transition elements in $LaGaO_3$ and $LaAlO_3$ matrices.

Two main features were found on studying the magnetic susceptibility of a large amount of solid solutions. The first is that no oxidation of transition elements was observed upon heterovalent doping of lanthanum gallate. In the case of cobalt and nickel heterovalent doping results in the changes in the spin states. The second and the most significant feature lies in the clustering of paramagnetic atoms. Clustering is stronger in lanthanum gallate than in aluminate. Upon heterovalent doping with Ca and Ba clustering increases compared to strontium doped lanthanum gallate. Introduction of magnesium into gallium sites increases clustering to the extent that the clusters behave as superparamagnetics and the susceptibility in some cases becomes field dependent. The clusters in heterovalent doped lanthanum gallate include transition element atoms, bivalent elements and vacancies in the oxygen sublattice accompanying them. The sizes of clusters and the exchange interactions in them exert an important and ambiguous impact on electrophysical properties of doped lanthanum gallate, which must be taken into account for optimization of the composition of electron-ionic conductors.

Chapter VI - Gallates, salt or ester of gallic acid (GA) are found widely in plants as phenolic compounds. Many forms of gallates are available in plants namely, epigallocatechin-3-gallate (EGCG), epicatechin-3-gallate (ECG), epigallocatechin (EGC), GA, ethyl gallate (EG), methyl gallate, propyl gallate, gallocatechin and theaflavin-3-gallate to name a few. Among these compounds, EGCG, GA and EG have attracted many researchers around the world for their antioxidant, anticancer, antidiabetic, anti-arthritic, anti-HIV and neuroprotective properties. Food sources of each compound vary from fruits, nuts, green tea and carob flour for EGCG; blueberries, apples, flax seeds, oak bark, walnut, green tea and watercress for GA; and walnuts, *Terminalia chebula* and *T. myriocarpa* for EG. The efficacy of these individual compounds varies based on their chemical structures and bioavailability in circulation. There are numerous reports available on their sole therapeutic properties using cell lines and animal models. In addition, these compounds are also reported to be used as a sensitizer or as an adjuvant to enhance the cytotoxic potential of some anticancer drugs. In this article, we have compared and compiled the beneficial effects of these compounds against major diseases like cancer, diabetes, inflammation, free radical generation and neurodegeneration using cell line, animal and human system. Compilation of the previous work carried out so far could form a basis for future research work related to identifying the mechanism behind each pharmaceutical property. Moreover, this review will give an insight in reasoning the differences in action of these compounds based on their structure-activity relationship, pharmacology and toxicology.

In: Recent Advances in Gallate Research   ISBN: 978-1-63117-071-3
Editor: Amanda L. Kinsey   © 2014 Nova Science Publishers, Inc.

Chapter I

Health Benefits of Nongallated and Gallated Flavan-3-ols: A Prospectus

Luís R. Silva[1,] and Rui Costa[2]*

[1]REQUIMTE/Laboratório de Farmacognosia, Departamento de Química,
Faculdade de Farmácia, Universidade do Porto,
R. Jorge Viterbo Ferreira, Porto, Portugal
[2]CERNAS, Instituto Politécnico de Coimbra,
Escola Superior Agrária, Bencanta, Portugal

Abstract

Flavonoids represent the most common and widely distributed group
of plant phenolics, and can be further divided into classes including
mainly flavones, flavonols, flavan-3-ols, anthocyanins, flavanones and
isoflavones. Flavan-3-ols are the most structurally complex subclass of
flavonoids, ranging from the simple monomers (+) catechin and its
isomers (-)-epicatechin, which can be hydroxylated to form
gallocatechins (gallocatechin and epigallocatechin) and also undergo
esterification with gallic acid (epicatechin-3-O-gallate and

---

[*] Corresponding author: Tel.: + 351 222428500; fax number: +351 226093390. *E-mail address:*
lmsilva@ff.up.pt (L.R. Silva).

epigallocatechin-3-*O*-gallate), through to complex structures including the oligomeric and polymeric proanthocyanidins, which are also known as condensed tannins.

Flavan-3-ols and their derivatives are a class of phenolic compounds found in green tea leaves, chocolate, grape and grape seeds, having several healthy properties. Epidemiological studies suggest that long term consumption of diets rich in nongallated and gallated flavan-3-ols offers protection against development of cancers, cardiovascular disease, diabetes, osteoporosis and neurodegenerative diseases.

Therefore, the objective of the present review is to provide a perspective on the health benefits associated with food consumption rich in nongallated and gallated flavan-3-ols through critical analysis of the available literature on the chemistry, bioavailability and biological potential of these bioactive compounds and the current level of scientific evidence for these health benefits.

Keywords: phenolic compounds, nongallated and gallated flavan-3-ols, bioactive compounds

1. Introduction

The positive relationship between diet and health has increasedconsumer demand for more information related to healthy diets, including fruits and vegetables, with functional characteristics that help to delay the aging processes and reduce the risk of various diseases, mainly cardiovascular diseases (CVDs) and cancer, as well as other disorders [1]. These beneficial effects of fruits and vegetables have been attributed to non-essential food constituents, which are known as phytochemicals or bioactive compounds, that possess a relevant bioactivity when they are frequently consumed as a part of a regular diet [2].

The class of natural compounds with biological properties, such as phenolic compounds (PCs) has attracted attention in terms of beneficial effects on human health, due their low toxicity, low cost and high availability. PCs form one major group of phytochemicals, they are a group of aromatic secondary metabolites ubiquitously distributed in fruits, vegetables, cereals and beverages [3,4]. PCs are secondary metabolites of plants and are involved in defense against ultraviolet radiation or aggression by pathogens [5]. In food, they may contribute to the bitterness, astringency, color, flavour, odor and oxidative stability [6]. In the last few years, great attention has been paid to the

PCs due their ability to promote benefits for human health. The diets rich in plant PCs offered some protection against development of cancers, CVDs, diabetes, osteoporosis, neurodegenerative diseases, among others [7, 8] (Figure 1).

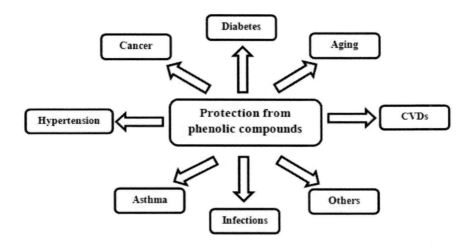

Figure 1. Protection from phenolic compounds.

The most important food sources of PCs are fruits, vegetables, red wine, coffee, chocolate, extra virgin olive oil, herbs, spices, nuts and algae [4]. Foods contain complex mixtures of PCs and numerous factors may affect their content in plants and food items. These factors can be environmental in nature, such as sun exposure, rainfall, different type of culture, fruit yield for tree, the degree of ripeness, the storage and the methods of culinary preparation [9, 10].

PCs can be divided in non-flavonoids and flavonoids. Flavonoids can be further divided into classes including mainly flavones, flavonols, flavan-3-ols, anthocyanins, flavanones and isoflavones. Flavan-3-ols are the most structurally complex subclass of flavonoids, ranging from the simple monomers (+) catechin (C) and its isomers (-)-epicatechin (EC), which can be hydroxylated to form gallocatechins (gallocatechin and epigallocatechin) and also undergo esterification with gallic acid (epicatechin-3-O-gallate and epigallocatechin-3-O-gallate), through to complex structures including the oligomeric and polymeric proanthocyanidins, which are also known as condensed tannins.

Flavan-3-ols are considered functional ingredients of beverages, fruits and vegetables, being reported to exhibit several health beneficial effects by acting as antioxidant, antimicrobial, anti-viral, anti-parasitic, anti-inflammatory, antidiabetic, neuro-protective, cardiopreventive and anticarcinogen agents. This review present information on nongallated and gallated flavan-3-ols rich food sources, bioavailability and metabolism and functional properties.

2. Classification of Phenolic Compounds

The term "phenolic" or "polyphenolic" describes the compounds that possess at least a benzenic ring substituted by one or several hydroxyl groups (-OH). Their reactivity is due to the acidic character of the phenolic function and to the nucleophilic character of the benzene ring. Based on their carbon skeleton, polyphenols are classified in non-flavonoid and flavonoid compounds.

Phenolics range from simple, low molecular weight, single-aromatic-ring compounds to the large and complex tannins and derived polyphenols. They can be classified by the number and arrangement of their carbon atoms (Table 1) and are commonly found conjugated to sugars and organic acids. More than 8000 phenolic structures have been identified in various plant species [11], many occur in food.

2.1. Non-Flavonoids Compounds

The main non-flavonoids of dietary significance are the phenolic acids and other phenolic derivatives, such as stilbenes (Table 1). Phenolic acids are found abundantly in foods and divided into two classes: hydroxybenzoic and hydroxycinnamic acids. The content of hydroxybenzoic acids of edible plants is generally low, with the exception of certain red fruits, black radish and onions, which can have concentrations of several tens of milligrams per kilogram of fresh weight [12]. The hydroxycinnmic acids are more common than hydroxybenzoic acids, with p-coumaric, caffeic, ferulic and sinapic acids being the most common. These occur as conjugates, for example with tartaric or quinic acids, collectively referred to as chlorogenic acids.

Stilbenes have a C_6-C_2-C_6 structure (Table 1) and are phytoallexins produced by plant (skins, leaves and roots) in response to disease, injury and stress [13]. The main dietary source of stilbenes is resveratrol (3,5,4'-trihydroxystilbene) from grapes and red wine [12].

Table 1. Basic structural skeletons of phenolic and polyphenolic compounds

Skeleton	Classification	Basic structure
C_6-C_1	Hydroxybenzoic acids (1)	
C_6-C_2	Acetophenones (2)	
C_6-C_2	Phenylacetic acid (3)	
C_6-C_3	Hydroxycinnamic acids (4)	
C_6-C_3	Coumarins (5)	
C_6-C_4	Naphthoquinones (6)	
C_6-C_1-C_6	Xanthones (7)	
C_6-C_2-C_6	Stilbenes (8)	
C_6-C_3-C_6	Flavonoids (9)	

2.2. Flavonoids Compounds

Flavonoids constitute the largest group of plant phenolics, found vegetables, fruits, nuts, seeds, stem, flowers, tea, wine, etc. The dietary intake of flavonoids is estimated to be 1-2g/day [14]. More than 4000 varieties of flavonoids have been identified, many of which are responsible for the attractive colours of the flowers, fruits and leaves [3].

Largely investigated for their health beneficial activity, the flavonoids comprise a group of phenolic secondary plant metabolites, the phenylbenzopyran chemical metabolites characterized by a phenylbenzopyran chemical structure [15]. They comprise 15 carbons, with two aromatic rings connected by a three carbon bridge, hence C_6-C_3-C_6 joined to a chromatogram ring (benzopyran moiety) that in turn bears an aromatic ring at C-2, C-3 or C-4 (Table 1). The heterocyclic benzopyran ring is known as the "C" ring, the fused aromatic ring as the "A" ring, and the phenyl constituent as the "B" ring. The A ring can be of two types: a phloroglucinol type that is a *meta*-trihydroxylated or a resorcinol type that is *meta*-dihydroxylated [16]. The B ring can be monohydroxylated, ortho-dihydroxylated or vicinal-trihydroxylated.

Flavonoids are mainly present in plants as glycosides. Aglycones (the forms lacking sugar moieties) occur less frequently. At least 8 different monosaccharides or combinations of these (di- or trisaccharides) can bind to the different hydroxyl groups of the flavonoid aglycone. The large number of flavonoids is a result of the many different combinations of flavonoid aglycones and these sugars. The most common sugar moieties include D-glucose and L-rhamnose. The glycosides are usually *O*-glycosides, with the sugar moiety bound to the hydroxyl group at C-3 or C-7 position.

The chemical nature of the flavonoids depends on structural class, degree of hydroxylation, other substitutions and conjugations and degree of polymerization [17]. In plants, they are relatively resistant to heat, oxygen, dryness and moderate degree of acidity but can be modified by light [18]. Photostability of the flavonoid molecule depends on the nature of the hydroxyl group attached to C-3 of ring C. The absence of glycosylation of this hydroxyl group results in high photostability of the molecule [19].

The main groups of dietary flavonoid compounds are flavonols, flavones, flavanones, flavan-3-ols, anthocyanins and isoflavones (Table 2). Within each group, compounds differ by the number and the localization of the hydroxyl and methoxyl groups located in the B ring. These basic structures can also present *O*-glycosylation, and these glycosides, in turn, can be acylated.

Kaempferol, quercetin, myricetin and catechins, etc are some most common flavonoids. Except for catechins, flavonoids do not occur in plants as aglycones; the most frequently occurring forms are the glycoside derivatives in plants [17, 20].

Table 2. Chemical structures of sub-classes of flavonoids

Flavonols (10)   Flavanones (11)   Flavanols (12)

Basic flavonoid structure(13)

Flavones (14)   Anthocyanins (15)   Isoflavones (16)

2.2.1. Flavan-3-ols

Flavan-3-ols are non-planar by virtue of their saturated C3 element and are the most structurally complex subclass of flavonoids, ranging from simple monomers (+)-catechin (C) (17) and (+)-epicatechin (EC) (19) and its isomers (18, 20), which can be hydroxylated to form gallocatechins (21, 22) and also undergo esterification with gallic acid (23, 24), through to complex structures including the oligomeric and polymeric proanthocyanidins, which are also known as condensed tannins. The two chiral centres at C2 and C3 of the flavan-3-ols produce four isomers for each level of B-ring hydroxylation, two of which, (+)-C(17) and (-)-EC(20), are widespread in nature whereas (-)-C

(18) and (+)-EC (19) are comparatively rare [21]. The four major flavan-3-ols found in plants are grouped in gallated [(-)-epigallocatechin-3-O-gallate (EGCG) (24), (-)-epicatechin-3-O-gallate (ECG) (23)]and non gallated [(-)-epicatechin (EC) (20), (-)-epigallocatechin (EGC) (22)] [22]. Two flavan-3-ols (EGCG, EGC) contain a gallic acid moiety at position 3 on the C ring (Table 3).

Table 3. Chemical structures of sub-classes of flavan-3-ols

(+)-Catechin (17)

(-)-Catechin (18)

(+)-Epicatechin (19)

(-)-Epicatechin (20)

(+)-Gallocatechin (21)

(-)-Epigallocatechin (22)

(-)-Epicatechin-3-O-gallate (23)

(-)-Epigallocatechin-3-O-gallate (24)

Gallic acid (25)

The C and EC are epimers. The structural difference between EGC and (-)-EC is an additional hydroxyl group at 5' position of the ring for EGC. EGCG is an EGC ester derivative, resulting from an esterification at 3 hydroxyl position of the C ring with a gallate moiety [23, 24].

The processing of foods, as the manufacture of tea-based beverages, the naturally occurring forms of some flavan-3-ols can suffer epimerization and (-)-EC can be converted to (-)-C, and (+)-C to (+)-EC. In the same way, (-)-EGCG can be converted to (-)-GCG [25]. Scholz and Williamson [26] reported that the epimers seem to have much lower absorption than the naturally occurring forms. However this effect has not been fully investigated.

Various terms have been used to describe polymeric flavan-3-ols in literature. As such, nomenclature used to describe these compounds can be confusing and is often erroneously employed. Of the various terms used in reference to proanthocyanidins (condensed tannins, vegetable tannins, flavans, flavolans, polyflavans, catechins, macromolecular phenolic substances, leucoanthocyanidins, condensed proanthocyanidins, polymeric proanthocyanidins, oligomeric proanthocyanidins, procyanidins, procyanidolic oligomers, plant polyphenols and pycnogenols [27]. The therms proanthocyanidins and condensed tannins are used most frequently in the literature. However, the use of the term "tannin" must be carefully considered as it used ambiguously in reference to other classes of plant polyphenols such as the hydrolysable and complex tannins [28].

The proanthocyanidins are formed from the association of several (+)-C and (-)-EC monomeric units: 2-5 units for C oligomers (Figure 2), over 5 units for C polymers. The procyanidins differ in the position and configuration of their monomeric linkages. Type B proanthocyanidins are formed from (+)-C and (-)-EC with oxidative coupling occurring between the C4 of the heterocycle and the C6 or C8 positions of the adjacent unit to create oligomers or polymers. Type A proanthocyanidins have an additional ether bond between C2 and C7. Proanthocyanidins can occur as polymers of up to 50 units. Proanthocyanidins that consists exclusively of (epi)catechin units are called procyanidins, and are the most abundant type of proanthocyanidins in plants [28]. The less common proanthocyanidins containing (-)-epiafzelechin and (+)-afzelechin or (epi)gallocatechin subunits are called propelargonidins and prodelphinidins, respectively. Many proanthocyanidins contain more than one monomer.

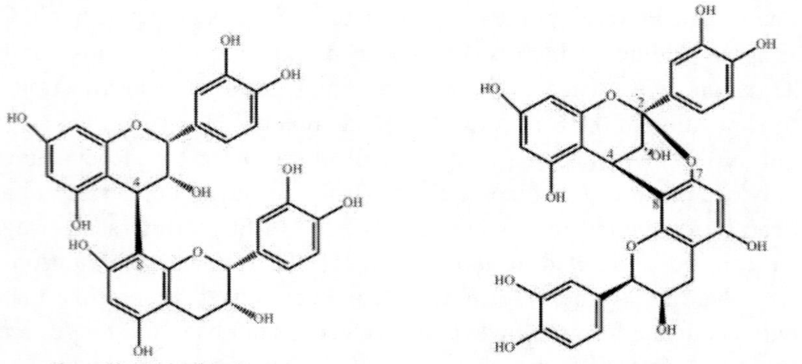

Proanthocyanidin B₂ dimer   Proanthocyanidin A₂dimer

Figure 2. Proanthocyanidin examples.

2.3. Sources of Nongallated and Gallated Flavan-3-ols

The most common group of flavonoids in the diet, flavan-3-ols and their derivatives are considered functional ingredients of beverages, fruits and vegetables, food grains, herbal remedies, dietary supplements and dairy products [27, 29].

Tea is one of the world's most popular beverages, ranking second after water, prepared by water infusion of dried leaves from *Camellia sinensis*.Teas are a rich source of polyphenols, with the phenolic content dependent on the degree of fermentation. Green tea is unfermented and the dried leaves are rich source of flavan-3-ols [31]. During preparation of black tea, leaves are crushed allowing fermentation by polyphenol oxidase and the flavan-3-ols are converted to complex condensation products, the theaflavins and their polymers, thearubigins [33].

The major phenolics present in teas are catechins (flavan-3-ols). The main flavan-3-ols in green tea are free catechins [(-)-EC, (+)-C] including gallocatechins [(-)-EGC and (+)-GC] and gallate esters [(-)-EGCG and (-)-ECG] [34, 35]. These compounds are present in lower amounts in black tea being replaced by theaflavins and thearubigins (Table 4) [36, 37, 38]. De Pascual-Teresa et al. [35] identified 14 flavan-3-ols (catechins and proanthocyanidin dimers and trimmers) in black and green tea, with amounts of 26.8 and 43.8 mg/100 mL, respectively. EGC and EC were the main compounds in green and black teas. Del Rio et al. [31] identified six flavan-3-ols in black and green tea infusions, their combined level was 4572 mg.L^{-1} in green tea, while only 101 mg.L^{-1} was present in black tea, being (-)-EGC and (-)-EGCG the major ones in green tea, on the other hand, (-)-ECG and (-)-EGC the main compounds found in black tea (Table 4). Green tea contained no theaflavin, theaflavin-3-gallate, theaflavin-3'-gallate, or theaflavin-3,3'-digallate, but all four compounds were detected in black tea in concentrations ranging from 35 to 64 mg.L^{-1} (Table 4). The albeit approximate estimate of the thearubigin content of black tea was 1681 mg.L^{-1} of gallic acid equivalents indicating that during fermentation there is substantial condensation of flavan-3-ols yielding these high molecular weight derivatives [31]. The percentages of the contents on different flavonoid and phenolic groups in the green and black tea are summarized in Figure 3.

Table 4. Concentration of flavan-3-ols and theaflavins in black and green tea infusions (adapted from [31])[a]

Compound	Green tea	Black tea
Flavan-3-ols		
(-)-Gallocatechin	383 ± 3.1	ND
(-)-Epigallocatechin	1565 ± 18	33 ± 0.8
(+)- Catechin	270 ± 9.5	12 ± 0.1
(-)-Epicatechin	738 ± 17	11 ± 0.2
(-)-Epigallocatechin gallate	1255 ± 63	19 ± 0.0
(-)-Epicatechin gallate	361 ± 12	26 ± 0.1
Σ	4572	101
Theaflavins		
Theaflavin	ND	64 ± 0.2
Theaflavin-3-gallate	ND	63 ± 0.6
Theaflavin-3'-gallate	ND	35 ± 0.8
Theaflavin-3,3'-digallate	ND	62 ± 0.1
Σ	ND	224

[a] Data expressed as mg.L^{-1} ± standard error ($n = 3$); ND, not detected.

Flavan-3-ols may occur as major compounds in leaves from other edible plants species, Cabana et al. [39] quantified the pair EGCG plus ECG as dominant in the infusion from *Satureja parvifolia* collected from Argentina.

De Pascual-Teresa et al. [35] quantified flavan-3-ols concentrations in 56 different kinds of Spanish food products including fruits, vegetable, legumes, beverages and chocolate. This work provides data on the content and distribution of 15 different flavan-3-ols (monomers, dimers and trimers) as well as the detection of 5 unquantified flavanols. Similar flavanol profiles were found in the different samples of a similar type of product, even though important variations could exist in the concentrations of total and individual flavanols among them. This was attributed to factors such as sample origin, stage of ripeness, post-harvesting conservation and processing.

In analyzed foods by De Pascual-Teresa et al. [35], the highest flavan-3-ol contents were found in broad beans sample (154.5 mg/100 g fresh weight). The total amounts in vegetables ranged from 0 to 154 mg/ 100g of fresh weight. Important amounts were found in pinto bean and lentil, which contains 7 and 1.5 mg/ 100g, respectively. Substantial amounts were also found in fruits ranging between 10 to 50 mg/100 g of fresh weight, obtaining 49 mg/100 g in plums, 10-43 mg/100 g in apples, 5-20 mg/100 g in strawberry and others berries, 8 mg/100 g in peach and 13 mg/100g in cherry.

The authors reported important amounts in wines varying between 0.2-2.7 mg/100 mL. In general way, EC was the most abundant flavan-3-ol, followed by C and proanthocyanidin B2. Catechins were found in all the flavanol-containing products, but the presence of gallocatechins was only relevant in pomegranate, broad bean, lentil, grape, wine, beer, tea and berries. Galloyled flavanols were only detected in strawberry, medlar, grape and tea.

Carando et al. [40] reported a total of 177 mg/L of flavan-3-ols in red wine, distributed by six compounds, namely C, EC, proanthocyanidin B_1-B_4. C and proanthocyanidin B_3 were quantified as the main ones. Silva et al. [41] identified the EC as majority PC in red wine obtained from Touriga Nacional grapes from Dão region (Portugal).

Beer is an alcoholic beverage made from malted grains, usually barley (*Hordeum vulgare*) or wheat (*Triticum vulgare*), hops (*Humulus lupulus*), yeast (*Sacharomyces* spp.) and water. Flavan-3-ols are found in both hops and malt. These include monomers such as C and EC, and the dimer procyanidin B_3, trimmers also occur [42, 43]. Cider is an alcoholic beverage from apples (*Malus domestica*), the main PCs were 5-*O*-caffeoylquinic acids and proanthocyanidins, and also present C and EC [43].

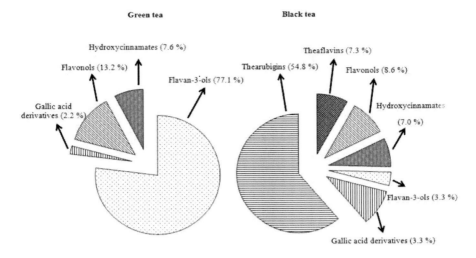

Figure 3. Percentile composition of the different classes of phenolics in green and black tea (adapted from [31]).

3. Biovailability

3.1. Definition

Bioavailability is defined as the amount of the compound that reaches the blood circulation system and to the tissue. It's determined by the combination of its rate of absorption, metabolism, distribution and excretion [44, 45]. Absorption is the passage of the compound to the systemic circulation after oral administration. Metabolism (biotransformation) is the transformation of the compound that may occur in different organs. Distribution is related to the circulation to the tissues. Excretion is the elimination from the systemic circulation. After these four actions, only the free form of the compound can reach the tissue to interact with the molecular target [46].

Especially important to the bioavailability assessment is the result of the metabolism. This can occur in liver, small intestine and colon, leading to changes such as methylation, glucuronidation, sulfation as well as degradation into phenolic acids or other compounds. This biotransformation can dramatically alter the biological properties, increasing or depleting the effects of the parent molecule [44].

3.2. Metabolism

Apart from the liver, which is the major metabolism site, small intestine, colon and even kidney play important roles in the metabolism of flavonoids. Unabsorbed compounds reach the colon, where they undergo extensive bacterial degradation [47] with the microbiota being able to break down the flavonoids into several low molecular- weight metabolites [48].

Metabolism is a detoxification process where xenobiotic compounds are transformed into more hydrophilic and polar ones to make it easier its excretion from the body. It can include four main types of transformations designated phase I, II and III types and the colonic metabolism. Phase I, including hydroxylation and demethylation (mediated by cytochrome 450), lead to oxidation and reduction reactions as well as hydrolysis of esters, amides and ether linkages, introducing stronger hydrophilic groups such as − OH, $-NH_2$, −SH, and −COOH. Phase II, involves conjugation reactions, link the hydrophilic groups described above to even stronger hydrophilic groups, such as glucuronic acid or sulphate [49]. Phase III is being attributed to the active efflux by multidrug resistance-associated proteins (MRP) at the apical surface of the intestine [22, 50]. All metabolites differ from their parent compounds in the structure and bioactivity.

Flavan-3-ols are extensively metabolized during absorption in epithelial cells in the small intestine, and subsequently go through liver metabolism, which includes conjugates of O-methylation, sulfation and glucuronidation. The nonabsorbed fraction reach the colon degraded by colonic microflora [44]. The conjugated metabolites are then transported into the circulation by MRP transport. MRP leads to efflux of flavanols to the apical side back into the intestinal lumen, limiting absorption of flavanols. Conjugated flavanols are further metabolized in the liver and finally excreted in the urine [51]. All metabolites are eliminated through biliary or urinary routes [44]. Large conjugates are more likely to be excreted through the biliary way, whereas small conjugates preferentially are excreted through the urine.

Although changes occur mainly in the intestine, they may occur right in the first step of ingestion, in the mouth. The flavan-3-ol EGCG can be hydrolyzed to EGC in human saliva by the esterase [50].

Phase II conjugation competes with phase I metabolism. Methylation and conjugation with glucuronic acid or sulfate are the major forms of conjugated metabolites of flavonoids[44]. Lambert et al. [50] have reported that the green tea polyphenols (EGCG) undergo methylation, glucuronidation, sulfation metabolism on phase II, which reduces its biological activity.

EGC and EGCG can be methylated to 4'-O-methyl-EGC and 4''-O-methyl-EGCG or 4',4''-O-dimethyl-EGCG, respectively, by the catechol-O-methyltransferase (COMT) [52]. Lower concentrations of EGCG lead to more dimethylated metabolite whereas higher concentrations, lead mainly to monomethylation.

The extent of glucuronidation of flavan-3-ols is influenced by the number of the available hydroxyl. Flavonoids containing catechol or pyrogallol B ring are susceptible to glucuronidation, whereas those containing monohydroxylated B ring are less susceptible to glucuronidation [53]. EGCG-4''-O-glucuronide and EGC-3'-O-glucuronide are the major metabolites formed in human, rat and mouse microsomes [50].

EC undergoes sulfation reaction in the human liver and intestine [50]. In fact, this was pointed as a preferred mechanism over glucuronidation of EC in humans, where glucuronidation was mainly observed in studies in mouse and mice [45].

Conjugated EGCG (methylated, glucuronated or sulfated) can be further conjugated with methylation, glucuronidation and/or sulfation to form mixed EGCG metabolites [50].

3.3. Colonic Metabolism

Bacterial metabolism of flavonoids in the colon has been studied in animal and human models. Unlike enzymes in animal and human tissues, bacterial enzymes catalyze the breakdown of polyphenols to small molecules catalyzing many reactions such as hydrolysis, hydrogenation, dehydroxylation, decarboxylation, deconjugation, oxidation, and heterocyclic oxygen ring split (ring fission) [45]. Thirteen metabolites of (−)-EC and (+)-C were found *in vitro* and in animal and human systems [45].

Li and Ho [45] generalizes the bacteria metabolic pathway of green tea polyphenols as: "(1) hydrolysis of gallate ester for ECG and EGCG; (2) ring fission at the C-ring, cleavage between O1 and C2 of the flavanol bond by enzyme-catalyzed reduction, and proton transfer to the O1 and C2; (3) formation of lactones and partially de-oxygenated B-ring lactones; (4) formation of phenyl-substituted aliphatic acids from hydrolysis, enzymatic oxidation, and coupling with glycine; and (5) formation of benzoic acids and their derivatives by enzyme-catalyzed oxidative cleavage, methylation or de-oxygenation of phenolic benzoic acids, and coupling with glycine."

In contrast to the cleavage of heterocyclic C ring of other flavonoids, flavan-3-ols reveal a different structure of diphenylpropan-2-ols as the precursors of the lactones. After ingestion of 20 mg/kg decaffeinated green tea, the compounds 5-(3',4',5'-trihydroxyphenyl)-γ-valerolactone, 5-(3',4'-dihydroxyphenyl)- γ-valerolactone and 5-(3',5'-trihydroxyphenyl)-γ-valerolactone were detected in the human urine and plasma [50]. These specific colonic metabolites of catechins are also observed in their oligo- and polymeric forms, procyanidins. The case of proanthocyanidins (oligomers or polymers of flavan-3-ols) is different from the other flavan-3-ols. The procyanidin oligomer is not depolymerized into monomeric flavan-3-ols during passage through stomach and gastrointestinal tract and thus suffer mainly colonic metabolism [54].

A high proportion of the *in vivo* studies performed so far suggests that only procyanidin dimers can be absorbed [55]. The authors showed that not only anthocyanins and flavan-3-ols may cross the Caco-2 cell barrier model with similar efficiency, but also dimeric structures containing both anthocyanins and flavan-3-ols, although with a lower efficiency.

3.4. Bioavailability of Flavan-3-ols

Measure of bioavailabilty implies, at least, blood (plasma) analysis and urine analysis after the ingestion of a single dose of polyphenol, provided as pure compound, plant extract, or whole food/beverage.

Studies have been analyzing mostly urine since blood analyses are not standardized [48]. Evaluation of bioavailability is also dependent on the time period after ingestion. Calani et al. [48] obtained considerably higher bioavailability's until 48 h when compared to previous studies done until 24 h. Mean values for the maximal plasma concentration, the time to reach the maximal plasma concentration, the area under the plasma concentration-time curve, the elimination half-life, and the relative urinary excretion for major polyphenols have been studied [56].

The main sources of flavan-3-ols are tea, chocolate, apples, pears, grapes, and red wine with the daily intake of C and proanthocyanidin dimers and trimers estimated to be 18–50 mg/day. However, bioavailability of catechins has been studied mainly on ingestion of tea [56].

Manach et al. [56] reviewed 97 bioavailability studies and conclude that gallic acid and isoflavones are the most absorbed polyphenols, followed by catechins, flavanones, and quercetin glucosides, but with different kinetics.

The least well-absorbed polyphenols are the proanthocyanidins, the galloylated tea catechins, and the anthocyanins. Proanthocyanidins, their polymeric nature and high molecular weight are likely to limit their absorption through the gut barrier.

Parent molecules or metabolites have been found in plasma and urine. EGCG is the polyphenol present in plasma in the largest proportion (77-90%) in a free form. C and EC are readily detected in plasma after their consumption from food or beverages but are rapidly eliminated from the organism, probably by the bile [56]. EGC was found in plasma, but with a concentration 5 times less than its metabolite 4'-O-methyl-EGC and 3 times less in urine. Other catechins highly conjugated with glucuronic acid and/or sulfate groups, such as EC-3'-O-glucuronide, 4'-O-methyl-EC-3'-O-glucuronide, 4'-O-methyl-EC-5- or 7-Oglucuronide,and the aglycones EC and 4'-O-methyl-EC were found in the plasma. Microbial metabolites, namely, 5-(3',4',5'-trihydroxyphenyl)-valerolactone, 5-(3',4'-dihydroxyphenyl)-valerolactone, and 5-(3',5'-dihydroxyphenyl)-valerolactone, were also identified in plasma and urine after ingestion of green tea and with levels 8 to 25 higher than the parent compounds EGC and EC [56].

Flavonoids and, in particular, flavan-3-ols from green tea have been attributed a low bioavailability in humans. It has been hypothesized that several processes contribute to the low bioavailability, including chemical degradation, intestinal metabolism, microbial metabolism, hepatic metabolism, poor membrane permeability and efflux transporter-mediated intestinal excretion [45].

Summing phase II metabolites formed in the small intestine and liver, estimated bioavailability values are around 8 to 9% [47]. This may be related to the assumptions that flavan-3-ols are absorbed and eliminated rapidly with a peak concentration reached at 1.3–1.6 h and excretion between 0 and 8 h [22]. The bioavailability increased to 39% when colon-derived valerolactones were considered [31].

Analyzing only the urine for 48 h, Calani et al. [48] recovered 41 different flavan-3-ol metabolites in urine from phase II conjugates and microbial ring-fission products, obtained an average bioavailability of tea flavan-3-ols close to 62%, higher than all the individual studies previously published in the literature. The authors attribute this higher bioavailability value to the longer urinary collection period, which lasted 2 days after tea ingestion, allowing an almost complete excretion of flavan-3-ol metabolites from phase II and microbial metabolism. In fact, during the first 24 h, 44% of the ingested dose of catechins from tea was bioavailable, a similar value to previous works [32] of the same authors. However, very different results in humans were found. Some showed a 100% absorption/excretion, whereas others were unable to efficiently absorb/excrete this class of flavonoids. Calani et al. [48] suggests that colonic ring fission metabolism could be relevant and that the main factor responsible for the inter-individual variability was the g-valerolactones.

3.5. Bioavailability Enhancement

Due to the low availability pointed in most of the studies, new approaches to the increase bioavailability of flavonoids have been postulated such as: improving the intestinal absorption via use of absorption enhancers, novel delivery systems, improving metabolic stability and changing the site of absorption from large intestine to small intestine [51].

Increased total flavan-3-ol recovery to 52, 55, and 69% after digestion was obtained mixing tea flavan-3-ols with 50% bovine, soy, and rice milk, respectively. The recovery of flavan-3-ols after the addition of 30 mg of ascorbic acid showed differential effects on EGC, EGCG, EC and ECG (74, 54, 82 and 45%, respectively). The addition of up to 50% of fruit juice (grapefruit, orange, lemon, or lime) also improved the recovery of EGC (81–98%), EGCG (56–76%), EC (86–95%) and ECG (30–55%)[22].

Lambert et al. [50] increased the stability and bioavailability through the synthesis of peracetylated EGCG (AcEGCG) that in an *in vitro* study observed that AcEGCG was rapidly converted to EGCG in HCT116 human colon adenocarcinoma cells.

Another approach is to inhibit metabolic changes of flavonol by administration with of piperine (from black pepper). Piperine may inhibit EGCG glucuronidation only in small intestinal microsomes and not in the hepatic microsomes which can lead to EGCG absorption in the intestine and glucuronidation only in the liver.

4. Health Benefits of the Flavan-3-ols

4.1. Antioxidants

Flavan-3-ols have been shown to behave as antioxidants via several mechanisms including the scavenging of free radicals, chelation of transition metals, as well as the mediation and inhibition of enzymes [57].

Today, free radicals are of major interest being involved in molecular transformations and gene mutation in many types of organisms. Oxidative stress is well-known to cause many diseases and scientists in many different disciplines became more interested in natural sources that could provide active components to reduce their impact on cells [6]. The generation of free radicals by living systems can potentially cause oxidative damage to DNA, lipids, carbohydrates and proteins, to eventually result in impairment of cellular function that in turn causes aging and initiates onset of disease [58]. Reactive species can be oxygen (ROS) or nitrogen (RNS) radicals, or non-radicals that either oxidize or easily convert to oxidizing radicals. Common radicals include superoxide anion, hydroxyl, alkoxyl, peroxyl and nitric oxide. Examples of non-radicals include hydrogen peroxide, hypochlorous acid, ozone, singlet oxygen and peroxynitrite [59]. The common free radicals used to test antioxidant activity include 1,1-diphenyl-2-picrylhydrazyl (DPPH$^{\bullet}$) and 2,2'-azinobis-3-ethylbenzthiazoline-6-sulfonic acid (ABTS$^{\bullet+}$). ABTS$^{\bullet+}$ is used in the trolox-equivalent antioxidant capacity (TEAC) assay [59].

Flavan-3-ols structure determines relative ease of oxidation and free radical scavenging activity. Although the presence of galloyl groups, number and position of hydroxyl groups (based on redox potential) are said to enhance activity, methoxylation and glycosylation of position 3 apparently inhibit activity [57, 60].While (-)-EC is more easily oxidized than (+)-C, the type of interflavanoid bond determines relative ease of oligomer degradation, with C-4→C-8 linked dimers such as B-3 and B-4 oxidizing more readily than their C-4→C-6 linked counterparts. However, dimers B-6 and B-7 oxidize less readily than B-1 and B-2 due to the nature of their lower structural monomeric unit [61]. Although, proanthocyanidin B-2 has been shown to scavenge hydroxyl radical and superoxide anion better than proanthocyanidin B-4 or (-)-EC [62]. Additionally, flavan-3-ols antioxidant activity is said to increase from monomer to trimer and then decrease from trimer and tetramer [63].

Generally, the health promoting activities of flavan-3-ols, including the antiproliferative effect, are mainly attributed to their antioxidant capacity and ability to scavenge ROS [64]. The antioxidant effects have been proven on several cellular and molecular targets associated with cell death and cell survival [23, 24]. These properties are due to the presence of the phenolic hydroxyl groups on the B ring in ungalloylated catechins (EC and EGC) and on the B and D rings of the galloylated catechins (ECG and EGCG) (Table 3). The presence of 3,4,5-trihydroxy B ring has been shown to be for the antioxidant and radical scavenging activities, and the order of their effectiveness being EGCG>EGC>EC>C.

Flavan-3-ols are highly hydrophilic molecules and act as antioxidant in aqueous environments [65]. Antioxidant activity of EGCG at physiological concentrations (0.1-1μM) [66], underline the interdependency between the scavenging of radicals in the hydrophilic and hydrophobic environments [67]. Thus, it is suggested that the presence of the gallate group at the 3 position plays the most important role in their free radical-scavenging abilities and an additional insertion of a hydroxyl group at the 5' position in the B ring also contributes to their scavenging activities [66, 68].

Braicu et al. [29] confirms that the specific structural components in catechins are responsible for the different biological activities by testing EGCG, EGC, EG, C and gallic acid at the same concentration (10 μM). Literature data suggest that the number of hydroxyl groups on the B ring contributes significantly to the ROS scavenging of flavan-3-ols [69]. Recently, the view has changed, and flavonoids are now thought to act as direct antioxidants but rather as inhibitors of prooxidants enzymes or as chelators of transition metals that mask prooxidant actions RNS and ROS [70].

The presence of hydroxyl groups from the three different rings also enhance the inhibition of ROS or induce prooxidant effect. This may be explained by the presence of the galloyl moiety is responsible for quenching the hydroxyl radicals [71].

It has been established that the B ring, hydroxyl group and galloyl moiety of the catechins are the main contributing factors to their scavenging activities and the presence of the *ortho*-dihydroxyl group in the B ring and the galloyl moiety are important in maintaining the effectiveness of the radical scavenging ability [30].

4.2. Antimicrobials, Anti-Virals and Anti-Parasitics

Increasingly, flavonoids are becoming the subject of medical research. Flavan-3-ols have been reported to possess many useful properties, including antimicrobial, anti-viral and anti-parasitic activities. The antimicrobial effects of several tannins extracts on yeast, filamentous fungi, bacteria and viral toxicity have been reviewed by Chung et al. [72], however the review references several types of tannins and sources, it does not offer structural information about condensed tannins extracts.

Polymeric proanthocyanidins which is mainly composed of EC, was reported to act as inhibitory properties against HIV-1 protease in water extracts of *Cynomorium songaricum*[73]. Hashimoto et al. [74] evaluated the inhibitory effects of tea flavan-3-ols against HIV-1 replication in H9 lymphocytes, it should be noted that ECG and EGCG did not demonstrate an inhibitory effect, which were reported previously as potent inhibitors of HIV-reverse tanscriptase [76].

Preliminary investigation of the antibacterial activity indicated that their crude extract had moderate effect on methicillin-resistant *Staphylococcus aureus* (MRSA) [76]. Chung et al. [77] reported that the tannins possess bacteriostatic or bactericidal activity against *S. aureus*. Akiyama et al. [78] were found inhibitory activity of the tannins against intestinal bacteria such as *Bacteroides fragilis*, *Clostridium perfringens*, *Escherichia coli* and *Enterobacter cloacae*.

Several flavan-3-ols, including tea polyphenol ECG [79] and polymeric proanthocyanidins isolated from the fruit peel of *Zanthoxylum piperitum* can supress the antibiotic resistance of MRSA or act synergistically when used with some antibiotics [80].

EGCG and its oxidative products is the most abundant polyphenol in tea leaves (*Camellia sinensis* L., Theaceae) to have bacterial activity against MRSA and they markedly decrease the minimum inhibitory concentrations (MIC) of oxacillin and other antibiotics [76, 81].

Oxacillin, ampicillin and cefalexin showed increased antibacterial activity against MRSA in the presence of C [82]. EGC markedly lowered the MIC of oxacillin and other β-lactams, but not of other antimicrobial agents, for strains of MRSA [79]. Stapleton et al. [81] reported that EGC is more effective in its capacity to modulate β-lactam resistance than EGCG when used in combination with β-lactams against MRSA, this effect may have therapeutic potential.

Li et al. [83] were reported the antifungal activity of the EGCG isolated from *Coccoloba dugandiana*, being observed inhibitory capacity against *Cryptococcus neoformans*. *Candida albicans* is a fungal pathogen that undergoes dimorphism (transformation from a yeast form to a hyphal form), wherein, the yeast form is identified as a disseminating form that plays a critical role in the early stages of *Candida* disease progression, while the hyphal form is found to exert additional pathogenicity by adapting to various environmental conditions. Saito et al. [84] suggested that C possesses anti-dimorphism activity by interfering with *in vitro* signal transduction. Similarly, this highlights the possible application of C in clinical therapy for the mnagement and prevention of candidosis.

Internal parasites infecting large food animals cause production losses to farmers resulting in higher prices to consumers. As the effectiveness of current antihelmintic drenches is being reduced by the emergence of drench resistance and significant production losses may still occur as a result of continuing larval challenge, alternative strategies for nematode control are urgent required [85]. Paveto et al. [86] tested the trypanocidal action of green tea catechins against two different development stages of *Trypanosome cruzi*, this activity was assayed with the nonproliferative bloodstream trypomastigote and with the intracellular replicative amastigote parasite forms. The most active compounds were GCG and EGCG.

The effects of the catechins on the recombinant *T. cruzi* arginine kinase, a key enzyme in the energy metabolism of the parasite, were also assayed. The activity of this enzyme was inhibited by about 50% by nanomolar concentrations of CG or GCG, whereas the other members of the group were less effective.

Min and Hart [87] suggested that proanthocyanidins in forages have the potential to aid in the control of gastrointestinal parasites. Their publication lists proanthocyanidin contents of various forage species, including molecular weight ranges and subunit composition data. According to the authors, proanthocyanidin-containing forages possess potential to aid in the control of antihelmintic-resistant gastrointestinal parasites, to decrease fecal egg counts in sheep and goats, and to decrease hatch rate as well as larval development feces. Molan et al. [84] evaluated the effect of water infusion and aqueous acetone extracts of green tea (*Camellia sinensis*) on the motility of infective larvae of the sheep nematodes *Teladorsagia circumcincta* and *Trichostrongylus colubriformis*.

The results obtained in this work revealed that the extracts of green tea, specially the gallated flavan-3-ols and proanthocyanidin oligomers have inhibitory activity against the motility of infective larvae of *T. circumcincta* and *T. colubriformis* under *in vitro* conditions.

4.3. Anti-Inflammatory

The health benefits of consuming fruits and vegetables are often attributed, in part, to their high content of PCs. Dietary flavonoids have many interesting *in vitro* properties, including antioxidant and anti-inflammatory effects, which have been postulated to underlie their beneficial health effect [88].

Flavonoids undergo extensive first-pass metabolism, and the chemical forms of flavonoids present in fruits and vegetables, usually glycosides and aglycones, are quite different from their *in vivo* metabolites. In the mucosa and the liver, flavonoids are subjected to extensive glucuronidation, methylation and sulfation [88]. Thus, after the intake of flavonoid rich food, these flavonoid metabolites are the main forms found in the circulatory system, where they are present for up to 4-6 h (e.g. catechins) [89]. As with pharmaceutical drugs and other xenobiotics, biotransformation greatly affects the physical and chemical properties of flavonoids, making them more water-soluble and readily excreted in bile and urine [90].

Inflammation is a normal physiological response of the immune system to counteract pathological states such as irritation and infection caused by chemicals, microbial pathogens and/or wounding. The most evident physical signs of inflammation are redness, swelling, pain and heat. These symptoms are associated with increased blood flow, metabolism, vasodilatation, release of intracellular mediators, fluid leakage and cellular influx [91]. However, unbalanced or prolonged inflammation leads to progressive tissue damage and has been implicated in the development of many chronic diseases, such as cancer, neurodegenerative disorders as well as diabetes and CVDs.

The onset of inflammation is characterised by recruitment of a wide range of immune cells (e.g. neutrophils, macrophages monocytes, etc.) to the inflamed sites and the release of various pro-inflammatory cytokines and ROS/RNS. Oxidative stress through continuous overproduction of ROS/RNS by activated phagocytes constitutes the major tissue-destructive force *in vivo*, and in turn promotes inflammation by stimulating production of inflammatory mediators and cytokines [92]. Evidence has shown that ROS/RNS are involved in the activation of a variety of kinases and transcription factors, whose regulation is dependent on the redox changes. For example, the transcription factors nuclear factor-kappa B (NF-κB) and activator protein (AP)-1 are redox-sensitive and become activated under oxidative/nitrosative stress. Once activated, NF-κB and AP-1 translocate from the cytoplasm to the nucleus, leading to the up-regulation of numerous inflammatory genes, such as those coding for inducible nitric oxide synthase (iNOS) and cyclooxygenase (COX-2), among others [93]. Hence, ROS/RNS and pro-inflammatory cytokines work in a synergistic manner through a ROS/RNS-cytokine-transcription factor regulatory loop, thereby augmenting the inflammatory response and tissue damage. The production of NO and prostaglandins by iNOS and COX-2, respectively, are considered to be the most prominent molecular mechanisms in the inflammatory processes, and are also involved in the multistage carcinogenesis, especially the promotion stage [94]. Excessive and prolonged NO generation caused by overexpression of iNOS has also been implicated in inflammational tumourigenesis; while COX-2 mediated prostaglandin production stimulates cell proliferation, invasion and angiogenesis in cancer development [95].

Anti-inflammatory agents can block ROS/RNS and cytokine-involved inflammatory cascade. Compared to steroidal or non-steroidal chemical drugs for treating inflammation, naturally derived substances are readily available at lower costs, while have limited side effects and intolerance.

Polyphenols found in abundantly in plant foods have been studied for their anti-inflammatory activities in suppressing the synthesis (gene expression) and action (enzyme activity) of many pro-inflammatory mediators. Green tea consumption has been suggested to have health benefits in preventing or mitigating the development of a variety of diseases including autoimmune, inflammatory, neurodegenerative diseases, obesity and cancer [96]. These effects of green tea are mainly attributed to its most abundant and biologically active catechin –EGCG.

Inflammation has been shown to play an important role in the initiation and/or development of these diseases, and thus viewed as a target for preventive and therapeutic strategies. EGCG have been reported to exhibit anti-inflammatory activity through their ability to scavenge NO, peroxynitrite ($ONOO^-$) and other ROS/RNS, to inhibit the translocation of NF-κB and AP-1 from the cytoplasm to nucleous and to inhibit the activity of iNOS and COX-2 [97]. EGCG was shown to inhibit the production of proinflammatory cytokines such as interleukin (IL)-1β, IL-6 and tumor necrosis factor (TNF)-α in human monocyte cell line U937 [98], and TNF-α in human monocyte cell line THP-1 cells [99], murine macrophage cell line, J774.1 cells [100] and RAW264.7 cells [101]. Another important proinflammatory mediator, prostaglandin (PG)-E_2, and the key rate limiting enzyme for its synthesis, COX-2 were also inhibited by EGCG in human chondrocytes [102] and various tumor cell lines [103-105].

4.4. Antidiabetic Activity

Epidemiological, *in vitro* and animal studies support the beneficial effects of dietary flavonoids on glucose and lipid homeostasis. It is encouraging that the beneficial effects of some flavonoids are at physiological concentrations and comparable to clinically used anti-diabetic drugs; however, clinical research in this field and studies on the anti-diabetic effects of flavonoid metabolites are limited [106]. Flavonoids act on various molecular targets and regulate different signalling pathways in pancreatic β-cells, hepatocytes, adipocytes and skeletal myofibers. Flavonoids may exert beneficial effects in diabetes by (i) enhancing insulin secretion and reducing apoptosis and promoting proliferation of pancreatic β-cells; (ii) improving hyperglycemia through regulation of glucose metabolism in hepatocytes; (iii) reducing insulin resistance, inflammation and oxidative stress in muscle and fat and (iv) increasing glucose uptake in skeletal muscle and white adipose tissue [106].

Diabetes mellitus is an emerging health problem in western societies. The scientific community is searching for new natural compounds with antidiabetic properties to overcome any resistance developed by patients to the currently used drugs. α-Glucosidase inhibitors act by reversible inhibition of α-glucosidase, an enzyme responsible for the breakdown of α-glycosidic bonds in complex carbohydrates to release absorbable monosaccharides [107]. α-Glucosidase inhibition is one of the currently selected and preferred targets for development of anti-type II diabetes agents. Some inhibitors of this enzyme have been developed as clinical drug, such as acarbose [108].

Epidemiological studies suggest correlation between tea consumption and reduced risk of type 2 diabetes, although the mechanisms for these observations are uncertain. A study conducted in Japan reported that the regular average consumption of six or more cups of green tea per day had a decreased risk for diabetes [109]. Odegaard et al. [110] investigated the prospective association between intakes of coffee, black tea and green tea with the risk of type 2 diabetes in Singaporean Chinese men and women. These authors concluded that consumption of coffee and tea was associated with lower risk of type 2 diabetes. Huxley et al. [111] reported that consumption of more than 3 to 4 cups of tea per day had an approximate one-fifth lower risk of type 2 diabetes than those consuming no tea.

Several studies reported the anti-diabetic effect of EGCG in animal and cell culture studies. Hosoda et al. [112] studied the effect of green tea catechins in twenty type-2 diabetics consumed, in addition to their normal medication, either 1.5 L oolong tea or water (control). The consumption of oolong tea, which contained 386 mg of EGCG, resulted in a significant reduction in plasma levels of glucose and fructosamine, suggesting that diabetic patients may benefit from ingestion of oolong tea, high in EGCG. EGCG may protect against the development of long-term complications of diabetes [113]. The oxidative stress in erythrocytes induced by tert-butyl hydroxyperoxide was measured in response to EGCG, EGC, ECG and EC in 31 type-2-diabetics and compared to 31 healthy control subjects. EGCG (1-10 μmol/L) was the most potent C in reducing oxidative stress thereby reducing an important factor in the development of glucose metabolism disorders.

The optimal dose of EGCG for glucose control has not yet been established. Based on the available literature a dose range of 84-386 mg EGCG/day may be adequate to support glucose homeostasis [112, 114].

In EGCG-treated but not ECG-treated male Sprague-Dawley rats, serum levels of protein, fatty acids and glycerol were not altered, but significant reductions of up 32% in serum glucose were observed [115]. Similar changes in these serum nutrients induced by EGCG were observed in male lean and (genetically induced) obese Zucker rats and in mice of high-fat diet [115]. Low levels of plasma glucose are known to reduce oxidative stress and osmotic pressure due to glucose in the cells which thereby improves diabetic complications, such as vascular disease, retinopathy, nephropathy and neuropathy, as well as the subsequent long-term morbidity and mortality in people with type 1 and 2 diabetes [116]. Accordingly, reductions of oxidative stress-induced DNA breakage, glycation end-products, inflammation and lipid oxidation by green tea or EGCG should help the possible curative and preventive effects against diabetic complications by green tea.

Collectively, EGCG can elicit a number of changes that are associated with beneficial effects on diabetes, including improvements in insulin secretion, glucose uptake, insulin resistance, glucose tolerance, oxidative stress, inflammation and mitochondrial function. EGCG appears to act thought multiple signalling pathways to exert these beneficial effects in diabetes. For example, the ability of green tea EGCG to reduce blood levels of glucose in rats may be dependent on changes in appetite [115]. EGCG of green tea extracts reduce carbohydrate absorption from the intestine of rats with a saccharide-supplemented diet *via* inhibition of the activity of intestinal α-amylase, sucrose or α-glucosidase [117]. Green tea EGCG ameliorates decreases in islet mass induced by multiple low doses of streptozotocin in mice (118). Green tea polyphenols reduce oxidative stress in rats with alloxan-induced diabetes as evidence by decreased hepatic ALP, GPT and LPO and by decreased renal BUN and creatinine levels [119].

4.5. Neurodegenerative Effects

Neurodegenerative disorders such as Parkinson's and Alzheimer's diseases represent an increasing problem in our aging societies, primarily as there is an increase prevalence of both Alzheimer's disease and Parkinson's disease with age [120]. These and other neurodegenerative disorders appear to be triggered by multi-factorial events including neuroinflammation, glutamatergic excitotoxicity, increases in oxidative stress, iron and/or depletion or endogenous antioxidant [121]. In terms of dietary modulation of these diseases, epidemiological studies have suggested that moderate wine consumption may reduce the incidence of certain age-related neurological disorders including Alzheimer's disease [122]. Furthermore, regular dietary intake of flavonoid-rich food have been associated with 50% reduction in the risk of dementia [123], a preservation of cognitive performance with aging [124], a delay in the onset of Alzheimer's disease and reduction of risk of developing Parkinson's disease [125].

Tea is the most widely consumed beverage after water. Green tea preparation precludes the oxidation of leaf polyphenols which are thought to contribute to the health/promoting effects. Ng et al. [126] observed that the total tea intake was significantly associated with lower prevalence of cognitive impairment in Chinese adults although the effect was most evident for black and oolong teas. In another study, Niu et al. [127] observed that the more frequent consumption of green tea was associated with lower prevalence of depressive symptoms in Japanese elderly. Interestingly, two epidemiological studies reported that tea consumption has been suggested to reduce (by 30-60%) the risk of Parkinson's disease [128, 129], and represents a main source of flavonoid intake found to diminish the risk of stroke and dementia, suggesting that catechins are responsible for its potential therapeutic benefits in the aging brain [123]. In support of this hypothesis, flavan-3-ols have been reported to exert neuroprotective effects in various models of toxicity induced by ischaemia, glutamate, MPTP, oxidative stress and Aβ peptides [130].

Flavan-3-ols such as EGCG and (-)-EC are able to cross the blood brain barrier (BBB) by *in vitro* cell culture and rat models[131]. Zini et al. [132] evaluated the presence of flavan-3-ol metabolites in plasma and blood cerebrospinal fluid (CSF) collected from subjects after acute ingestion of green tea. Flavan-3-ols metabolites were detected in plasma however no flavan-3-olsor any of their metabolites were detected in the CSF. Since CSF contains material that penetrate the BBB, it can be considered as an indirect method for evaluating if a compound cross the BBB [133].

Green tea extract and catechins suppressed the Aβ-induced oxidative stress and expression of apoptotic proteins which are known to be activated by ROS [134]. Co-treatment of PC12 cells with green tea extract attenuated Aβ-induced cell death, intracellular ROS levels, 8-oxodG formation, activation of p53 and capase-3 and increased ratio of Bax to Bcl-2 [134]. Moreover, in cultured hippocampal neurons, EGCG had neuroprotective effects against Aβ-induced apoptosis by particularly scavenging ROS and inhibiting subsequent oxidative damage such as lipid peroxidation [135]. In rat cortical neurons, EGCG prevented Aβ-induced neuronal cell death by reducing the increase of cytosolic calcium levels, glutamate release, generation of ROS and activation of caspase-3 [136].

4.6. Flavan-3-ols and Cardiovascular Disease

Cardiovascular disease (CVD), in particular coronary heart disease and stroke, is a major cause of mortality in developed nations. CVD is a chronic, multifactorial disease in which a range of genetic and environmental factors play a role in its initiation, progression and development. For example, smoking, high saturated fat diets and physical inactivity are well known environmental factors that are known to increase the risk of CVD [137]. Numerous epidemiological and human intervention studies have suggested that regular consumption of polyphenol/rich foods, such as fruits, vegetables, cocoa, tea and wine, may exert cardio-protective effects in humans [87, 138].

Free radicals and oxidative stress are key contributors to CVDs such as congestive heart failure, valvular heart disease, cardiomyopathy, hypertrophy, atherosclerosis and ischemic heart disease [64]. Flavan-3-ols may interfere in the pathogenesis of CVD via several mechanisms: antioxidative, antithrombogenic and anti-inflammatory. In particular, proanthocyanidins and flavan-3-ols monomers aid in lowering plasma cholesterol levels, inhibit the oxidation of LDL, and activate endothelial nitric oxide synthase to prevent platelet adhesion and aggregation that contribute to blood clot formation [139, 140]. Flavan-3-ols also influence oxidative stress via enzyme modification and modulation of cell signalling pathways; the extent of the effect relies greatly on flavan-3-ol structure-related protein reactivity [141].

The majority of epidemiological studies demonstrate that tea consumption benefits the cardiovascular system [142] and more recently an inverse correlation between green tea consumption and mortality due to CVD was found [143].

Imai and Nakachi [144] found an inverse association between green tea consumption and markers of CVD in 1371 men. The prevalence of heart disease was 26.0, 29.4 and 39.8 per 1000 in populations with a daily consumption of >10, 4-9 and <3 cups of green tea per day, respectively. These observations were supported by the fact that the population showed significantly reduced levels of cholesterol and triacylglycerides.

Recent evidences suggest that tea consumption improves endothelium-dependent vasodilation. Some studies suggest that flavan-3-ols increase nitric oxide (NO) production and therefore could have a positive effect on CVD [27]. Shenouda and Vita [145] reviewed the effect of flavonoid-containing beverages and EGCG on endothelial function. According to these authors, clinical studies have shown that the consumption of such beverages leads to improve endothelium function. Red wine flavan-3-ols cause endothelium-dependent vasorelaxation (EDR) associated with marked formation of NO. The same red wine extract also causes extracellular calcium ion increases in endothelial cell, but not in smooth muscle cells [146]. Grape proanthocyanidin trimmers, tetramers, pentamers and polymers and their gallates as well as a dimer gallate provide EDR of blood vessels *in vitro* by increasing NO production. Flavan-3-ols monomers did not investigated the same EDR result [147].

Oxidized LDL is recognized as a risk factor for arterosclerosis. Antioxidants such as those found in fruits, vegetables, herbs and beverages prevent the oxidation of LDL [148]. Consumption of flavan-3-ols reduces cholesterol, restore lipid balance and prevent conversion of LDL to harmful oxidized chemical states [148]. Flavan-3-ols and oligomeric procyanidins decrease LDL oxidative susceptibility with increasing chain length; however, equivalent concentrations of monomers equally inhibit LDL, suggesting that antioxidant power of procyanidins on biologic substrate depends on ring structure and number of catechol groups, not chain length alone [149]. Two clinical trials substantiate this finding. A single consumption of 300 mL green tea containing 6g green tea solids by healthy subjects, increased total plasma antioxidant capacity and efficiently protected LDL from oxidation compared to the control beverage [150]. Similarly, in a 4 week study with a daily consumption of 600 mL green tea, containing 5.2 g of tea solids, significantly decreased the levels of oxidized LDL [151].

Flavan-3-ols influence angiotension I (Ang-I) converting enzyme (ACE), this glycoprotein catalyses the hydrolysis of angiotensin I to angiotensin II (a potent vasoconstrictor) [141]. The authors also suggest that despite the number of (-)-EC units (high hydroxyl moiety count capable of binding protein), other factors determine flavan-3-ol enzyme interactions and that ACE activity and Ang-I hydrolysis are dependent on Cl- binding. Actis-Goretta et al. [152] demonstrated that procyanidins as well EGC all inhibit ACE activity, while flavan-3-ol monomers such as (+)-C and (-)-EC do not. ACE activity inhibition thus depends on both phenolic and flavan-3-ol content of foods.

4.7. Anticancer Activity

Cancer is a major public health problem in the world. The clinical management of cancer invariably involves diverse conventional modalities, including surgery, radiation and chemotherapy [153, 154]. Because of the complexity of human cancer, alternative management may be needed to improve the efficacy of therapeutic treatments and the quality of life of patients [155]. Cancer chemoprevention of treatment may combine natural products with chemotherapeutic agents to inhibit tumour development.

Polyphenolic phyto-constituents of dietary origin have been shown potent preventive and therapeutic properties. Dietary polyphenols, such as catechins and theaflavins have been critically evaluated to their pharmacological effects in several serious illnesses [156]. Dietary polyphenols owe their therapeutic effects to their ability to modulate several enzymes and signalling pathways [157]. Antioxidants are compounds that protect cells against the damaging effects of ROS released to create an imbalance between antioxidants and ROS. Oxidative stress has been linked to many different medical conditions, including cancer [158].

Catechins, theaflavins and therubigins are powerful antioxidants, they have shown considerable promise in their ability to prevent as well mitigate several chronic ailments [159]. Effects of green tea on cancer chemoprevention have been attributed to its antioxidant activities [160].

Numerous studies have provided promising evidence for the anticarcinogenic and chemopreventive properties of tea polyphenols [161]. The chemopreventive and anticarcinogenic activities of tea flavan-3-ols have been studied in cancers of several major organ systems, such as bladder, breast, colon, esophagus, head and neck, kidney, liver, lung, pancreas, prostate, stomach, skin and uterus [162]. Green tea polyphenols have effectively inhibited multiple stages of carcinogenesis: initiation, promotion and progression stages. However, the mechanisms of growth inhibition and apoptosis were not well understood or easy to identify. The majority of studies investigating green tea extract effect on cancer focus on monomeric flavan-3-ols [27].

Li et al. [163] reported that ROS accumulated in ginseng-treated colorectal cancer cells activated a cellular signalling defense pathway, and that ROS levels were reduced by a combination treatment with ginseng antioxidants. In another study, Rodriguez et al. [164] showed that the anticancer activity of panaxadiol (PD), a purified ginseng compound, was enhanced by EC, but not C. In a subsequent study, synergistic effects were observed in treating colon cancer cells with a combination of panaxadiol and EGCG, a major C found in green tea [165].

EGCG is the most abundant and powerful antioxidant in green tea for cancer chemoprevention [165]. The use of this C has been shown to inhibit cancer process *in vitro* and in animal models, not only during the initiation but also during progression and metastasis in a high variety of cancer types, including skin, breast, prostate, colorectal, liver and lung cancers [166]. In the study developed by Du et al. [167] evaluated the chemopreventive effects of 10 tea polyphenols on human colorectal cancer cells, EGCG showed the most potent antiproliferative effect. Their antiproliferative effect is even more potent than 5-fluorouracil, which is a chemotherapy drug on colorectal cancer [168].

Additionally, EGCG induced significant cell apoptosis in HCT-116 cells suggesting that the antiproliferative effects of EGCG in human colorectal cancer cells is at least in part thought the apoptosis pathway. Structure-activity relationship analysis showed that the galloylated catechins showed even more potent activity.

For example, the antiproliferative effects of GC, EGC, GCG and EGCG were stronger than their corresponding compounds C, EC, CG and ECG [165]. In other words, when the C unit is esterified with gallic acid, its antiproliferivative effect is increased significantly.

Singh et al. [169] suggest that EGCG inhibits cell viability or induces cytotoxicity in skin cancer cells through inactivation of β-caterin signalling, and that the inactivation of β-caterin involves the downregulation of: (i) inflammatory mediators; (ii) cell cycle regulatory proteins; (iii) cAMP levels; and (iv) cell survival signals in the human skin cancer cell lines.

One of the key chemopreventive mechanisms of EGCG is their ability to inhibit NF-κB activation via prevention of its binding to DNA [170]. Yang et al. [101] suggest that green tea polyphenols-induced production of H_2O_2 that plays a role in apoptosis mediation. Investigation of the effect of green tea flavan-3-ols on the growth and apoptosis of human prostate cancer DU 145 cells indicates that apoptosis induction occurs through increase ROS formation and mitochondrial depolarization. In this study, apoptosis induction appeared unrelated to members of the Bcl-2 family of cell cycle regulating genes [171]. EGCG also increases AP-1 factor associated responses via MAPK signalling [172]. Chen et al. [173] report EGCG potently induces MAPK induction in human cell lines HepG1, Ht-29 and HeLa (hepatoma, colon and cervical squamous, respectively).

Tea polyphenols have been shown to be hepatoprotective, several cases of liver toxicity have been reported after consumption of high doses of dietary supplements containing green tea [174]. A study by Lambert and colleagues (175) has demonstrated the hepatotoxic effects of high oral dose of EGCG. Thus, the overall toxic portfolio of tea polyphenols, especially the high doses consumed as dietary supplements, need through investigation.

Grape seeds proanthocyanidin extracts regulates the expression of cell cycle-related genes such as p53, Bcl-2- and c-myc [176]. Grape seed proanthocyanidins treatments decreases the expression of p53 and c-myc in Chang liver cells, indicating that proanthocyanidins ameliorate toxic effects associated with cancer therapy treatments. Grape seeds proanthocyanidin extract cytotoxicity to human breast, lung and gastric adenocarcinoma cells may coincide with up-regulation of Bc1-2 and down regulation of the oncogene c-myc [176].

Ramljak et al. (177) reported that the procyanidin pentamer from cocoa proved to be potent inhibitor of tyrosine kinase expression and thus an inhibitor of angiogenesis, additionally inhibits proliferation of human breast cancer cells by causing depolarization of mitochondrial membranes of MDA MB-231 cells and down-regulation of G1 modulatory proteins CdC-2 and p53 of MDA Mb-468 cells.

Recently, blueberry has received great deal of attention due to their anti-promotion and anti-proliferative activity against various forms of cancer [178]. Blueberry proanthocyanidins provide anti-proliferation activity against human prostate and mouse liver cancer cell lines [179].

Studies in cell lines have also demonstrated that flavan-3-ols can affect a range of signalling and metabolic pathways. These molecular events may result in cancer cell growth inhibition, apoptosis and inhibition, apoptosis and inhibition of invasion, angiogenesis and metastasis.

Conclusion

In conclusion, flavan-3-ols are flavonoids with various health benefits. They are ubiquitously in fruits, vegetables, tea and wine, being commonly present in the human diet. Interest in the biological properties of flavan-3-ols has emerged from *in vitro* and *in vivo* experimental evidence, indicating they have been shown antioxidant, antimicrobial, anti-viral, anti-parasitic activities. Their consumption has been suggested to have health benefits in preventing or mitigating the development of a variety of health problems, including diabetes, inflammatory, cardiovascular and neurodegenerative diseases and cancer. However, further studies are required to elucidate the several mechanisms involved in the prevention and treatment of the diseases with flavan-3-ols.

References

[1]   Paredes-López, O., Cervantes-Ceja, M. L., Vigna-Pérez, M. & Hérnandez-Pérez, T. (2010). Berries: Improving human health and healthy aging, and promoting quality — A review. *Plant Foods for Human Nutrition, 65*, 299–308.

[2]   Mudgal, V., Madaan, N., Mudgal, A. & Mishra, S. (2010). Dietary polyphenols and human health. *Asian Journal of Biochemistry, 5*, 154–162.

[3]   Pandey, K. B. & Rizvi, S. I. (2009). Plant polyphenols as dietary antioxidants in human health and disease. *Oxidative Medicine and Cellular Longevity, 2* (5), 270-278.

[4]   Visioli, F., Lastra, C. A., Andres-Cueva, C., Aviram, M., Calhau, C., Cassano, A., D'Archivio, M., Faria, A., Favé, G., Fogliano, V., Llorach, R., Vitaglione, P., Zoratti, M. &, Edeas, M. (2011). Polyphenols and human health: a prospectus. *Critical Reviews in Food Science and Nutrition, 51*, 524-546.

[5]   Beckman, C. H. (2000). Phenolic-storing cells: keys to programmed cell death and periderm formation in wilt disease resistance and in general defence responses in plants? *Physiological and Molecular Plant Pathology, 57*, 101-110.

[6]   Silva, L. R., Valentão, P. & Andrade, P. (2012). Phenolic compounds in honey as a health promoters. In:. Bondurand, H. Bosch (Eds.). Honey:

Production, *Consumption and Health Benefits. Nova Science Publishers,*
Inc.; pp 81-111.

[7]   Graf, B. A., Milbury, P. E. & Blimberg, J. B. (2005). Flavonols,
flavonones, flavanones and human health: epidemiological evidence.
Journal of Medicinal Food, 8, 281–290.

[8]   Arts, I. C. W. & Hollman, P. C. H. (2005). Polyphenols and disease risk
in epidemiologie studies. *American Society for Clinical Nutrition,* 81,
317-325.

[9]   Napolitano, A., Cascone, A., Graziani, G., Ferracane, R., Scalfi, L., Di
Vaio, C., Ritieni, A. & Fogliano, V, (2004). Influence of variety and
storage on the polyphenol composition of apple flesh. *Journal of
Agricultural and Food Chemistry,* 52, 6526–6531.

[10]   Miglio, C., Chiavaro, E., Viscont,i A., Fogliano, V. & Pellegrini, N.
(2008). Effects of different cooking methods on nutritional and
physicochemical characteristics of selected vegetables. *Journal of
Agricultural and Food Chemistry,* 56, 139–147.

[11]   Strack D. (1997). Plant Biochemistry. In: P. M. Dey & J. B. Harborne
(Eds.), London: Academic Press, pp. 387-416.

[12]   Monagas., M, Bartolomé, B. & Gómez-Cordovés, C. (2005). Updated
knowledge about the presence of phenolic compounds in wines. *Critical
Reviews in Food Science and Nutrition,* 45, 85-118.

[13]   Crozier ,A., Jaganath, I. B. & Clifford, M. N. (2009). Dietary phenolics:
chemistry, bioavailability and effects on health. *Natural Product
Reports,* 26(8), 965-1096.

[14]   Fernandez, S. P., Wasowski, C., Loscalzo, L. M., Granger, R. E.,
Johnston, G. A.R, Paladini, A. C. & Marder, M. (2006) Central nervous
system depressant action of flavonoid glycosides. *European Journal of
Pharmacology,* 539, 168-176.

[15]   Marais, J. P., Deavours, B., Dixon, R. A. & Ferreira, D. (2006). The
Science of Flavonoids. In: Grotewold, E. (Eds.), Ohio, USA: Springer
Science and Business Media, Inc, Columbus, pp. 1-46.

[16]   Haslam, E. (1998). Practical polyphenols: from structure to molecular
recognition and Physiological Action. Cambridge, UK: Cambridge
University Press.

[17]   Harbone, J. B. (1986). Nature, distribution, and function of plant
flavonoids. In: Cody V., Middleton, E., Harbone, J. B. (Eds.). Plant
flavonoids in biology and medicine: biochemical, pharmacological, and
structure-activity relationship. New York: Alan R. Liss.

[18] Kühnau, J. (1976). The flavonoids, a class of semi-essential food components: their role in human nutrition. *World Review of Nutrition and Dietetics,* 24, 117.

[19] Smith, G., Thomsen, S. J., Markham, K. R., Andary, C. & Cardon, D. (2000). The photostabilities of naturally occurring 5-hydroxyflavones, flavonols, their glycosides and their aluminium complexes. Journal of Photochemistry and Photobiology. *A, Chemistry,* 136, 87.

[20] Erlund, I. (2004). Review of the flavonoids quercetin, hesperetin, and naringenin. Dietary sources, bioactivities, bioavalability, and epidemiology. *Nutrition Research,* 24, 851-874.

[21] Clifford, M. N. (1986). Interations of Food Components. In: G. G. Birch and M. G. Lindley (Eds.). London: *Elsevier Applied Science,* pp. 143-164.

[22] Henning, S. M., Choo, J. J., & Heber. D. (2008). Nongallated compared with gallated flavan-3-ols in green and black tea are more bioavailable. *The Journal of Nutrition, Proceedings of the Fourth International Scientific Symposium on Tea and Human Health,* 1529S-1534S.

[23] Thangapazham, R. L., Passi, N. & Maheshwari, R. K. (2007). Green tea polyphenol and epigallocatechin gallate induce apoptosis and inhibit invasion in human breast cancer cells. *Cancer Biology & Therapy,* 6, 1938-1943.

[24] Velayutham, P., Babu, A. & Liu, D. (2008). Green tea catechins and cardiovascular health: an update. *Current Medicinal Chemistry,* 15, 1840-1850.

[25] da Silva Pinto, M. (2013). Tea: a new perspective on health benefits. Food Research International. In press. http://dx.doi.org/10.1016/j. foodres.2013.01.038.

[26] Scholz, S. & Williamson, G. (2007). Interactions affecting the bioavailability of dietary polyphenols in vivo. *International Journal for Vitamin and Nutrition Research. Supplement,* 77, 224-235.

[27] Aron, P. M. & Kennedy, J. A. (2008). Flavan-3-ols: nature, occurrence and biological activity. *Molecular Nutrition & Food Research,* 52, 79-104.

[28] Bruneton, J. (2009). Pharmacognosie, phytochimie, plantes médicinales, Lavoisier, Editions Tec & Doc.

[29] Braicu, C., Pilecki, V., Balacescu, O., Irimie, A. & Neagoe, I. B. (2011). The relationships between biological activities and structure of flavan-3-ols. *International Journal of Molecular Sciences,* 12, 9342-9353.

[30] Braicu, C., Rugina, D., Chedea, V. S., Balacescu, L., Brie, I., Soritau, O., Socaciu, C. & Irimie, A. (2010). Protective action of different natural flavan-3-ols against aflatoxin B1-related cytotoxicity. *Journal of Food Biochemistry*, 34, 595–610.

[31] Del Rio, D., Stewart, A. J., Mullen, W., Burns, J., Lean, M. E., Brighenti, F. & Crozier, A. (2004). HPLC-MS[n] analysis of phenolic compounds and purine alkaloids in green and black tea. *Journal of Agricultural and Food Chemistry*, 52, 2807-2815.

[32] Del Rio, D., Calani, L., Cordero, C., Salvatore, S., Pellegrini, N., Brighenti, F. (2010). Bioavailability and catabolism of green tea flavan-3-ols in humans. *Nutrition*, 26(11–12):1110–1116.

[33] Duthie, G. G. & Crozier, A. (2003). Beverages. In: Goldberg, G. (Eds.). Plants: Diet and Health. London: British Nutrition Foundation, *Chapman Hall*, pp 147-182.

[34] Ashihara, H., Deng, W-W., Mullen, W. & Crozier, A. (2010). Distribution and biosynthesis of flavan-3-ols in Camellia sinensis seedlings and expression of genes encoding biosynthetic enzymes. *Pytochemistry*, 71, 559-566.

[35] De Pascual-Teresa, S., Santos-Buelga, C. & Rivas-Gonzalo, J C (2000). Quantative analysis of flavan-3-ols in Spanish foodstuffs and beverages. *Journal of Agriculture and Food Chemistry*, 48, 5331-5337.

[36] Finger, A., Kuhr, S., Engelhardt, U. H. (1992). Chromatography of tea constituents. *Journal of Chromatography*, 624, 293-315.

[37] Balentine, D. A., Wiseman, S. A. & Bouwens, L. C. M. (1997). The chemistry of tea flavonoids. *Critical Reviews in Food Science and Nutrition*, 37, 693-704.

[38] Yiannakopoulou, E. C. (2013). Effect of green tea catechins on breast carcinogenesis: a systematic review of in-vitro and in-vivo experimental studies. *European Journal of Cancer Prevention*. In press.

[39] Cabana, R., Silva, L. R., Valentão, P., Viturro, C. I. & Andrade, P. B (2013). Effect of different extraction methodologies on the recovery of bioactive metabolites from Satureja parvifolia (Phil.) Epling (lamiaceae). *Industrial Crops and Products*, 48, 49-56.

[40] Carando, S., Teissedre, P–L., Pascual-Martinez, L. & Cabanis, J-C (1999).Levels of flavan-3-ols in French wines. *Journal of Agriculture and Food Chemistry*, 47, 4161- 4166.

[41] Silva, L. R., Andrade, P. B., Valentão, P., Seabra, R. M., Trujillo, M. E. & Velazquez, E. (2005). Analysis of non-coloured phenolics in red

wine: Effect of Dekkera bruxellensis yeast. *Food Chemistry,* 89, 185–189.

[42] Gu, L., Kelm, M. A., Hammerstone, J. F., Beecher, G., Holden, J., Haytowitz, D. & Prior, R. L. (2003). Screening of foods containing proanthocyanidins and their structural characterization using LC-MS/MS and thiolytic degradation. *Journal of Agriculture and Food Chemistry,* 51, 7513-7521.

[43] Marks, S. C., Mullen, W. & Crozier, A. (2007). Flavonoid and hydroxycinnamate profiles of english apple ciders. *Journal of Agriculture and Food Chemistry,* 55, 8723-8730.

[44] Wang, Y. & Ho, C. T. (2009). Metabolism of Flavonoids. In Yoshikawa T. (Eds.), Food Factors for Health Promotion. Forum Nutrition Basel, *Karger,* 61, pp 64–74.

[45] Li, S. & Ho, C.T. (2013). Metabolism, bioavailability, and safety features of green tea polyphenols. In Lekh R. Juneja, Mahendra P. Kapoor, Tsutomu Okubo, Theertham P. Rao Eds.), Green tea polyphenols: nutraceuticals of modern life. Boca Raton: CRC Press.

[46] van de Waterbeemd, H., Lennernas, H. & Artursson, P. (2003). Drug bioavailability. Estimation of solubility, permeability, absorption and bioavailability. Weinheim: Wiley-VCH.

[47] Auger, C., Mullen, W., Hara, Y. & Crozier, A. (2008). Bioavailability of polyphenols. Flavan-3-ols in humans with an ileostomy. *The Journal of Nutrition, Proceedings of the Fourth International Scientific Symposium on Tea and Human Health.*

[48] Calani, L., Del Rio, D., Callegari, M. L., Morelli, L. & Brighenti, F. (2012). Updated bioavailability and 48 h excretion profile of flavan-3-ols from green tea in humans. *International Journal of Food Sciences and Nutrition,* 63(5), 513–521.

[49] Yan, Z. & Caldwell, G. W. (2001). Metabolism profiling, and cytochrome P450 inhibition and induction in drug discovery. *Current Topics in Medicinal Chemistry,* 1, 403–425.

[50] Lambert, J. D., Sang, S. & Yang, C. S. (2007). Biotransformation of green tea polyphenols and the biological activities of those metabolites. *Molecular Pharmaceutics,* 4 (6), 819–825.

[51] Thilakarathna, S. H. & Rupasinghe, H. P. V. (2013). Flavonoid bioavailability and attempts for bioavailability enhancement. *Nutrients,* 5, 3367-3387.

[52] Feng, Y. W. (2006). Metabolism of green tea catechins: An overview. *Current Drug Metabolism,* 7, 755–809.

[53] Prior, R. L., Wu, X. & Gu, L. (2006). Perspective flavonoid metabolism and challenges to understanding mechanics of health effects. *Journal of the Science of Food and Agriculture*, 86, 2487–2491.

[54] Tsang, C., Auger, C., Mullen, W., Bornet, A., Rouanet, J. M., Crozier, A. & Teissedre, P. L. (2006). The absorption, metabolism and excretion of flavan-3-ols and procyanidins following the ingestion of a grape seed extract by rats. *The British Journal of Nutrition*, 95, 847.

[55] Fernandes, I., Nave, F., Gonçalves, R., de Freitas, V. & Mateus, N. (2012). On the bioavailability of flavanols and anthocyanins: Flavanol–anthocyanin dimers. *Food Chemistry*, 135, 812–818.

[56] Manach, C., Williamson, G., Morand, C., Scalbert, A. & Rémésy, C. (2005). Bioavailability and bioefficacy of polyphenols in humans. I. Review of 97 bioavailability studies. *The American Journal of Clinical Nutrition*, 8, 230S–242S.

[57] Cos, P., De Bruyne, T., Hermans, S., Apers, S., Berghe, D. V. & Vlietinck, A. J. (2003). Proanthocyanidins in health care: current and new trends. *Current Medicinal Chemistry*, 10, 1345-1359.

[58] Beecher, G. (2004). Proanthocyanidins: biological activities associated with human health. *Pharmaceutical Biology*, 42, 2-20.

[59] Socha, R., Baczkowicz, M., Fortuna, T., Kura, A., Labanowska, M. & Kurdziel, M. (2013). Determination of free radicals and flavan-3-ols content in fermented and unfermented teas and properties of their infusions. *European Food Research and Technology*, 237, 167-177.

[60] Rice-Evans, C. A., Miller, N. J. & Paganga, G. (1996). Structure-antioxidant activity relationships of flavonoids and phenolic acids. *Free Radical Biology & Medicine*, 20, 9333-956.

[61] deFreitas, V. A. P., Glories, Y. &, Laguerre, M. (1998). Incidence of molecular structure in oxidation of grape seed procyanidins. *Journal of Agriculture and Food Chemistry*, 46, 376-382.

[62] Zhao, M. M., Yang, B., Wang, J. S., Li, B. Z. & Jiang, Y. M. (2006). Identification of the major flavonoids from pericarp tissues of lychee fruit in relation to their antioxidant activity. *Food Chemistry*, 98, 536-544.

[63] Plumb G. W., De Pascual-Teresa, S., Santos-Buelga, C., Cheynier, V. & Williamson, G. (1998). Antioxidant properties of catechins and proanthocyanidins: effect of polymerization, galloylation and glycosylation. *Free Radical Research*, 29, 351-358.

[64] Kavanagh, K. T., Hafer, L. J., Kim, D. W., Mann, K. K., Sherr, D. H., Rogers, A. E. & Sonenshein, G. E. (2001). Green tea extracts decrease

carcinogen-induced mammary tumor burden in rats and rate of breast cancer cell proliferation in culture. *Journal of Cellular Biochemistry, 82,* 387-398.

[65] Guo, Q., Zhao, B., Shen, S., Hou, J., Hu, J. & Xin, W. (1999). ESR study on the structure–antioxidant activity relationship of tea catechins and their epimers. *Biochimica et Biophysica Acta, 1427,* 13–23.

[66] Chobot, V., Huber, C., Trettenhahn, G. & Hadacek, F. (2009). (±)-Catechin: Chemical weapon, antioxidant, or stress regulator. *Journal of Chemical Ecology, 35,* 980–996.

[67] Nanjo, F.., Mori, M., Goto, K. & Hara, Z. (1999) Radical scavenging activity of tea catechins and their related compounds. *Bioscience, Biotechnology, and Biochemistry, 6,* 1621–1623.

[68] Heim, K. E., Tagliaferro, A. R. & Bobilya, D. J. (2002). Flavonoid antioxidants: Chemistry, metabolism and structure-activity relationships. *The Journal of Nutritional Biochemistry, 13,* 572–584.

[69] Yang, C. S., Kim, S., Yang, G. Y. & Lee, M. J. (1999). Inhibition of carcinogenesis by tea: Bioavailability of tea polyphenols and mechanisms of actions. *Proceedings of the Society for Experimental Biology and Medicine, 220,* 213–217.

[70] Dwibedy, P., Dey, G. R., Naik, D. B., Kishore, K. & Moorthy, P. N. (1999). Pulse radiolysis studies on redox reactions of gallic acid: One electron oxidation of gallic acid by gallic acid–OH adduct. *Physical Chemistry Chemical Physics, 1,* 1915–1918.

[71] Weisburg, J. H., Weissman, D. B., Sedaghat, T. & Babich, H. (2004). In vitro cytotoxicity of epigallocatechin gallate and tea extracts to cancerous and normal cells from the human oral cavity. *Basic & Clinical Pharmacology & Toxicology, 95,* 191–200.

[72] Chung, K-T., Wong, T. Y., Wei, C-I., Huang, Y-W. & Lind, Y. (1998). Tannins and human health: a review. *Critical Reviews in Food Science and Nutrition, 38(6),* 421-464.

[73] Ma, C. M., Nakamura, N., Miyashiro, H., Hattori, M. & Shimotohno, K. (1999). Inhibitory effects of constituents from Cynomorium songaricum and related triterpenes derivatives on HIV-1 protease. *Chemical & Pharmaceutical Bulletin, 47,* 141-145.

[74] Hashimoto, F., Kashiwada, Y., Nonaka, G., Nishioka, I., Nohara, T., Cosentino, L. M. & Lee, K. H. (1996). Evaluation of tea polyphenols as anti-HIV agents. *Bioorganic & Medicinal Chemistry Letters, 6,* 695-700.

[75] Nakane, H. & Ono, K. (1990). Differential inhibitory effects of some catechin derivatives on the activities of human immunodeficiency virus

reverse transcriptase and cellular deoxyribonucleic and ribonucleic acid polymerases. *Biochemistry,* 29, 2841-2845.

[76] Jin, S., Eerdunbayer, Doi, A., Kuroda, T., Zhang, G., Hatano, T. & Chen, G. (2012). Polyphenolic constituents of Cynomorium songaricum Rupr. And antibacterial effect of polymeric proanthocyanidin on methicillin-resistant Staphylococcus aureus. *Journal Agriculture of Food Chemistry,* 60, 7297-7305.

[77] Chung, K-T., Stevens, S. E. Jr., Lin, W-F. & Wei, C. I. (1993). Growth inhibition of selected food-borne bacteria by tannic acid, propyl gallate and related compounds. *Letters in Applied Microbiology,* 17, 29-32.

[78] Akiyama, H., Fujii, K., Yamasaki, O., Oono, T. & Iwatsuki, K. (2001). Antibacterial action of several tannins against Staphylococcus aureus. Journal of Antimicrobial Chemotherapy, 48, 487-491.

[79] Shiota, S., Shimizu, M., Mizushima, T., Ito, H., Hatano, T., Yoshida, T. & Tsuchiya, T. (1999). Marked reduction in the minimum inhibitory concentration (MIC) of β-lactams in methicillin-resistant Staphylococcus aureus produced by epicatechin gallate, an ingredient of green tea (Camellia sinensis). *Biological and Pharmaceutical Bullentin,* 22, 1388-1390.

[80] Kusuda, M., Inada, K., Ogawa, T. O., Yoshida, T., Shiota, S., Tsuchiya, T. & Hatano, T. (2006). Phenolic constituent structures of Zanthoxylum pipericum fruit and the antibacterial effects of its polymeric procyanidin on methicillin-resistant Staphylococcus aureus. *Bioscience, Biotechnology, and Biochemistry,* 70, 1423-1431.

[81] Stapleton, P. D., Shah, S., Anderson, J. C., Hara, Y., Hamilton-Miller, J. M. T. & Taylor, P. W. (2004). Modulations of β-lactam resistance in Staphycococcus aureus by catechins and gallates. *International Journal of Antimicrobial Agents, 23,* 462-467.

[82] Takahashi, O., Cai, Z., Toda, H., Hara, Y. & Shimamura, T. (1995). Appearance of antibacterial activity of oxacillin against methicillin resistant Staphylococcus aureus (MRSA) in the presence of catechin. *Journal of the Japan Association for Infectious Disease,* 69, 1126-1134.

[83] Li, X. C., ElSohly, H. N., Nimrod, A. C. & Clark, A. M. (1999). Antifungal activity of (-)-epigallocatechin gallate from Coccoloba dugandiana. Planta Medica, 65(8), 780.

[84] Saito, H., Tamura, M., Imai, K., Ishigami, T. & Ochiai, K. (2013). Catechin inhibits Candida albicans dimorphism by disrupting Cek1 phosphorylation and cAMP synthesis. *Microbial Pathogenesis,* 56, 16-20.

[85] Molan, A. L., Sivakumaran, S., Spencer, P. A. & Meagher, L. P. (2004). Green tea flavan-3-ols and oligomeric proanthocyanidins inhibit the motility of infective larvae of Teladorsagia circumcincta and Trichostrongylus colubriformis in vitro. *Research Veterinary Science*, 77, 239-243.

[86] Paveto, C., Guida, M. C., Esteva, M. I., Martino, V., Coussio, J., Flawiá, M. M. & Torres, H. N. (2004). Anti-Trypanosoma cruzi activity of green tea (Camellia sinensis) catechins. *Antimicrobial Agents and Chemotherapy*, 48(1), 69-74.

[87] Min, B. R. & Hart, S. P. (2003). Tannins for suppression of internal parasites. *Journal of Animal Science*, 81, E102-E109.

[88] Yang, C. S., Sang, S., Lambert, J. D. & Lee, M. J. (2008). Bioavailability issues in studying the health effects of plant polyphenolic compounds. *Molecular Nutrition & Food Research*, 52 (Suppl.1), S139-S151.

[89] Lee, M. J., Maliakal, P., Chen, L., Meng, X., Bondoc, F. Y., Prabhu, S., Lambert, G., Mohr, S. & Yang, C. S. (2002). Pharmacokinetics of tea catechins after ingestion of green tea and (-)-epigallocatechin-3-gallate by humans: formation of different metabolites and individual variability. *Cancer Epidemiology, Biomarkers & Prevention*, 11, 1025-1032.

[90] Alavijeh, M. S., Chishty, M., Qaiser, M. Z., Palmer, A. M. (2005). Drug metabolismo and pharmacokinetics, the blood barrier, and central nervous system drug discovery. *NeuroRx*, 2, 554-571.

[91] Ferrero-Miliani, I., Nielsen, O. H., Andersen, P. S. & Girardini, S. E. (2007). Chronic inflammation: importance of NOD2 and NALP3 in interleukin-1beta generation. *Clinical and Experimental Immunology*, 147, 227-235.

[92] Shahidi, F. & Zhong, Y. (2009). Antioxidants, polyphenols and adipose inflammation. In A. B. Awad & P. G. Bradford (Eds.). Adipose tissue and inflammation Boca Raton, FL: CRC Press, Taylor & Francis Inc, pp. 233-234.

[93] Kamada, H. & Hirata, H. (1999). Redox regulation of cellular signaling. *Cellular Signalling.*, 11, 1-14.

[94] Pan, M. H., Yang, J. R., Tsai, M. L. & Ho, C. T. (2009). Anti-inflammatory effect of Momordica grovesnori Swingle extract through suppressed LPS-induced upregulation of iNOS and COX-2 in murine macrophages. *Journal of Functional Foods*, 1, 145-152.

[95] Mann, J. R., Backlund, M. G. & DuBois, R. N. (2005). Mechanisms of disease: inflammatory mediators and cancer prevention. *Nature Clinical Practice Oncology,* 2, 202-210.

[96] Chaudhuri, A. K., Karmakar, S., Roy, D., Pal, S., Pal, M. & Sen, T. (2005). Anti-inflammatory activity of Indian black tea (Sikkim variety). *Pharmacological Research,* 51, 169-175.

[97] Tedeschi, E., Menegazzi, M., Yao, Y., Suzuki, H., Forstermann, U. & Kleinert, H. (2004). Green tea inhibits inducible nitric-oxide synthase expression by down-regulating signal transducer and activator of transcription-1α activation. *Molecular Pharmacology,* 65, 111-210

[98] Bodet, C., Chandad, F. & Grenier, D. (2006). Anti-inflammatory activity of high-molecular-weight cranberry fraction on macrophages stimulated by lipopolysaccharides from periodontopathogens. *Journal of Dental Research,* 85, 235-239.

[99] Singh, U., Tabibian, J., Venugopal, S. K., Devaraj, S. & Jialal, I. (2005). Development of na in vitro screening assay to test the anti-inflammatory properties of dietary supplements and pharmacologic agents. *Clinical Chemistry,* 51, 2252-2256.

[100] Ichikawa, D., Matsui, A., Imai, M., Sonoda, Y. & Kasahara, T. (2004). Effect of various catechins on IL-12p40 production by murine peritoneal macrophages and a macrophage cell line J774.1. *Biological & Pharmaceutical Bulletin,* 27, 1353-1358.

[101] Yang, G-Y., Liao, J., Kim, K., Yurkow, E. J. & Yang, C. S. (1998). Inhibition of growth and induction of apoptosis in human cancer cell lines by tea polyphenols. *Carcinogenesis,* 19, 611-616.

[102] Ahmed, S., Rahman, A., Hasnain, A., Lalonde, M., Goldberg, V. M. & Haqqi, T. M. (2002). Green tea polyphenol epigallocatechin-3-gallate inhibits the IL-1 beta-induced activity and expression of cyclooxygenase-2 and nitric oxide synthase-2 in human chondrpcytes. *Free Radical Biology & Medicine,* 33, 1097-1105.

[103] Cui, Y., Kim, D. S., Park, S. H., Yoon, J. A., Kim, S. K., Kwon, S. B. & Park, K. C.. (2004). Involvement of ERK and p38 MAP kinase in AAPH-induced COX-2 expression in Hacat cells. *Chemistry and Physics of Lipids,* 129, 43-52.

[104] Hussain, T., Gupta, S., Adhami, V. M. & Mukhtar, H. (2005). Green tea constituent epigallocatechin-3-gallate selectively inhibits COX-2 without affecting COX-1 expression in human prostate carcinoma cells. *International Journal of Cancer,* 113, 660-669.

[105] Porath, D., Riegger, C., Drewe, J. & Schwager, J. (2005). Epigallocatechin-3-gallate impairs chemokine production in human colon epithelial cell lines. *The Journal of Pharmacology and Experimental Therapeutics*, 315, 1172-1180.

[106] Babu, P. V. A. & Liu, D. (2013). Recent advances in understanding the anti-diabetic actions of dietary flavonoids. *Journal of Nutritional Biochemistry*, 24, 1777-1789.

[107] Li, D.-Q., Quia, Z.-M. & Li, S.-P. (2010). Inhibition of three selected beverages extracts on a-glucosidase and rapid identification of their active compounds using HPLC–DAD-MS/MS and biochemical detection. *Journal of Agriculture and Food Chemistry*, 58(11), 6608–6613.

[108] Ma, C.-M., Sato, N., Li, X-Y., Nakamura, N. & Hattori, M. (2010). *Flavan-3-ol contentes, anti-oxidative and α-glucosidase inhibitory activities of Cynomorium songaricum. Food Chemistry*, 118, 116-119.

[109] Iso, H., Date, C., Wakai, K., Fukui, M. & Tamakoshi, A. (2006). The relationship between green tea and total caffeine intake and risk for self-reported type-2 diabetes among Japanese adults. *Annals of Internal Medicine*, 144, 554.562.

[110] Odegaard, A. O., Pereira, M. A., Koh, W-P., Arakawa, K., Lee, H-P. & Yu, M. C. (2008). Cofee, tea and incident type 2 diabetes: The Singapore Chinese health study. *American Journal of Clinical Nutrition*, 88, 979-985.

[111] Huxley, R., Lee, C. M. Y., Barzi, F., Timmermeister, L., Czernichow, S., Perkovic, V., Grobbee, D. E., Batty, D. & Woodward, M. (2009). Coffee, decaffeinated coffe, and tea consumption in relation to incident type 2 diabetes mellitus: A systematic review with meta-analysis. *Archives of Internal Medicine*, 169, 2053-2063.

[112] Hosoda, K., Wang, M. F., Liao, M. L., Chuang, C. K., Ilha, M., Clevidence, B. & Yamamoto, S. (2003). Antihyperglycemic effect of oolong tea in type-2 diabetes. *Diabetes Care*, 26, 1714-1718.

[113] Rizvi, S. I., Zaid, M. A., Anis, R. & Mishra, N. (2005). Protective role of tea catechins against oxidation-induced damage of type 2 diabetic erythrocytes. *Clinical and Experimental Pharmacology & Physiology*, 32, 70-75.

[114] Tsuneki, H., Ishizuka, M., Terasawa, M., Wu, J. B., Sasaoka, T. & Kymura, I. (2004). Effect of green tea on blood glucose levels and serum proteomic patterns in diabetic /db/db) mice and on glucose metabolism in healthy humans.BMC Pharmacology, 4, 18.

[115] Kao, Y. H., Hiipakka, R. A., Liao, S. (2000). Modulation of endocrine systems and food intake by green tea epigallocatechin gallate. *Encodrinology,* 141, 980-987.

[116] Besser,G.M. & Thorner, M. O. (2002). Comprehensive Clinical Endocrinology (3rd edn.), MOSBY, an affiliate of Elsevier Science, London.

[117] Matsumoto, N., Ishigaki, F., Ishigaki, A., Iwashina, H. & Hara, Y. (1993).Reduction of blood glucose levels by tea catechin. Bioscience, *Biotechnology, and Biochemistry,* 57, 525-527.

[118] Ortsäter, H., Grankvist, N., Wolfram, S., Kuehn, N. & Sjöholm, A, (2012). Diet supplementation with green tea extract epigallocatechin gallate prevents progression to glucose intolerance in db/db mice. *Nutrition & Metabolism,* 9, 11.

[119] Sabu, M. C., Smitha, K. & Kuttan, R. L. (2002). Anti-diabetic activity of green tea polyphenols and their role in reducing oxidative stress in experimental diabetes. *Journal of ethnopharmacology,* 83, 109-116.

[120] Nussbaum, R. L. & Ellis, C. E. (2003). Alzheimer's disease and Parkinson's disease. *The New England Journal of Medicine,* 348(14), 1356-1364.

[121] Jellinger, K. A. (2001). Ell death mechanisms in neurodegeneration. *Journal of Cellular and Molecular Medicine,* 5, 1-17.

[122] Lindsay, J., Laurin, D., Verreault, R., Hebert, R., Helliwell, B., Hill, G. B. & McDowell, I. (2002). Risk factors for Alzheimer's disease: A prospective analysis from the Canadian study of health and aging. *American Journal of Epidemiology,* 156, 445-453.

[123] Commenges, D., Scotet, V., Renaud, S., Jacqmin-Gadda, H., Barberger-Gateau, P. & Dartigues, J. F. (2000). Intakes of flavonoids and risk of dementia. *European Journal of Epidemiology,* 16, 357-363.

[124] Letenneur, L., Proust-Lima, C., Le, G. A., Dartigues, J. F. & Barberger-Gateau, P. (2007). Flavonoid intake and cognitive decline over a 10 year period. *American Journal of Epidemiology,* 165, 1364-1472.

[125] Dai, Q., Borenstein, A. R., Wu, Y., Jackson, J. C. & Larson, E. B. (2006). Fruit and vegetable juices and Alzheimer's disease: the kame project. *The American Journal of Medicine,* 119, 751-759

[126] Ng, T-P., Feng, I., Niti, M., Kua, E-H. & Yap, K-B. (2008). Tea consumption and cognitive impairment and decline in older Chinese adults. *American Journal of Clinical Nutrition,* 88, 224-231.

[127] Niu, K., Hozawa, A., Kuryama, S., Ebihara, S., Guo, H., Nakaya, N.. et al., (2009). Green tea consumption is associated with depressive

symptoms in the elderly. *The American Journal of Clinical Nutrition,* 90, 1615–1622

[128] Tan, E. K., Fook-Chong, S. M., Lum, S. Y., Chai, A., Chung, H., Shen, H., Zhao, Y., Teoh, M. L., Yih, Y., Pavanni, R., Chandram, V. R. & Wong, M. C. (2003). Dose-dependent protective effect of coffee, tea and smoking in Parkinson's disease: a study in ethnic Chinese. *Journal of the Neurological Sciences,* 216, 163-167.

[129] Chekoway, H., Powers, K., Smith-Weller, T., Franklin, G. M., Longstreth, W. T. Jr. & Swanson, P. D. (2002). Parkinson's disease mumption, and caffeine intake. *American Journal of Epidemiology,* 155, 732-738.

[130] Bastianetto, S., Yao, Z-X., Papadopoulos, V. & Quirion, R. (2006). Neuroprotective effects of green and black teas and their catechin gallate esters against β-amyloid-induced toxicity. *European Journal of Neuroscience,* 23, 55-64.

[131] Youdim, K. A., Qaiser, M. Z., Begley, D. J., Rice-Evans, C. A. & Abbott, N. J. (2004). Flavonoid permeability across an in situ model of the blood-brain barrier. *Free Radical Biology & Medicine,* 36, 592-604.

[132] Zini, A., Del Rio, D., Stewart, A. J., Mandrioli, J., Merelli, E., Sola, P., Serafini, M., Serafini, M., Brighenti, F., Edwards, C. A. & Crozier, A. (2006). *Do flavan-3-ols From Green tea reach the human brain? Nutritional Neuroscience,* 9, 57-61.

[133] Kerns, E. H. & Di, L. (2008). Blood-brain barrier. In E. H. Kerns & I. Di (Eds.), Drug-like properties: concepts, structure design and methods, from ADME to toxicity optimization. London: Academic Press-Elsevier, pp. 122-136.

[134] Lee, S. Y., Lee, J. W., Lee, H., Yoo, H. S., Yun, Y. P., Oh, K. W., Ha, T. Y. & Hong, J. T. (2005). Inhibitory effect of green tea extract on β-amyloid-induced PC12 cell death by inhibition of the activation of NF.kB and ERK/p38 MAP kinase pathway through antioxidant mechanisms. Brain Research. *Molecular Brain Research,* 140, 45/54.

[135] Choi, H. T., Pae, H. O., Choi, B. M., Billiar, T. R. & Kim, Y. M. (2001). Nitric oxide as a bioregulator of apoptosis. *Biochemical and Biophysical Research Communications,* 282, 1075-1079.

[136] Ban, J. Y., Jeon, S. Y., Bae, K., Song, K. S. & Seong, Y. H. (2006). Catechin and epicatechin from Smilacis chinae rhizome protect cultured rat cortical neurons against amyloid β protein (35)-induced neurotoxicity through inhibition of cytosolic calcium elevation. *Life Science,* 79, 2251-2259.

[137] Tanasescu, M., Leitzmann, M. F., Rimm, E. B., Willet, W. C., Strampfer, M. J. & Hu F. B. (2002). Exercise type and intensity in relation to coronary heart disease in men. *JAMA,* 288, 1994-2000.

[138] Hooper, L., Kay, C., Abdelhamid, A., Kroon, P., Chn, J. S., Rimm, E. B. & Aedín-Cassidy (2012). Effects of chocolate, cocoa, and flavan-3-ols on cardiovascular health: a systematic review and meta-analises of randomized trials. *The American Journal of Clinical Nutrition,* 95, 740-751.

[139] Bagchi, D. B., Sen, C. K., Ray, S. D., Das, D. K., Bagchi, M., Preuss, H. G. & Vinson, J. A. (2003). Molecular mechanisms of cardioprotection by a novel grape seed proanthocyanidin extract. *Mutation Research-Fundamental and Molecular Mechanisms of Mutagenesis,* 523, 87-97.

[140] Rasmussen, S. E., Frederiksen, H., Krogholm, K. S. & Poulsen, L. (2005). Dietary proanthocyanidins: occurrence, dietary intake, bioavailability, and protection against cardiovascular disease. *Molecular Nutrition & Food Research,* 49, 159-174.

[141] Ottaviani, J. I., Actis-Goretta, L., Villordo, J. J. & Fraga, C. G. (2006). Procyanidin structure defines the extent and specificity of angiotensin I converting enzyme inhibition. *Biochimie,* 88, 359-365.

[142] Vita, J. A. (2003). Tea consumption and cardiovascular disease: effects on endothelial function. *The Journal of Nutrition,* 133, 3293S-3297S.

[143] Kuriyama, S., Shimazu, T., Ohmori, K., Kikuchi, N., Nakaya, N., Nishino, Y., Tsubono, Y. & Tsuji, I. (2006). Green tea consumption and mortality due to cardiovascular disease, cancer, and all causes in Japan: the Ohsaki study. *Jama,* 296, 1255-1265.

[144] Imai, K. & Nakachi, K. (1995). Cross sectional study of effects of drinking green tea on cardiovascular and liver diseases. *BMJ,* 310, 693-696.

[145] Shenouda, S. M. & Vita, J. A. (2007). Effects of flavonoid-containing beverages and EGCG on endotelial function. *Journal of the American College of Nutrition,* 26, 366S-372S.

[146] Stoclet, J. C., Kleschyov, A., Andriambeloson, E., Diebolt, M. & Andriantsitohaina, R. (1999). Endothelial NO release caused by red wine polyphenols, *Journal of Physiology and Pharmacology,* 50, 535–540.

[147] Fitzpatrick, D. F., Fleming, R. C., Bing, B., Maggi, D. A., O'Malley, R. M. (2000). Isolation and characterization od endothelium-dependent vasorelaxing compounds from grape seeds. *Journal of Agriculture and Food Chemistry,* 48, 6384-6390.

[148] Tomero, J. F. (1999). Current knowledge of the health benefits and disadvantages of wine consumption. *Trends in Food Science & Technology,* 10, 129-138.

[149] Steinberg, F. M., Holt, R. R., Schmitz, H. H. & Keen, C. L. (2002). Cocoa procyanidin chain lenght does not determine ability to protect LDL from oxidation when monomer units are controlled. *The Journal of Nutritional Biochemistry,* 13, 645-652.

[150] Serafini, M., Laranjinha, J. A., Almeida, L. M. & Maiani, G., (2000). Inhibition of human LDL lipid peroxidation by phenol-rich beverages and their impact on plasma total antioxidant capacity in humans. *The Journal of Nutritional Biochemistry,* 11, 585–590.

[151] Sung, H., Min, W. K., Lee, W., Chun, S., Park, H., Lee, Y. W., Jang, S. & Lee, D. H. (2005). The effects of green tea ingestion over 4 weeks on atherosclerotic markers. *Annals of Clinical Biochemistry,* 42, 292–297.

[152] Actis-Goretta, L., Ottaviani, J. I. & Fraga, C. G. (2006). Inhibition of angiotensin converting enzyme activity by flavanol-rich foods. *Journal of Agriculture and Food Chemistry,* 54, 229-234.

[153] Wood, C. G. (2007). Multimodal approaches in the management of locally advanced and metastic renal cell carcinoma: combining surgery and systemic therapies to improve patient outcome. *Clinical Cancer Research,* 13, 697s-702s.

[154] Randhawa, M. A. & Alghamdi, M. S. (2011). Anticancer activity of Nigella sativa (black seed) – A review. *The American Journal of Chinese Medicine, 39,* 1075-1091.

[155] Xu, Z., Chen, X., Zhong, Z., Chen, L. & Wang, Y. (2011). Ganoderma lucidum polysaccharides: immunomodulation and potential anti-tumor activities. *American Journal of Chinese Medicine,* 39, 15-27.

[156] Huang, W. Y., Cai, Y. Z. & Zhang, Y. (2010). Natural phenolic compounds from medicinal herbs and dietary plants: potential use of cancer prevention. *Nutrition and Cancer,* 62, 1-20.

[157] Lambert, J. D., Hong, J. & Yang, G. Y. (2005). Inhibition of carcinogenesis by polyphenols: evidence from laboratory investigations. *The American Journal of Clinical Nutrition,* 81, 284-291.

[158] Lawless, M. W., O'Byrne, K. J. & Gray, S. G. (2010). Targeting oxidative stress in cancer. *Expert Opinion on Therapeutic Targets,* 14, 1225-1245.

[159] Zaveri, N. T. (2006). Green tea and its polyphenolic catechins: medicinal uses in cancer and noncancer applications. *Life Science,* 78, 2073-2080.

[160] Mak, J. C. (2012). Potential role of green tea catechins in various disease therapies: *progress and promise. Clinical and Experimental Pharmacology & Physiology,* 39, 265-273.

[161] Yuan, J-M. (2013). Cancer prevention by green tea: evidence from epidemiologic studies. *The American Journal of Clinical Nutrition,* Doi:10.3945/ajcn.113.058271.

[162] Yang, C. S., Wang, X., Lu, G. & Picinish, S. C. (2009). Cancer prevention by tea: animal studies, molecular mechanisms and human relevance. Nature Reviews. *Cancer,* 9, 429-439.

[163] Li, B., Zhao, J., Wang, C. Z., Searle, J., He, T. C., Yuan, C. S. & Du, W. (2011). Ginsenoside Rh2 induces apoptosis and paraptosis-like cell death in colorectal cancer cell through activation of p53. *Cancer Letters,* 301, 185-192.

[164] Rodriguez, M., Du, G. J., Wang, C. Z. & Yuan, C. S. (2010). Letter to the editor: Panaxadiol's anticancer activity is enhanced by epicatechin. *The American Journal of Chinese Medicine,* 38, 1233-1235.

[165] Du, G-J., Zhang, Z., Wen, X-D., Yu, C., Yu, C., Calway, T., Yuan, C-S. & Wang, C-Z. (2012). Epigallocatechin gallate (EGCG) is the most effective cancer chemopreventive polyphenol in green tea. *Nutrients,* 4, 1679-1691.

[166] Singh, B. N., Shankar, S. & Srivastava, R. K. (2011). Green tea catechin, epigallocatechin-3-gallate (EGCG): mechanisms, perspectives and clinical applications. *Biochemistry & Pharmacology,* 82, 1807-1821.

[167] Du, G. J., Wang, C. Z., Qi, L. W., Zhang, Z. Y., Calway, T., He, T. C., Du, W. & Yuan, C. S. (2012). The synergistic apoptotic interaction of panaxadiol and epigallocatechin gallate in human colorectal cancer cells. *Phytotherapy Research.* Doi:10.1002/ptr.4707.

[168] Wang, C. Z., Luo, X., Zhang, B., Song, W. X., Ni, M., Mehendale, S., Xie, J. T., Aung, H. H., He, T. C. & Yuan, C. S. (2007). Notoginseng enhances anti-cancer effect of 5-fluorouracil on human colorectal cancer cells. *Cancer Chemotherapy and Pharmacology,* 60, 69-79.

[169] Singh, T. & Katiyar, S. K. (2013). Green tea polyphenols, (-)-epigallocatechin-3-gallate, induces toxicity in human skin cancer cells by targeting β-catenin signaling. *Toxicology and Applied Pharmacology,* doi: org/10.1016/j.taap.2013.09.021.

[170] Lin, Y. L. & Lin, J. K. (1997). (-)-Epigallocatechin-3-gallate blocks the induction of nitric oxide synthase by down-regulating lipopolysaccharide-induced activity of transcription factor nuclear factor-kappa B. *Molecular Pharmaceutics,* 52, 465-472.

[171] Chung, L. Y., Cheung, T. C., Kong, S. K., Fung, S. K., Fung, K. P., Choy, Y. M., Chan, Z. Y., Kwok, T. T. (2001). Induction of apoptosis by green tea catechins in human prostate cancer DU 145 cells. *Life Sciences,* 68, 1207-1214.

[172] Jeong, W., S., Kim, I. W., Hu, R. & Kong, A. N. T. (2004). Modulation of AP-1 by natural chemopreventive compounds in human colon HT-29 cancer cell line. *Pharmaceutical Biology,* 21, 649-660.

[173] Chen, C., Shen, G., Hebbar, V., Hu, R., Owuor, E, D. & Kong, A. N. (2003). Epigallocatechin-3-gallate induced stress signals in HT-29 human colon adenocarcinoma cells. *Carcinogenesis,* 24, 1369-1378.

[174] Mazzanti, G., Menniti-Ippolito, F., Moro, P. A., Cassetti, F., Raschetti, R., Santuccio, C. & Mastrangelo, S. (2009). Hepatotoxicity from green tea: a review of the literature and two unpublished cases. *European Journal of Clinical Pharmacology,* 65, 331-341.

[175] Lambert, J. D., Kenett, M. J., Sang, S., Reuhl, K. R., Ju, J. & Yang, C. S. (2010). Hepatotoxicity of high oral dose (-)-epigallocatechins-3-gallate in mice. *Food Chemical Toxicology,* 48, 409-416.

[176] Bagchi, D., Bagchi, M., Stohs, S. J., Das, D. K., Ray, S. D., Kuszynski, C. A., Joshi, S. S. & Pruess, H. G. (2000). Free radicals and grape seed proanthocyanidin extract: importance in human health and disease prevention. *Toxicology,* 148, 187-197.

[177] Ramljak, D., Romanczyk, L. J., Metheny-Barlow, L. J., Thompson, N., Knezevic, V., Galperin, M., Ramesh, A. & Dickson, R. B. (2005). Pentameric procyanidin from Theobroma cacao selectivity inhibits growth of human breast cancer cells. *Molecular Cancer Therapeutics,* 4, 537-546.

[178] Schmidt, B. M., Erdman, J. W. & Lila, M. A. (2006). Differential effects of bluberry proanthocyanidins on androgen sensitive and insensitive human prostate cancer cell lines. *Cancer Letters,* 231, 240-246.

[179] Schmidt, B. M., Howell, A. B., McEniry, B., Knight, C. T., Seigler, D., Erdman, J. W. Jr. & Lila, M. A. (2004). Effective separation of potent anti proliferation and anti-adhesion components from wild bluberry (Vaccinium angustifolium Ait) fruits. *Journal of Agriculture and Food Chemistry,* 52, 6433-6442.

In: Recent Advances in Gallate Research
Editor: Amanda L. Kinsey

ISBN: 978-1-63117-071-3
© 2014 Nova Science Publishers, Inc.

Chapter II

Epigallocatechin-3-Gallate, GRP78 and Unfolded Protein Response

Simona Martinotti, Bruno Burlando and Elia Ranzato[*]

DiSIT - Dipartimento di Scienze e Innovazione Tecnologica,
University of Piemonte Orientale "Amedeo Avogadro",
Alessandria, Italy

Abstract

The unfolded protein response (UPR) is an evolutionarily conserved mechanism that activates both pro-apoptotic and survival pathways to allow eukaryotic cells to adapt to endoplasmic reticulum (ER) stress. A major UPR protective response is the induction of the ER chaperone protein GRP78/BIP, which is required for the proper folding and assembly of membrane and secretory proteins.

GRP78 is up-regulated under stress conditions, such as glucose deprivation, hypoxia, or the presence of toxic agents. Overexpression of GRP78 is prominent in a wide variety of tumors and protects tumor cells against ER stress as well as a range of cancer therapeutic agents.

---

[*] E-mail: ranzato@unipmn.it.

(-)-Epigallocatechin-3-gallate (EGCG), the major component of green tea, has been found to directly interact with GRP78 at the ATP-binding site of protein and regulates its function by competing with ATP binding, resulting in the inhibition of ATPase activity. EGCG binding results in the conversion of GRP78 from its active monomer to the inactive form.

Some studies have reported that EGCG has anticancer effects on various tumors, however, the exact molecular mechanism of this kind of activity is not well understood. Improving the knowledge about the implications of EGCG/GRP78 interaction in cancer cells could throw light on EGCG antitumor properties and provide a new rationale for its therapeutic use.

Endoplasmic Reticulum and Unfolded Protein Response

The endoplasmic reticulum (ER) is an intracellular organelle of all eukaryotic cells, consisting of an extensively interlinked network of membranaceous tubules, sacs and cisternae.

The ER is the cellular site for Ca^{2+} storage and for the synthesis, folding and maturation of most secreted and trans-membrane proteins, detoxification reactions, lipid biosynthesis, assembly of lipid bilayers, and transport of different molecules to their subcellular destinations (Xu et al., 2005).

Protein folding represents a well-orchestrated process involving pathways for folding, assembly, modification, quality control, and recycling. Such a complex of events is possible by means of participation of chaperone proteins, glycosylating enzymes, appropriately high calcium levels, and an oxidizing environment (Schonthal, 2013).

Physiological or pathological processes that disturb protein folding cause ER stress and activate a set of signaling pathways known as Unfolded Protein Response (UPR). Glucose deprivation also leads to ER stress, by interfering with N-linked protein glycosylation. Aberrant Ca^{2+} regulation in the ER causes protein unfolding, while viral infection may also trigger the UPR, representing one of the ancient evolutionary pressures for linking ER stress to cell suicide in order to avoid the spread of viruses (Ma and Hendershot, 2004).

A certain amount of basal protein misfolding occurs in the ER, normally ameliorated by retrograde transport of misfolded proteins into the cytosol for proteasome-dependent degradation. Hence, situations that impair proteasome function can create a veritable protein traffic jam and can even cause inclusion body diseases associated with neurodegeneration (Rao and Bredesen, 2004).

UPR can be viewed as an adaptation to a changing environment, acting to reestablish normal ER functions. Such an adaptive mechanism involves transcriptional programs that induce the expression of genes enhancing the UPR protein folding capacity, and promoting ER-associated protein degradation to remove misfolded proteins. However, excessive or prolonged ER stress triggers cell suicide, usually in the form of apoptosis (Ma and Hendershot, 2004).

UPR is initially mediated by three molecules, PKR-like ER kinase (PERK), activated transcription factor 6 (ATF6), and inositol-requiring enzyme 1 (IRE1).

The ER luminal domains of PERK, IRE1 and ATF6 normally interact with the ER chaperone 78 kDa glucose related protein 78 (GRP78). Upon accumulation of unfolded proteins, GRP78 dissociates from these molecules, leading to their activation (Gardner et al., 2013). However, the activation of ER stress sensors is modulated by other cellular factors, in addition to dissociation from GRP78 (Bravo et al., 2013).

The GRP78 also referred to as BiP or HSPA5, is a highly abundant endoplasmic reticulum chaperone. The upregulation of GRP78 relieves ER stress by increasing the folding capacity of the ER. Notably, if ER homeostasis cannot be restored, the UPR is capable of inducing apoptosis.

GRP78 expression can be stimulated by a variety of environmental and physiological stress conditions that perturb ER function and homeostasis, as well as by pharmacological reagents affecting protein folding, glycosylation or the ER calcium pool (Schonthal, 2013)

GRP78 Role in Tumorigenesis

As its name implies, GRP78 was originally identified as a protein whose expression levels are regulated by available glucose, where hypoglycemia or aglycemia are strong stimuli for an increase of GRP78 expression. Hypoglycemia combined with hypoxia and acidosis represent micro environmental conditions that are frequently present in solid tumor tissue.

Elevated GRP78 is among the most critical pro-survival mechanisms of tumor cells under detrimental microenvironmental conditions, and is frequently described in tumor cell lines and primary tumor samples (Luo and Lee, 2013).

While the presence of high GRP78 levels defends against ER stress, the protein also confers increase chemoresistance to tumor cells. Various studies have shown that elevated levels of GRP78 protect cancer cells from killing by some of the most common chemotherapeutic drugs.

Overexpression of GRP78 is detected in most malignant, but not benign, cancers and it is correlated with poor prognosis of patients (Lee, 2007).

Chronic ER stress and permanently elevated levels of GRP78 expression provide a survival advantage to tumor cells proliferating in sub-optimal microenvironment. Yet, this phenotype sets tumor cells apart from normal cells, thus possibly representing an opportunity for therapeutical intervention (Healy et al., 2009). In this sense, an obvious approach would entail the blockage of the system's pro-survival agent GRP78.

GRP78 and Epigallocatechin-3-Gallate

With emerging data suggesting the UPR role in tumor survival and therapeutic resistance, identifying this pathway as a form of molecularly-targeted cancer therapy represents an active area of research.

It was recently discovered that epigallocatechin-3-gallate (EGCG), the main active polyphenol in green tea, accounting for 50-80% of total catechin, directly interacts with GRP78 (Zhang and Zhang, 2010).

Huge numbers of research studies have investigated the effect of EGCG on cell death, while the compound has been reported to either induce or suppress apoptosis in a variety of cancer cell lines. Very importantly, the pro-apoptotic effects of EGCG appear to target only cancer cells with little effect on normal cells, suggesting the use of EGCG in combination with chemotherapeutical drugs.

Identifying the EGCG "receptor" is the first step in understanding the molecular and biochemical mechanisms of this polyphenol's anticancer effects. A few proteins have been described to bind EGCG, including several plasma proteins, fatty acid synthase, the 67-kDa laminin receptor, and GRP78.

EGCG has been shown to directly interact with GRP78 at the protein's ATP-binding site, competing with GRP78 ATP binding and resulting in the inhibition of ATPase activity (Ermakova et al., 2006).

The GRP78 protein exists in multiple forms, including ATP-mediated monomeric, dimeric, and oligomeric ones (Blond-Elguindi et al., 1993). The GRP78 monomeric species reflects maximal activity, whereas the various dimeric or oligomeric species are less active or inactive. Available data demonstrate that EGCG converts GRP78 from the active monomeric to the inactive dimeric or oligomeric forms. Such a property is shared by other epigallocatechin analogues, suggesting that the gallate group might be critical for the binding to GRP78 and the inhibition of GRP78 ATPase activity.

Research findings also indicate that EGCG interferes with the formation of the antiapoptotic GRP78-casapse-7 complex, a mechanism that can at least in part explain the EGCG-induced apoptosis in cancer cells (Ermakova et al., 2006).

Conclusion: Future Perspectives

Trials are currently underway to test the potentials of EGCG as a strategy for both cancer treatment and prevention (Khan et al., 2009). However, the clinical use of EGCG is still inspired by empirical observations.

Much work has been done on the molecular mechanisms underlying EGCG interactions with cancer cells, but such a bulk of knowledge has not yet been translated into a well-defined pharmacological strategy. The improvement of knowledge about the interaction of EGCG with GRP78, and its implications in tumor cells, could help to set the basis for a pharmacological characterization of EGCG as an antitumor drug.

References

Blond-Elguindi, S., Fourie, A.M., Sambrook, J.F., Gething, M.J., 1993. Peptide-dependent stimulation of the ATPase activity of the molecular chaperone BiP is the result of conversion of oligomers to active monomers. *J. Biol. Chem.* 268, 12730-12735.

Bravo, R., Parra, V., Gatica, D., Rodriguez, A.E., Torrealba, N., Paredes, F., Wang, Z.V., Zorzano, A., Hill, J.A., Jaimovich, E., Quest, A.F., Lavandero, S., 2013. Endoplasmic reticulum and the unfolded protein response: dynamics and metabolic integration. *Int. Rev. Cell Mol. Biol.* 301, 215-290.

Ermakova, S.P., Kang, B.S., Choi, B.Y., Choi, H.S., Schuster, T.F., Ma, W.Y., Bode, A.M., Dong, Z., 2006. (-)-Epigallocatechin gallate overcomes resistance to etoposide-induced cell death by targeting the molecular chaperone glucose-regulated protein 78. *Cancer Res.* 66, 9260-9269.

Gardner, B.M., Pincus, D., Gotthardt, K., Gallagher, C.M., Walter, P., 2013. Endoplasmic reticulum stress sensing in the unfolded protein response. *Cold Spring Harb. Perspect. Biol.* 5, a013169.

Healy, S.J., Gorman, A.M., Mousavi-Shafaei, P., Gupta, S., Samali, A., 2009.Targeting the endoplasmic reticulum-stress response as an anticancer strategy. *Eur. J. Pharmacol.* 625, 234-246.

Khan, N., Adhami, V.M., Mukhtar, H., 2009. Review: green tea polyphenols in chemoprevention of prostate cancer: preclinical and clinical studies. *Nutr. Cancer* 61, 836-841.

Lee, A.S., 2007. GRP78 induction in cancer: therapeutic and prognostic implications. *Cancer Res.* 67, 3496-3499.

Luo, B., Lee, A.S., 2013. The critical roles of endoplasmic reticulum chaperones and unfolded protein response in tumorigenesis and anticancer therapies. *Oncogene* 32, 805-818.

Ma, Y., Hendershot, L.M., 2004. ER chaperone functions during normal and stress conditions. *J. Chem. Neuroanat.* 28, 51-65.

Rao, R.V., Bredesen, D.E., 2004. Misfolded proteins, endoplasmic reticulum stress and neurodegeneration. *Curr. Opin. Cell Biol.* 16, 653-662.

Schonthal, A.H., 2013. Pharmacological targeting of endoplasmic reticulum stress signaling in cancer. *Biochem. Pharmacol.* 85, 653-666.

Xu, C., Bailly-Maitre, B., Reed, J.C., 2005. Endoplasmic reticulum stress: cell life and death decisions. *J. Clin. Invest.* 115, 2656-2664.

Zhang, L.H., Zhang, X., 2010. Roles of GRP78 in physiology and cancer. *J. Cell Biochem.* 110, 1299-1305.

In: Recent Advances in Gallate Research   ISBN: 978-1-63117-071-3
Editor: Amanda L. Kinsey   © 2014 Nova Science Publishers, Inc.

Chapter III

Antioxidant and Cytoprotective Effects of Gallates

Sandhya Khurana[1], Collin J. Byrne[*1,2],
Krishnan Venkataraman[5], Aseem Kumar[3,4]
and T. C. Tai[1,2,3,4]

[1]Medical Sciences Division, Northern Ontario School of Medicine,
Sudbury, ON, Canada
[2]Department of Biology, Laurentian University, Sudbury, ON, Canada
[3]Department of Chemistry and Biochemistry,
Laurentian University, Sudbury, ON, Canada
[4]Biomolecular Sciences Program, Laurentian University,
Sudbury, ON, Canada
[5]Department of Gerontology, Huntington University,
Sudbury, ON, Canada

Abstract

Oxidative stress resulting from increased reactive oxygen species (ROS) can overwhelm cellular antioxidant defenses and cause significant damage to macromolecules such as proteins, lipids, DNA and RNA,

---

* S.K. and C.J.B contributed equally to this work

resulting in compromised cellular function. Oxidative damage is a critical determinant for several disease pathologies. It exacerbates inflammatory responses, and damages amongst others, the respiratory, neurological and the cardiovascular systems, which, cumulatively then effect age-related physiological changes. Further, oxidative damage is the leading cause of cancer in aging. In tumor cells, altered redox balance and ROS-mediated signaling pathways trigger cellular proliferation in the context of dysregulated cell replication genes. Hence, the argument for stemming oxidative damage to our cells is indisputable. Nature's potent antioxidants, polyphenols, are biologically active plant-based molecules that can aid in the restoration of cellular redox potential due to their ability to accept and release electrons. Also, polyphenols indirectly reduce the burden of oxidative stress by altering cellular signaling pathways. The urgency to reduce oxidative stress-induced disease pathologies, and thereby their psychological and socioeconomic consequences, has accelerated research on developing polyphenols as natural therapeutic agents. Additionally, acquired drug resistance and toxicity to chemotherapeutic agents has necessitated the development of novel therapeutic strategies to selectively target cancer cells. This review will provide a summary of the research advancements suggesting that gallate polyphenols such as methyl gallate and EGCG may be responsible for improved outcomes in cardiovascular function, toxicity associated with carcinogenesis, and cognitive decline in aging, amongst other health benefits.

Keywords: Cardiovascular, polyphenols, aging, neurodegeneration, cancer, ROS, gallate, tea, EGCG, theaflavin, gallic acid

Abbreviations

Aβ	Amyloid β protein
ACE	Angiotensin converting enzyme
AD	Alzheimer's disease
AGE	Advanced glycation end products
Ang II	Angiotensin II
ApoE	Apolipoprotein E deficient mice
CVD	Cardiovascular disease
EGCG	Epigallocatechin gallate
ET-1	Endothelin-1
eNOS	Endothelial nitric oxide synthase
GA	Gallic acid

GPx   Glutathione peroxidase
GST   Glutathione S-transferase
HDL   High density lipoprotein
HO-1   Hemoxygenase-1
ICAM-1   Intercellular cell adhesion molecule-1
LDL   Low density lipoprotein
MCP-1   Monocyte chemoattractant protein -1
MG   Methyl gallate
MI   Myocardial infarction
MMPs   Matrix metalloproteinases
PD   Parkinson's disease
ROS   Reactive oxygen species
SOD   Super oxide dismutase
SHR   Spontaneously hypertensive rat
TF   Theaflavin
TF2A   Theaflavin-3-gallate
TF2B   Theaflavin-3'-gallate
TF3   Theaflavin-3-3'-gallate
TNF α   Tumor Necrosis Factor α
VCAM-1   Vascular endothelial adhesion molecule-1
VSMC   Vascular smooth muscle cell

1. Introduction

1.1. Oxidative Stress and Cellular Damage

Conventionally, oxidative stress implies an imbalance between the generation of free radicals and the ability of cellular antioxidant system to counteract these radicals. Reactive oxygen species (ROS) are byproducts of cellular respiration formed during electron transfer in normal energy generation and metabolism. ROS are also signaling molecules rendering them capable of modulating a variety of cellular pathways such as ERK, JNK, p38 MAPK, and P13K/Akt, as well as redox sensitive transcription factors such as Nrf-2, NF-κB and COX amongst others. This makes ROS key players in cellular responses to stress, metabolism, proliferation and senescence [1]. Molecules such as hydrogen peroxide (H_2O_2), the hydroxyl radical (OH•) and superoxide ($O_2^{•-}$), are classically referred to as ROS, and in excess are the main contributors to oxidative stress within cells. Additionally, several nitrogen species, metal intermediates such as Fe, Co, Cu, Cr, and advanced glycation end products (AGE) contribute to cellular oxidative stress [2–4]. The major source of free radicals in cells is the mitochondrion with free radicals being generated when free electrons bind with oxygen to generate superoxide during reduction of NADH (complex I) or during renewal of coenzyme Q from semiquinone (complex III) [5,6]. The NOX family of NAD(P)H oxidases are the predominant sources of ROS generation at the limiting membrane and membranes of endocytic vesicles, with NOX 1 and 2 being primarily responsible [7]. Xanthine oxidase can also generate superoxide during the oxidation of xanthine and hypoxanthine; superoxide generated can then participate in the Haber-Weiss or Fenton reaction to generate more ROS [8,9]. Reactive nitrogen species (RNS) are formed when free nitric oxide (NO) reacts with excess superoxide to form peroxynitrite ($ONOO^-$), nitrogen dioxide (NO_2) and dinitrogen trioxide (N_2O_3) [3]. AGEs are modified protein and lipid products that are generated upon non-enzymatic glycation and oxidation by sugars. AGEs feed into the oxidative stress cycle, for example, by activating NADPH oxidase to generate ROS [10]. ROS and RNS, sometimes collectively recognized as RONS, are the primary sources of endogenous oxidative stress. ROS can also be derived from exposure to exogenous sources including pollutants, UV irradiation, drugs and toxins [11].

Cellular antioxidant systems are usually adequate to combat excessive free radicals and prevent cellular damage. This is achieved either by antioxidant enzymes such as superoxide dismutase (SOD) that can neutralize excess $O_2^{\cdot-}$ to H_2O_2 in the mitochondria (manganese-containing MnSOD or SOD2) or in the cytosol (copper-containing CuSOD or SOD1). H_2O_2 is then broken down by catalase (CAT) to non-toxic water. Additionally, H_2O_2 can be neutralized by glutathione peroxidase (GPx) through the conversion of reduced glutathione (GSH), a powerful antioxidant tripeptide, to its oxidized form (GSSG) [12]. Glutathione reductase (GSR) can then regenerate GSH from GSSG.

Cellular insults resulting from oxidative stress are vast and include damage to proteins via carbonylation of amino acids such as leucine, threonine and proline, resulting in structural impairment and functional loss of proteins. Further, oxidized proteins are inefficiently targeted to the proteasome for removal and accumulate in the cells. Hydroxyl radicals can damage membranes leading to loss of integrity and alteration in fluidity, ultimately compromising membrane physiology. ROS can also modulate lipid peroxidation and alter lipoproteins such as LDL leading to an accumulation of oxidized LDL extracellularly. ROS-induced damage to DNA is pronounced, particularly in mitochondrial DNA (mtDNA) due to its proximity to the source of ROS. Damaged DNA is evidenced by increased DNA adducts, double stranded DNA breaks, mutations and increased modified bases such as 8-oxo-2'-deoxyguanosine (8-oxo-dG), FAPy-adenine and 5-hydroxycytosine [13].

1.2. Oxidative Stress in Cardiovascular and Neurological Disease, Aging and Cancer – A Brief Overview

Oxidative stress plays a crucial role in the pathogenesis of a variety of cardiovascular disorders. A vast body of literature supports the notion that ROS are largely responsible for vascular abnormalities underlying cardiovascular dysfunctions involved in atherosclerosis, hypertension, myocardial infarction (MI), and ischemic heart disease [14,15]. ROS are increased during ischemia/reperfusion (I/R) in the heart and lead to increased cardiac cell death due to apoptosis resulting in exacerbated injury [14,16]. ROS targets in the endothelium alter signaling pathways to promote endothelial damage by decreasing the vasodilatory molecule nitric oxide and increasing oxidized LDL, a precursor for foam cell formation involved in the initiation of atherosclerosis. ROS mediate increases in the synthesis of proinflammatory cytokines such as TNFα and IFNγ, and redox sensitive transcription factors like NFκB that increase synthesis of cytokines IL-6 and IL-8, and upregulates monocyte chemotactic protein-1 (MCP-1), intercellular cell adhesion molecule-1 (ICAM-1), vascular cell adhesion molecule-1 (VCAM-1) and CD-40 that promote migration of macrophages and adherence of leukocytes and platelets respectively. ROS also increases the proliferation and migration of vascular smooth muscle cells (VSMCs) into the intima, with all these processes ultimately contributing to the progression of atherosclerosis [17–20]. Furthermore, ROS augments the effects of potent vasoconstrictor molecules such as endothelin-1 (ET-1) and angiotensin II (AngII), the latter being a primary determinant in the renin angiotensin system, leading to exaggerated structural cardiac changes observed in hypertension and vascular stenosis [21–24].

ROS not only impact the cardiovascular system, but they can be especially damaging to tissues of the human brain, which are more susceptible to increased oxidative stress damage by virtue of an increased oxygen consumption as compared to the rest of the body, accounting for about 20% of the total oxygen consumed [25,26]. Additionally neurons have a higher number of mitochondria to meet the high ATP demands of the brain. The brain also has a higher polyunsaturated fatty acid composition and lower amount of GPx and CAT antioxidant enzymes making its membranes and cellular contents more prone to oxidative stress mediated damage [25,26]. Oxidative stress-mediated damage has been associated with Alzheimer's disease (AD), multiple sclerosis (MS), Parkinson's disease (PD), mild cognitive impairment (MCI), amongst other neurodegenerative conditions [26–29]. For example, the involvement of oxidative stress in AD patients is manifested in the form of oxidative damage markers such as 8-oxo-dG in both nuclear and mtDNA from brain regions of AD patients. This is accompanied by increases in lipid peroxidation evidenced by thiobarbituric acid reactive substances (TBARS) and 4-hydroxynonenal (HNE), byproducts of lipid peroxidation, and abnormal protein accumulation [26]. It has also been reported that AD brains have a higher content of Fe, a metal that is capable of generating OH• radical by utilizing H_2O_2 via the Fenton or Haber-Weiss reactions [30]. The accumulation of the amyloid β protein (Aβ) in the cerebellum, as well as the hyperphosphorylation of Tau protein, are widely accepted to be the major culprits in the loss of neuronal and neurotransmitter functions in AD; both of these have been reported to be AGE-modified in AD [30]. Further, exposure of microglia to Aβ leads to an increase in NO and eventually ONOO⁻ [30]. In case of PD, the accumulation of α-synuclein in intracytoplasmic Lewy bodies of neurons is one of the factors leading to the pathogenesis of this neurodegenerative disease. Aggregation of α-synuclein monomers into protofibrils, and then into fibrils, leads to disruption of dopamine metabolism, which then leads to increased ROS. This in turn leads to increased aggregation of α-synuclein into protofibrils, ultimately triggering apoptosis cascades and death of dopaminergic neurons [31].

The free radical theory of aging as postulated by Harman in 1956, proposes that free radicals generated either by endogenous or exogenous means are collectively responsible for impairment of cellular functionality and consequently lead to aging and its associated degenerative diseases [32]. The aging of various systems in the human body is not uniform; the organs with the greatest respiratory demands are the most susceptible to aging-related deterioration. The concept of non-uniform aging in large multicellular animals is important in understanding the incidence of age-related diseases in humans. Deterioration of the cardiovascular and neurological systems is augmented with age and is suggestive of common underlying mechanisms in the age-related accelerated decline, such as inflammation [1]. Age-related mitochondrial changes could also play a role; for example monoamine oxidases (MAOs), enzymes that degrade catecholamines and generate ROS, are found in the outer mitochondrial membrane. In aging systems, the MAO-B isoform is significantly increased and predisposes towards age-related neurodegenerative diseases such as PD [33]. The association between ROS reduction, increasing oxidative stress resistance and increased lifespan has been extensively studied in *C.elegans* and in mice. Further, limiting food intake, or calorie restriction (CR), has also proved beneficial in extending the lifespan of rodents, likely by reducing oxidative stress. CR aids in reducing age-related damage to DNA, lipid and proteins, protects mitochondrial functions, reduces inflammation and alters transcriptional changes in signaling pathways normally associated with age [1,34,35].

The Free Radical Theory of cancer proposed by Oberley, suggests that cancer cells have dysfunctional mitochondria leading to an accumulation of free radicals; this in conjunction with ROS-mediated upregulation of cellular pathways and transcription factor deregulation, primarily comprising of oncogenes, plays a significant role in establishing the malignant phenotype of cancers [36–39]. The establishment of cancer, a consequence of imbalance between cell proliferation and cell death, is a 3 step process: 1) Initiation, wherein a nonlethal mutation in cellular DNA generates an altered cell; 2) Promotion, which supports the expansion of the altered cell lineage by promoting proliferation; and 3) Progression, wherein additional genetic changes cumulatively give rise to neoplasms and support changes from the benign to the malignant phenotype [40]. Oxidative stress can thus participate in cancer establishment through the oxidation of DNA bases, which have been shown to be mutagenic and could be responsible for the initiation of a neoplasm. Additionally, the redox sensitive transcription factors such as p53, NFκB, AP-1 and HIF-1α which are important in cell growth and proliferation, cell survival and inflammation, can all be modulated by ROS and have been shown to play significant roles in the process of carcinogenesis [41].

2. Antioxidants Alleviate Oxidative Stress

2.1. Antioxidants

Antioxidants are compounds that inhibit or delay the oxidation of cellular constituents such as protein, lipids and DNA. The mechanisms include direct scavenging of ROS to limit oxidative damage or indirectly as a consequence of interfering with cellular signaling pathways that can then mitigate oxidative stress. Endogenous antioxidant machinery includes enzymes such as SOD, CAT and GPx as discussed previously [5]. Non-enzymatic antioxidants include flavanoids, carotenoids such as β carotene, vitamin C, vitamins E (or α-tocopherol) and GSH. GSH is a critical antioxidant within the cell as it can directly scavenge free radicals such as OH• and $O_2^{\bullet-}$, and serve as a substrate in the reaction carried out by GPx to reduce H_2O_2; the GSH/GSSG ratio is often used as an indicator of cellular oxidative health [5]. Moreover GSH is able to regenerate vitamins C and E back to their active forms [5]. Vitamin E is a potent scavenger of $ONOO^-$ and mitigates the oxidation of LDL as well as membrane phospholipids [42]. Vitamin C (or L-ascorbate) reacts directly with free radicals, preventing oxidative stress-induced damage; however, L-ascorbate can also lose an electron, and function as a pro-oxidant [42]. β carotene scavenges peroxyl radicals by converting it to a stable carotenoid adduct, scavenges singlet oxygen radicals, and prevents lipid peroxidation reactions, thereby protecting from oxidative damage [43].

2.2. Polyphenols as Antioxidants

2.2.1. Polyphenols – Historical Perspectives

Polyphenols are ubiquitously found naturally occurring compounds that are synthesized by plants as a defensive strategy against stressors [44]. They are classified into 4 categories based on the number of phenolic rings and their structural moiety: phenolic acids, flavonoids, stilbenes and lignans with the flavonoids further subdivided into 6 classes as flavonols, flavones, isoflavones, flavanones, anthocyanidins and flavanols [45]. In the past 2 decades, polyphenols have been extensively researched to understand the basis for their capacity to improve human health [44,46–48]. Polyphenols rose to fame primarily owing to epidemiological studies revealing a striking association between the consumption of polyphenol rich diets and reduced susceptibility to cardiovascular diseases, their associated complications and related mortality [49,50]. The term French paradox was coined to describe the anomaly observed in the French population, who, despite consuming a diet rich in saturated fats have low incidences of coronary heart disease, a trend not seen in populations of other countries with similar levels of fats in their diet; this was attributed to the high consumption of red wine, that is rich in the polyphenol resveratrol, in the French diet [51]. Similarly, the Mediterranean diet rich in olive oil is associated with reduced cardiovascular risk, longer lifespan, reduced incidences of cancer and benefits in neurodegenerative conditions [52].

The use of turmeric, or the golden spice, in South Asian cuisines has been correlated with reduction in inflammation and lower incidences of cancer [53]. The consumption of large amounts of tea, rich in polyphenols, in Eastern populations is associated with reduced incidences of cardiovascular disease and associated mortalities as well as inversely correlated with neurodegeneration seen in AD and PD, amongst others [54–56].

2.2.2. Polyphenols – Occurrence and Variability in Foods

The polyphenol composition of plants varies qualitatively and quantitatively with varied occurrence across different foods, that for the most part contain a complex mixture of polyphenols. Polyphenol content differs based on environmental factors such as location of cultivation, soil type, as well as factors such as ripeness of fruits, processing, and storage conditions [44]. For example, in wine, the Pinot Noir from grapes of Oregon has a higher resveratrol content as compared to that from New York state [57].

In case of quercetin content of onions, yellow onions have a higher content than the red or pink ones while white ones have negligible quantities [58]. Also, the storage temperature of onions affects the amount of quercetin, with lower temperatures conserving the content by preventing oxidation. In case of olives the more ripened they are, the lesser is the polyphenol content in the olive oil [59]. Preparation methods may also alter the polyphenolic content of foods; peeling fruits and vegetables could exclude the polyphenols present in the outer skin. Cooking can also vastly alter polyphenolic constituents of food; cooking tomato and onions by boiling for 15 min results in 75-80% loss of their quercetin content [45].

Other processing such as freezing, grinding, mashing, pasteurization, addition of food stabilizers and preservatives can also lead to significant variability in polyphenol content of food [45,60].

For the purpose of this review, we will elaborate on gallate polyphenols, specifically epigallocatechin gallate (EGCG the major polyphenolic constituent of green tea), theaflavin (TF) and its gallates, (the major polyphenolic constituents of black tea), gallic acid (GA) and methyl gallate (MG) in the sections outlined below.

3. Sources of Gallate Polyphenols

3.1. Tea

Tea, one of the most popular beverages in the world, is consumed by over two-thirds of the global population [61]. The two most common varieties of tea by far are black tea (constituting about 78% of global tea production) and green tea (constituting about 20% of global tea production) [61].

Both of these varieties, as well as oolong tea, are obtained from the plant *Camellia sinensis*; however, phytochemical compositions of these teas can be very different [62]. Flavan-3-ols are the main class of flavonoid in tea, and account for roughly 25% of the dry mass of fresh leaves [62]. Major flavan-3-ols found in fresh tea leaves include (−)-epicatechin (EC), (−)-epigallocatechin (EGC), and the gallic acid (GA) esters (-)-epicatechin gallate (ECG) and (-)-epigallocatechin gallate (EGCG) [62]. GA esters of flavan-3-ols such as EGCG and ECG account for a large proportion of the total polyphenols in green tea [62,63]. Black tea, on the other hand, is relatively low in EGCG and ECG, but is high in TFs (Table 1) [63].

Table 1. Content of catechin and theaflavin gallate esters in typical samples of green and black tea (Adapted from [70])

Compound	Tea (µg/ml)	
	Green	Black
Total catechins	1064	300
(-)-Epicatechin-3-gallate (ECG)	90	73
(-)-Epigallocatechin-3-gallate (EGCG)	444	128
Total theaflavins	0	64
Theaflavin-3-gallate	0	20
Theaflavin-3'-gallate	0	13
Theaflavin-3, 3'-digallate	0	9

Black tea is also higher than green tea in GA, which is liberated from esters during fermentation. Black tea leaves have approximately 2 mg/g of GA, twice as much as typical green teas; a similar effect is observed in Pu-erh tea (5.53 mg/g), which is also fermented but using microorganisms rather than the oxidation method used to ferment black tea [64]. This difference in composition of green and black teas is due to different methods of processing and fermentation [63]. The methods of processing green tea are designed to prevent the enzymatic oxidation of flavanols [61]. Manufacturing of black tea, however, involves a fermentation and oxidation process. During this process, flavan-3-ol monomers are oxidized by the enzyme polyphenol oxidase, and condense to form TFs and thearubigins [63].

TFs are the major polyphenolic components of black tea and are not present in green tea [63,65]. There are four main TFs in black tea, three of which contain galloyl moieties. These include theaflavin-3-gallate (TF2A), theaflavin-3'-gallate (TF2B), and theaflavin-3, s3'-digallate (TF3). The total TF content typically ranges between 0.3-2% of black tea leaves [62]. Due to its manufacturing process, black tea also has a much lower content of flavan-3-ols than green tea, comprising only 3-10% of black tea solids [66]. It should also be noted that the phenolic composition of tea brews can vary according to the origins of the tea blend used, its manufacturing process, and the methods of infusion [67,68]. For example tea from the Brahmaputra valley of India have a much higher TF content, (averaging 11.4 mg/g) than the tea grown in the Barak Valley, Terai or Dooars regions (averaging 8.9, 8.4 and 8.7 mg/g respectively)[69].

3.2. Fruits and Vegetables

Many of the galloylated catechins and TFs present in tea are uncommon in other food sources. In a study of 24 types of fruits and 27 types of vegetables and legumes commonly consumed in the Netherlands, none were found to contain EGCG [71]. Low levels of ECG can be found in rhubarb (~6 mg/kg fresh weight), and white grapes (~4 mg/kg fresh weight); moderate amounts can be found in black grapes (~28 mg/kg fresh weight) [71]. Although compounds abundant in tea may be difficult to obtain from common food sources, GA and it's other ester derivatives are found in a variety of plant foods. For example, GA, which is present in both tea and wine, is found in fruits such as grapes (skin and seeds), bananas, strawberries, blueberries, blackberries, and others [72–77]. The tropical fruit tree *Manilkara zapota (L.) P. Royen (Sapotaceae),* produces fruit commonly called sapota or chikoo, which is a source of GA and other polyphenols [78]. MG can be found in Lotus plants, consumed as an edible plant in India, China and other South Asian countries [79,80]. Pomegranate and Indian gooseberry (*Phyllanthus emblica,* commonly called amla) both contain GA and MG [81–83]. Among commonly consumed vegetables, broccoli has a high amount of GA (about 240 μg/g), whereas asparagus and eggplant have trace amounts [84]. Like tea, variation in chemical composition can be found within other plant sources. For example, the GA content of grapes varies from 99 mg/100 g dry matter for Muscadine seeds to 10 mg and 15 mg in Merlot and Chardonnay seeds respectively [73].

3.3. Processed Foods and Beverages

Catechins are often present only in trace amounts or are absent in processed foods [68]. This is typically due to methods of commercial preparation used, which result in complete or near-complete loss of catechins present in the original fruit component [68]. For example, iced tea, grape and apple juices contain very low catechin levels in comparison to their fresh plant sources [68]. Although grape juices are low in catechins, studies have found that they contain high content of GA relative to other phenolic acids [85]. Red wine contains substantial levels of catechins (27-96 mg/L); however, only (+)-catechin and (-)-epicatechin, and no catechin compounds bearing galloyl moieties (i.e. ECG, EGCG) are present [68]. Red wine is also a source of GA (about 95 mg/L); however, the content of these compounds can vary with grape cultivar, climate, soil, and wine-making process [86–88]. GA is a component of olive oil; the amount of this phenolic in olive oil depends on olive cultivar varieties and stage of ripening of the olive fruit at the time of harvest [89–91].

3.4. Medicinal Plants, Herbs and Other Sources

Some of the pants used in traditional Chinese medicine likely owe their healing properties to GA and the other phenolics they contain. GA is a major component of both *Areca catechu* and *Toona sinensis* extracts, which are used in traditional Chinese medicine, and have antioxidant properties along with many other diverse health effects [92–95].

Hamamelis virginiana (witch hazel) is another plant known for its medicinal properties, and its leaves and bark are sources of GA catechins and tannins [96]. Other sources of GA and its esters include pistachios and *Pimenta dioca* (commonly called pimento, all spice or Jamaica pepper). The Bronte pistachios from Catania, Italy have a high GA content both in the seed and the skin (12.66 µg/g and about 15.00 µg/g fresh weight respectively), and *Pimenta dioca*, used as a spice is South American cuisine, is a good source of MG and GA [97,98]. Finally, due to the wide distribution of polyphenols among plant species, GA and its derivatives are also found in a variety of non-dietary sources, including hard wood species such as oak (*Quercus robur*), chestnut (*Castanea sativa L.*) and many others [72].

4. Epigallocatechin Gallate (EGCG)

4.1. Epidemiological and Clinical Studies with Green Tea or EGCG

Numerous epidemiological studies have suggested the beneficial health effects of tea consumption, one of which being a positive correlation between tea consumption and reduced cardiovascular risk [99]. The Ohsaki study, conducted in Japan, followed 40,000 participants over a 11 year period and reported that individuals who consumed 5 cups/day (1 cup=100 mL) of green tea had a 16% reduced risk of mortality due to CVD and all other causes at the 11 year follow up. [99,100]. Another investigation of protective effects of green tea reported a 46% decrease in the risk of developing hypertension in individuals who consumed 120- 599 mL/d, and about 65% in those who consumed 600 mL/d or more [55]. Green tea intake over a 12 week period has also been shown to reduce body fat, improve BMI and lower oxidized LDL [101]. Tea consumption may have beneficial effects in regard to neurological disease as well, as it has been suggested to have a role in the reduced risk of incidence of age-related neurological decline in South Asian populations as compared to American and European populations [54]. Studies assessing a link between decline of cognitive functions and tea consumption have concluded that drinking 2 or more cups/d of green tea is inversely correlated with cognitive impairment [102]. The study also reported no impact of coffee, black or oolong tea consumption on cognitive impairment. Tea drinking may also have benefits in regard to ageing. Aging is associated with cognitive decline, neurodegeneration, and increased risk for cardiovascular disorders, and in a study on adults aged 80-115 y (mean age 91.4y, a cohort in the Chinese Longitudinal Health Longevity Survey (CLHLS), tea drinking demonstrated beneficial effects on cognitive function [103].

A majority of studies have concluded the positive impact of tea on cardiovascular and neurological health as well as in healthy aging; however the association of tea and cancer prevention remains unclear due to conflicting results from clinical studies [104]. Studies in the early 1970's had suggested a link between green tea consumption and an increased incidence of esophageal cancer in humans; but this finding was later extended to the consumption of any hot beverage. The increase in esophageal cancer was ultimately attributed to the damage inflicted on the epithelial cell lining of the esophagus by the extreme heat of beverages such as tea and coffee. Overall, as reviewed by Yuan in 2011, some studies demonstrated weak or non-significant inverse association between green tea and esophageal cancer, while others reported increased risk, and thus are inconclusive [105,106]. Similar to esophageal cancer, the connection between green tea consumption and oral cancer is somewhat ambiguous. A phase II clinical trial on green tea extract (GTE) and the development of leukoplakia (a precancerous lesion in the mouth) reported reduced lesion size, and warranted a phase III trial; however, more studies are needed to confirm the efficacy of green tea on oral cancer prevention [106]. In the case of prostate cancer, some studies have reported no chemopreventive effect of green tea or a flavonoid rich diet including EGCG, and other flavonoids [107,108]. No correlation was seen with lung cancer either, as reported by the Ohsaki study and by another investigation [100,107]. As for breast cancer, green tea might prevent carcinogenesis in premenopausal women and also prevent the recurrence of breast cancer; contrasting data were obtained from different cohorts [106,109]. Some studies, reviewed by Wu et al in 2011, have reported an influence of green tea consumption on circulating estrogen, mammographic density, insulin like growth factor (IGF) and serum adiponectin; all important biomarkers in breast cancer [109]. There is some evidence demonstrating the protective effect of tea on gastric, pancreatic and other cancers; these epidemiological studies have been elegantly reviewed by Yuan et al in 2011 [106].

4.2. Modes of Action of EGCG

The list of studies on the influence of EGCG in ameliorating pathological disease states in the cardiovascular system and promoting healthy physiological parameters in animal models is extensive. In these models, EGCG has demonstrated considerable benefits to the cardiovascular system ranging from protecting the endothelium and impeding atherosclerosis to preventing cardiac cell damage and gross morphological heart changes due to hypertrophy and hypertension [47,110].

The oxidation of LDL is an antecedent in the development of atherosclerosis; it induces the adhesion of monocytes to the endothelium by stimulating the synthesis of VCAM-1 and ICAM-1, and promotes chemotactic migration of monocytes into the arterial intima. Through this mechanism, the oxidation of LDL can lead to immunological changes that mediate the synthesis of proinflammatory cytokines that orchestrate the inflammatory response associated with atherosclerosis [17,18]. Eventually, migration and proliferation of VSMCs results in plaque formation and intima thickening in atherosclerotic lesions [111]. Activated platelets are also found in atherosclerotic lesions eventually and may lead to thrombotic events [20]. The anti-atherosclerotic properties of EGCG have been demonstrated in a variety of studies. EGCG treatment impedes the expression of LOX-1, the receptor for oxidized LDL [112]. By activating the PI3kinase pathway, EGCG mediates the upregulation of Nrf2, and downregulation of VCAM-1 and ICAM-1 on endothelial cells [113]. EGCG also stimulates HO-1, which can protect from H_2O_2-mediated oxidative stress in human aortic endothelial cells [114]. EGCG has also proved to be anti-inflammatory, and thus anti-atherosclerotic by impeding the synthesis of TNFα and other proinflammatory cytokines such as MCP-1 [115]. In Wistar Kyoto (WKY) rats fed a cholesterol-rich atherogenic diet, EGCG reduced the inflammatory marker C-reactive protein (CRP) as compared to controls [116]. Further EGCG treatment reduced the proliferation of VSMCs and subsequently reduced their migration by impeding the activity of MMP-2 and MMP-9, matrix metalloproteinases that are gelatinolytic and aid in the migration of VSMCs [117–120]. EGCG also prevents the activation of platelets, reduces the expression of Thromboxane 2 (TXA$_2$) and increases phosphorylation of Syk and SLP-76, both prerequisites for platelet activation [121,122]. EGCG affects cholesterol synthesis by regulating the activity of hydroxy-3-methyl-glutaryl-CoA (HMGR), the enzyme that controls the rate limiting step in cholesterol synthesis [123]. Apolipoprotein E deficient mice (*Apo-E -/-*) are an atherosclerotic animal model that develop atherosclerotic aortic plaques when fed an atherogenic diet high in cholesterol [124]. In *ApoE -/-* mice, the dietary supplementation of catechins rich in EGCG as a commercially available formulation called Polyphenon E resulted in decreased atheromatous areas in the aortas, and reduced aortic cholesterol and triglycerides [125]. A comprehensive microarray based study on *ApoE -/-* mice, using nutritional doses of 9 different polyphenols, including EGCG rich catechins, reported that the miRNA profiles of these animals were strikingly different from those not receiving the polyphenol supplementation. Interestingly, the miRNA signatures of the animals in the polyphenol groups were similar to wild type animals indicating the ability of polyphenols to modulate miRNA and reestablish wild type patterns of gene expression [126].

Green tea polyphenol is also anti-hypertensive. In the spontaneously hypertensive rat (SHR) as well as the stroke prone SHR (SP-SHR), dietary EGCG supplementation reduced blood pressure, mediated by eNOS- and NO-dependent vasorelaxation [127–129]. This increase in available NO is likely due an increased activity of eNOS, rather than protein content, mediated by activation of PI3-Kinase and Akt pathways by EGCG [110,130]. Tea flavonoids including EGCG inhibit the activity of angiotensin converting enzyme (ACE) subsequently reducing circulating AngII, a critical player in the Renin–Angiotensin system and blood pressure homeostasis [131–133]. EGCG also modulates ET-1, a potent vasoconstrictor molecule with important functions in vascular physiology [23,134]. In addition, EGCG has been found to attenuate cardiac hypertrophy resulting from aortic constriction and protect cardiomyocytes from ROS-mediated cellular injury and death in rat models [135–138]. In reperfusion injury, EGCG reduced the infarct size in rats [139] and damage in isolated rat hearts exposed to I/R stress [140,141]. The reduction in I/R-mediated damage is attributed to attenuated STAT-1 activation in cardiomyocytes, and reduced neutrophil migration; neutrophils being the primary source of oxygen radicals and ROS-mediated cellular damage [142–145]. EGCG's protective role against apoptosis is substantiated by the prevention of telomere attrition in cardiomyoblasts; telomere attrition and resulting cellular senescence are often correlated with oxidative stress encountered during I/R [146].

The role of EGCG in neuroprotection is gaining recognition and this area of research has become another focal point in understanding the beneficial effects of EGCG on health. The primary mechanisms involved in the neuroprotective properties of EGCG are attributed to its antioxidant capacity, its ability to chelate Fe and to modulate cellular signaling pathways that can regulate neuritogenesis [147]. In the case of AD, EGCG reduces Aβ production and the deposition of this amyloid protein in plaques. This isn't merely a consequence of EGCG acting as an antioxidant, but also its ability to diminish the synthesis of the amyloid precursor protein (APP), to interact with amyloidogenic monomeric proteins and prevent their aggregation into fibrils or via its metal chelating property [148]. EGCG can modulate metal-induced Aβ aggregation, metal-Aβ species being implicated in neurotoxic processes and the generation of ROS species in AD [149]. EGCG can also structurally alter mature Aβ and α-synuclein aggregates into smaller amorphous non-toxic protein aggregates [150]. EGCG can function by a variety of other mechanisms that influence Aβ aggregation, which have been extensively reviewed by Massimo et al. and Mahler et al. in 2013 [148,151] and by Weinreb *et al* in 2009 [147]. EGCG modulates the synthesis of α secretase, an enzyme which is active in the non-amyloidogenic pathway that is non-toxic to cells in Alzheimer Transgenic mice (TgAPP*sw*), an animal model used widely for studies on Alzheimer's disease [152]. At 12 months of age, the TgAPP*sw*, which overexpress APP in neurons, start exhibiting deposition of Aβ plaques in the brain; intraperitoneal injection of 20 mg/kg/d of EGCG for 60 days showed a 47-54% reduction in plaques and promoted non-amyloidogenic processing of APP in these animals [152]. In another investigation using the same animal model, both intraperitoneal and oral routes of EGCG administration not only reduced Aβ deposits but also reduced the sarkosyl-soluble fraction of phosphorylated tau, another marker of AD, and markedly improved the cognitive behavior of the mice [153].

Parkinson's Disease is characterized by the degeneration of dopaminergic neurons in the substantia nigra; 1-methyl-4-phenyl-1,2,3,6-tetrahydropyridine (MPTP) is a neurotoxin that leads to Parkinsonism and has been used in cell culture and animal models to mimic the disease. In PC12 cells, a culture model used extensively in neuroscience and for Parkinson's research, EGCG pretreatment protected cell viability from MPTP treatment by reducing ROS, inducing antioxidant enzymes GPx and SOD1, and inducing PGC1α and SIRT1 which are both central players in energy pathways, mitochondrial biogenesis and cellular metabolism [154,155]. Paraquat (PQ), an herbicide with structural similarity to MPTP, is an environmental toxin linked with the development of PD. In PC12 cells treated with PQ, EGCG rescued viability by inhibiting caspase-3 activity and apoptosis [156]. Another environmental toxin linked with neurodegeneration and PD is p,p'-dichlorodiphenyltrichloroethane (DDT); EGCG was found to increase viability of the dopaminergic neuroblastoma cell line SHSY-5Y protecting it from the toxicity of DDT treatment [157]. Neurotoxicity of 6-hydroxydopamine (6-OHDA) on SHSY-5Y cells was also attenuated by EGCG via Akt activation and diminished caspase-3 activity [158]. In animal models, mice injected with MPTP and an oral gavage of 25 mg/kg/d of EGCG or an equivalent dose of EGCG as prepared tea showed a reduction in loss of tyrosine hydroxylase (TH) positive cells in the substantia nigra and preserved levels of dopamine and its metabolites; further EGCG treatment led to reduced nNOS (neuronal NO synthase) and its associated toxicity in these animals [159]. In a comprehensive microarray study by Mandel, Youdim and colleagues (2002), a cDNA microarray analysis from substantia nigra samples of MPTP treated C57/BL6 mice revealed various gene expression changes that differed based on acute versus chronic MPTP treatment; EGCG treatment modulated a multitude of genes that offer neuroprotection [160,161]. Additionally, EGCG can inhibit NFκB nuclear translocation and the synthesis of TNFα, reducing neuroinflammation; it can upregulate HIF1α via Fe chelation and inhibiting HIF prolyl hydroxylase activity, correspondingly upregulating HIF1α regulated genes such as VEGF and GLUT4. EGCG also modulates the activity of a variety of cell signaling pathways via modulation of the phosphorylation states of kinases like MAPK, Akt, PKC and ERK 1/2 etc., associated with cell proliferation, apoptosis, neurite extension amongst others [147,162].

In the context of aging, the modes of protection by EGCG in cardiovascular and neurological systems are critical because of the complex interplay between the two physiological systems. The cause of mortality due to cardiovascular complications is about 80% in adults over 65 years of age [163]. Additionally, about 5-7% of the global population above the age of 65 suffers from neurological decline leading to dementia [164]. Moreover, the epidemiological correlation between vascular complications and neurological decline is striking, with peripheral atherosclerosis being a risk factor for the onset of AD in the elderly [165,166]. In a microarray study on the rat model of aging, Fisher 344 rats fed a low dose (50 mg/kg/d) or a high dose (500 mg/kg/d) of EGCG revealed a global alteration of gene expression in various tissues, including the heart and brain, with a gene profile that overlapped with the pattern obtained from rats fed a calorie restricted diet [167]. Not only does EGCG reduce oxidative stress and inflammation, both key in the decline of aging systems, but it also activates SIRT1 in healthy rats, a member of the sirtuin family associated with longevity and lifespan [168]. Moreover, EGCG also inhibits MAO-B activity in adult rat brains; MAO-B is increased with aging and results in ROS generation, making EGCG a good candidate for neurorescue from oxidative stress [169,170].

The detailed mechanism of EGCG's anti-tumorigenic effects is beyond the scope of this review primarily because of the multitude of cancer types and studies with numerous cancer cell lines. The general paradigm that emerges from these studies suggests that green tea inhibits tumorigenesis by altering signal transduction pathways and mitigating oxidative stress to modulate cell proliferation, migration, angiogenesis and expression of oncogenes amongst other processes involved in tumor formation [171,172]. EGCG can modulate oxidative stress-induced signaling pathways by regulating phosphorylation of MAPK, ERK 1/2, JNK kinases, and EGCG can regulate NFκB and AP-1, key transcription factors in the inflammatory process, cell proliferation, cell growth and apoptosis [173]. Further, EGCG can interact with epidermal growth factor receptor (EGF-R) and platelet-derived growth factor receptor (PDGF-R) to inhibit growth factor-mediated cellular proliferation and neoplasms. Interestingly, EGCG can also influence topoisomerase I and DNA replication, cyclin-dependent kinases (CDKs), and can inhibit telomerase to preserve telomere length, thereby influencing cell cycle and cellular senescence [171,173]. In the later stages of cancer metastasis, EGCG can influence urokinase and MMPs, enzymes with critical roles in tumor cell migration [171,173]. The biological consequences of EGCG behaving as a pro-oxidant are frequently overlooked; however, the ability of EGCG (and other polyphenols) to generate ROS are also a critical aspect of their mechanism, particularly in cancer cells. The pro-oxidant properties of EGCG have been evaluated in a variety of cancer cell types such as human lung cancer, cervical carcinoma, oral squamous carcinoma and many others [174,175]. The selective cytotoxicity of polyphenols such as EGCG against cancer cells can be a consequence of the overall oxidative status of cells as determined by endogenous antioxidants such as Catalase, SOD, GSH and content of divalent cations, all of which influence the behavior of the polyphenol and affect the mode by which cellular protection is offered [174].

In summary, the impact of EGCG on mitigating cardiovascular disease physiology, decelerating aging-related health decline, and its remarkable neuroprotective effects, make this polyphenol an indisputable component of a diet designed for conserving excellent health and in extending lifespan.

5. Theaflavin Gallate

5.1. Epidemiological and Clinical Studies with Black Tea or Theaflavins

TFs are the predominant polyphenols found in black tea. Similar to the primary catechins in green tea, consumption of TF gallates in black tea have been linked to numerous health benefits. Data from epidemiological and some clinical studies on the health benefits of tea are conflicting; however, the overall health benefits of both green and black tea is widely accepted [176].

Black tea has been linked to a lower incidence of MI in a European study of 340 subjects consuming 1 or more cups of black tea/d [177]. In the Determinants of Myocardial Infarction Onset Study, 1900 subjects with a diagnosis of MI were followed for a median of 3.8 years; persons drinking 14 cups or more of tea per week and rated as heavy tea drinkers had a much lower risk of all–cause mortality including cardiovascular mortality [178]. In the same study, the prevalence of ventricular arrhythmias was also assessed and reported lower prevalence in high tea drinkers [179]. One drawback of this study was that it did not differentiate between green or black tea or decaffeinated drinks; however the drink of choice in the US at the time was caffeinated black tea, and was likely the tea consumed by most participants in the study. Black tea consumption was also inversely correlated with severe atherosclerosis in individuals 55-94 years old from the Rotterdam study (black tea being the popular tea in the Netherlands); this correlation was more prominent in women than in men [180].

Studies assessing the effects of TFs on dyslipidemia have shown some conflicting results. A TF-enriched GTE (containing both TF and catechin) was reported to have inhibitory effects on total cholesterol, LDL and HDL cholesterol, and triglycerides in a randomized control clinical trial undertaken on 240 subjects with mild to moderate hypercholesterolemia [181]. However, another intervention study using purified TFs with or without catechins showed no effect on serum cholesterol [182]. The study by Maron *et al* used an extract of TF prepared from raw tea leaves, whereas in the study by Trautwein *et al*, TF was from a commercial source, and this could account for the different ratio of TF and its gallates in both studies even though the total amount used was the same. Further, the subjects enrolled in Maron's study were encouraged to reduce dietary fat while in the latter, diets of the subjects were not altered, thus explaining possible reasons for the discrepancy in the results obtained between the two studies [181,182].

Black tea also has putative protective effects against neurodegeneration. The risk of developing Parkinson's disease in a cohort of individuals in Seattle, that were followed for 8 years, was lower in those who consumed 2 or more cups of tea/d and was not influenced by cigarette smoking; however, since all tea drinkers were pooled regardless of the type of tea, the study did not differentiate between black or green tea [183]. The Hordaland Health Study (HUSK) conducted in Norway on 70-74 year old individuals investigated the outcome of habitual consumption of chocolate, wine and tea on a variety of cognitive tests in these older adults and also reported an inverse correlation between these polyphenol rich foods and cognitive decline [184].

Further, the PAQUID study in France also reported similar findings for adults (65 y and older) consuming a flavonoid rich diet, including tea, over a 10 y period [185].

In aging populations, tea consumption has been linked with a reduction in age-related cardiac and neurological decline. The Zutphen Elderly study as well as the Rotterdam study, on older adults, report better cardiovascular health and reduced incidences of mortality from coronary heart disease in the elderly [56,180,186,187]. Further, studies from the Rotterdam cohort also revealed reduced risk of MI in tea drinking older adults [56]. Although neither study clearly stated whether green or black tea was consumed, it is widely accepted that the popular drink of choice in these cohorts was black tea. A cohort of Chinese adults aged ≥ 55 years from the Singapore Longitudinal Ageing Study (SLAS) were identified to assess the association of tea intake and cognitive impairment and decline. Regardless of the type of tea consumed (green, black or oolong), tea consumption was correlated with reduced risk of cognitive impairment and decline, however black and oolong tea were the most influential [188].

Although experimental evidence has suggested that black tea and/or polyphenols therein are protective against cancer, the evidence from epidemiological studies is inconclusive. The Zuphen Elderly study reported no relationship between consumption of flavonoids in foods such as tea and reduced risk of all-cause cancer in this cohort [189]. The Netherlands Cohort study on Diet and Cancer reported no correlation between consumption of black tea and the risk of stomach, colorectal, lung or breast cancers [190]. A decreased risk of advanced stage III/IV prostate cancer was reported to be associated with a median black tea consumption of 2 cups/d [191]. No association of black tea and ovarian cancer risk, but a positive correlation with endometrial cancer risk was observed in a metanalyses conducted by Wu et al [192]. Singaporean women who consumed black tea had higher levels of circulating estrogen as compared to those who didn't suggesting that black tea increases estrogen; higher levels of this hormone have been associated with breast cancer, and thus, black tea has been speculated to promote cancer in this tissue [193,194]. Some protective evidence was demonstrated in oral leukoplakia by reduction in plaque size after a 6 month application of a formulation of mixed tea directly to the oral lesions [195]. A metanalyses by Sun et al reported no chemoprotective effects of either green or black tea on colorectal cancer [196].

5.2. Modes of Action of Theaflavin Gallate

Like green tea, black tea constituents have potent antioxidant effects. A comparative study analyzing the antioxidant activity of TFs and green tea showed that TFs are at least as effective as catechins in inhibiting Cu^{2+} mediated oxidation of human LDL. The order of antioxidant activity was TF3 > ECG > EGCG $\geq$ TF2B $\geq$ TF2A > TF $\geq$ EC > EGC, suggesting that fermentation during black tea manufacturing does not significantly alter radical scavenging activity [197]. Additionally, black tea consumption generated the greatest increase in *in vivo* plasma antioxidant activity when compared to green tea and alcohol-free red and white wines [198]. Experiments measuring antioxidant activity *in vitro* mirrored the phenolic concentration of the beverages; however, the antioxidant activity observed with black tea *in vivo* was unexpectedly high when compared to *in vitro* measurements. This discrepancy suggests that *in vivo* antioxidant activity is not merely dependent on phenolic content, but also dependent on factors such as the interaction of phenolics and other nutrients present in the beverages, as well as potential structural modifications of black tea polyphenols after ingestion. It was speculated that gastric acids might break down condensed polyphenols, restoring antioxidant capacity and releasing monomeric phenolics for absorption [198]. A key component of theaflavin's anti-tumorigenic properties may be directly due to their antioxidant effects. TF3 can inhibit xanthine oxidase, which is a ROS-generating enzyme involved in the formation of O_2^- [199]. Theaflavins also inhibit lipid peroxidation and mutation due to H_2O_2 treatment, effects which are likely attributable to radical scavenging by the galloyl moiety [63].

In addition to functioning as an effective antioxidant, TF gallates may also have anti-hypertensive effects. In the SP-SHR animal model, consumption of black tea polyphenols has been shown to attenuate increases in blood pressure [129]. Anti-hypertensive effects could be mediated by numerous mechanisms including, for example, the regulation of cholesterol metabolism. The cholesterol lowering effect of black tea has often been highlighted as one of the major mechanisms behind this polyphenol's ability to protect against CVD and related disorders. This quality can at least be partially attributed to the ability of TFs, specifically TF2A, to interfere with the incorporation of cholesterol into micelles resulting in reduced intestinal absorption [200]. This was further supported by a study on rats administered black tea polyphenols; TF monogallates decreased micellar solubility of cholesterol *in vitro* and also demonstrated decreased absorption of cholesterol via deceased lymphatic recovery *in vivo* [201]. Other studies have suggested that TFs, without a galloyl moiety, may have additional protective properties. In *ApoE-/-* mice, TF (64 mg/kg/d for 26 weeks) significantly attenuated atherosclerotic lesions in the aortic sinus and thoracic aorta; it also increased vascular NO, augmented HO-1, and reduced P-selectin, although the effects were less extensive than quercetin [202]. TF also protected young rat hearts from injury during I/R by opening K_{ATP} channels and protecting mitochondrial membrane integrity [203]. Cerebral I/R injury in Sprague Dawley rats was attenuated by TF administration; TF was anti-inflammatory by inhibiting COX-2 and phosphorylation of STAT-1 in the ischemic brain, and repressing ICAM-1 expression on leucocytes [204].

TF gallates have also demonstrated beneficial properties in regard to neurodegenerative disease. In an *in vitro* study using pooled human plasma, TF3's ability to inhibit plasminogen activator inhibitor-1 (PAI-1) was demonstrated; PAI-1 inhibits tPA-induced activation of plasmin, an enzyme responsible for the degradation of amyloid peptides [205–207]. TF3 showed stronger ability to inhibit PAI-1 in human plasma than both EGCG and the known PAI-1 inhibitor PAI039, implying a potential protective role of TF3 against AD [205]. Black tea extract, containing 80% TFs, has also shown protective effects against toxicity of Aβ aggregates by reduced apoptosis and abrogated Aβ aggregation in hippocampal neurons from Sprague Dawley rats [208]. TFs are also protective against 6-OHDA-induced oxidative stress and cell death in SH-SY5Y cells by inhibiting ROS, preserving mitochondrial potential and nuclear architecture thereby preventing apoptosis and increasing cell viability [209]. In the MPTP treated mouse model of PD, TF treatment protected against Parkinsonism in these animals by reducing oxidative stress parameters in the striatum and substantia nigra, increasing the expression of dopamine transporter (DAT) and vesicular monoamine transporter 2 (VMATs) in dopaminergic neurons, reduced nigral expression of TH and caspase 3, 8 and 9. Further, behavioral impairments due to MPTP, as assessed by open field test (test for acclimatization and motor activity), the performance on a rotarod (to assess coordinated motor skills), as well as the hang test (to assess neuromuscular strength), revealed much improved patterns due to TF treatment [210,211]. Interestingly, TF3 can inhibit the methylation of DNMT3a, a DNA methyl transferase that is important for the regulation of transcription of neurogenic genes, regulation of synaptic function in the forebrain as well as emotional behavior [212–215].

TFs have also been analyzed for their anti-tumorigenic properties in a wide variety of cell types [63]. In a study investigating a variety of phenolic compounds for their ability to inhibit mutagenesis by 2-amino1-methyl-6-phenylimidazo [4,5-b] pyridine (PhIP), a foodborne pro-carcinogen, the compounds with greatest anti-mutagenic activity (reported as IC_{50} values) were: tannic acid > TF3 > TF2 > TF > ECG > EGCG. Other phenolics tested included ungallated catechins, as well as GA and MG, none of which showed inhibition. In the same study, a similar experiment using 2-NF, a different mutagen, showed no inhibition with the same phenolic compounds suggesting that the anti-mutagenic effects of the gallated catechins and tannic acid, but not the ungallated catechins or GA, was specific and involved the inhibition of the cytochrome P450-mediated oxidation of the promutagen PhIP to its active form [216]. Other studies have supported the idea that cytochrome-P450 (CYP) oxidases are inhibited by galloyl groups of these compounds [217]. TFs can suppress CYP450 1A1 in RL-34 cells (from the rat liver epithelium), with TF3 having the greatest protective effect, TF2 the second greatest, and TF being the least protective [199]. Another environmental mutagen, benzo[a]pyrene or B[a]P is also activated by CYP450 1A1. TF2 or TF3 reduced the DNA damage caused by B [a] P due to their strong suppressive effect on CYP450 1A1 induction [199].

TFs have shown protective capacity against a number of other mutagenic agents, including, H_2O_2, cyclophosphamide (CP) and dimethylbenz(a) anthracene (DMBA) [61,199,218,219]. In Swiss albino mice TF significantly decreased chromosome aberrations (CA) and sister chromatid exchanges (SCE) mediated by CP and DMBA [219]. Theaflavins show considerable anti-mutagenic and anti-clastogenic effects against the procarcinogen B[a]P; TFs and B[a]P were administered to BALB/c mice by gavage, and bone marrow was later analyzed; all three concentrations of TF significantly decreased CA and SCE [218]. In RL-34 cells, black tea theaflavins demonstrated protective effects on H_2O_2 and tert-butyl hydroperoxide (tBuOOH)-induced oxidative stress, DNA damage, and cytotoxicity, with TF3 attenuating intracellular ROS even at the lowest dose used, and offered cytoprotection similar to EGCG [199]. Further, both co-treatment or pre-treatment with TFs, demonstrated dose-dependent protective effects against oxidative stress-induced cytotoxicity, with TF3 exhibiting the strongest protective effect in that 50 μM recovered more than 90% of the cell viability. Additionally, the effects of pretreatment suggest that cells are able to absorb and retain TFs.

The anti-tumorigenic properties of TFs are also discernible in the form of interference with signaling pathways and tumor growth inhibition. The effect of TF, TF2, TF3, EGCG, and EGC on the growth of 33BES and 21BES, human bronchial epithelial cells, showed growth inhibitory effects with TF3,

EGC and EGCG treatments; lower levels of inhibition with TF2 and even lower with TF were observed, suggesting that the number and organization of galloyl groups is important to the growth inhibitory effects of TFs. Apoptosis of these cells was attributed to TFs acting as pro-oxidants and generating H_2O_2, and to lowered activity of AP-1, a transcription factor fundamental in cellular proliferation [220]. TFs can also hinder signal transduction pathways and interfere with cell signaling. The IGF-I signal transduction pathway and downstream Akt phosphorylation, which has been linked to incidence of prostate cancer in humans, was inhibited by a black tea polyphenol mixture [221]. TF3 and penta-O-galloyl-β-D-glucose (5GG) were both found to inhibit rat liver microsomal 5α-reductase activity, an enzyme involved in androgen metabolism with potential involvement in prostate cancer development. TF3 and 5GG also inhibited growth of androgen-responsive LNCaP prostate cancer cells and suppressed expression/function of the androgen receptor, supporting their chemopreventive properties [222].

In conclusion, the studies summarized above illustrate that TF and its gallates, the predominant polyphenols found in black tea, the most widely consumed beverage globally, has favorable outcomes in attenuating pathophysiological consequences of cardiovascular and neurological sequelae associated with disease and with aging.

6. Gallic Acid

6.1. Epidemiological and Clinical Studies with Gallic Acid

GA displays a wide variety of biological effects that are primarily relevant in cancer and tumorigenesis. However, there is increasing evidence for the benefits of GA in other physiological systems such as the cardiovascular and neurobiological systems. Although epidemiological studies on the independent effects of GA are lacking, there is significant evidence suggesting that a diet rich in fruits, vegetables, olive oil and tea can be beneficial for cardiovascular and neurological health. These benefits are primarily owing to the high amount of polyphenolic compounds present in these dietary sources, of which GA is a constituent.

The FINRISK and the Kuopio Ischemic heart Disease (KIHD) studies in Finland compared the consumption of functional foods such as berries, vegetables and fruits with risk of CVD and reported a reduced risk of CVD with increased fruit and vegetable consumption [223,224]. Another investigation, the INTERHEART study, followed subjects from 52 countries and reported an inverse correlation of MI with a "prudent diet" rich in fruits and vegetables as opposed to the "western diet" rich in meat and fried foods [225]. Additionally, the Mediterranean diet, rich in olive oil, has been correlated with a decreased risk of AD and other neurodegenerative diseases [226].

In clinical studies, evidence has been found to support a role for GA in contributing to decreases in a number of cardiovascular risk factors. In a group of healthy volunteers, daily consumption of Mauritian black tea infusion (containing 50 ± 0.4 mg/L GA) over a course of 12 weeks, significantly decreased fasting serum glucose (18.4%; p<0.001), triglyceride levels (35.8%; p<0.01), LDL/HDL plasma cholesterol ratio (16.6%; p<0.05) and significantly improved plasma antioxidant status [227]. Additionally, a black Pu-Erh tea extract, high in GA, significantly decreased BMI, waist circumference, and visceral fat values in pre-obese Japanese adults [228]. Another study measured flow-mediated dilation of the brachial artery in male patients with coronary heart disease and found that administration of a red grape polyphenol extract (containing 2.07 mg/g GA) improved endothelial function, [229].

6.2. Modes of Action of Gallic Acid

GA has been reported to have profound cardioprotective effects, which are achieved primarily by its radical scavenging properties and induction of endogenous antioxidants. Isoproterenol-induced cardiotoxicity is a well-established model to study ischemia-induced MI; cardiac damage is induced by ROS generated by auto autoxidation of catecholamines. In this model of cardiotoxicity, oral intake of 15 mg/kg/d of GA for 10 days by Wistar rats ameliorated the effects of isoproterenol by reducing plasma and heart lipid peroxides, increasing GSH and reducing the activities of lysosomal enzymes such as Cathepsin-B and D, which are responsible for cell injury in ischemic hearts [230]. Sprague Dawley rats administered 100 mg/kg day of GA for 14 days induced the expression and increased activity of antioxidant enzymes Cu-SOD, GPx and CAT in the heart, accompanied by the upregulation of transcription factors Nrf2 and HO-1, both involved in cellular stress response and oxidative challenge [231]. Lindane, an agricultural pesticide, induces ROS-mediated cardiotoxicity; its effects in Wistar rats were alleviated by an oral GA dose of 50 mg/kg/d for 30 days. Similar to the other studies, GA aided in cardioprotection by increasing cardiac antioxidant enzymes SOD, CAT and GST, diminishing lipid peroxidation and by reducing circulating lactate dehydrogenase (LDH) and creatine kinase (CK), both indicators of injury to myocyte membranes [232]. The ability of GA to mitigate ROS and increase cell viability has been further demonstrated in a variety of cell lines. HeLa cells exposed to H_2O_2-mediated oxidative stress were protected from apoptosis by GA pretreatment by reducing intracellular ROS and the activity of Caspase-9 [233]. GA also reduced intracellular ROS generated in cardiomyoblasts by AGEs, increased the activity of antioxidant enzymes SOD, CAT and elevated GSH content while preserving mitochondrial potential [234]. In these cells, GA also impaired the AGE-induced induction of the key transcription factor NFκB and cytokines TNFα, TGFβ as well as MMP-2 and MMP-9, all mediators of AGE-induced matrix remodeling and cardiovascular complications [235]. GA's cardioprotective strengths are also affirmed by its roles in mitigating inflammation and activating platelet aggregation, both as discussed above are crucial processes in the development of atherosclerosis. By limiting the activation of NFκB and the proinflammatory cytokines TNFα and IL1β, GA successfully abolished inflammatory responses in NFκB transgenic mice stimulated with LPS [236]. Platelet activation was blunted in the presence of GA through the inhibition of P-selectin expression, and phosphorylation of MAPK and Akt/GSK3β on platelets thereby reducing their aggregation [237]. In addition to its antioxidant and anti-inflammatory properties, GA also has demonstrated beneficial effects with obesity, which is a risk factor for hypertension and other cardiac diseases and decreases antioxidant capacity of individuals. The negative effects of obesity induced by a high fat diet (HFD) in an animal model were abrogated by GA, evident in significant body weight and adipose tissue reduction, and reduced total and LDL cholesterol and triglycerides as compared to HFD without GA supplementation [238]. GA's cholesterol lowering capability likely stems from its ability to inhibit pancreatic cholesterol esterase, and its ability to reduce the solubility of cholesterol in micelles, delaying cholesterol absorption [239].

Like other protective antioxidants, GA has also been studied for its potential neuroprotective capabilities. In a study in which Wistar rats were injected with 6-OHDA directly into the medial forebrain bundle (MFB) to serve as an animal model for PD by inhibition of striatal dopamine, 200 mg/kg/d GA was administered orally for 10 days post-injection to analyze if these animals could recover from 6-OHDA-induced oxidative stress and resultant PD traits. The GA group showed decreased MDA levels (a product of lipid peroxidation and a biomarker for oxidative stress), and increased GPx in the hippocampus and striatum, and this was accompanied by a significant increase in passive avoidance memory, a test to judge fear-based learning and memory, as well as cognitive ability [240]. Interestingly, in such animals, GA also augmented motor dysfunctions associated with PD and improved EEG readings from the left globus pallidus in the basal ganglia, measured via a bipolar wire electrode implant [241]. GA may also act on the neuroinflammatory processes paramount in neurodegeneration through regulation of NFκB, a key signaling molecule with control over cytokine expression. The RelA or p65 subunit of NFκB has been reported to be present at higher concentrations in neurons, microglia cells and astrocytes in AD brains [242]. GA treatment blocked the histone acetylation of RelA in cultured glia cells and in mouse brain tissue, thereby diminishing the activation of NFκB, consequently mitigating Aβ toxicity and neuronal cell death [243]. In a mouse model of aging, the senescence accelerated mice, the antioxidant potential of GA extracted from rose flowers reestablished the antioxidants CAT and GPx and also reduced the levels of MDA in a variety of body tissues [244].

GA is selectively cytotoxic against a variety of tumor cells and shows irreversible anti-proliferative and cytotoxic activity for a number of cancer cell lines, with reversible effects toward healthy cells [72,245,246]. GA has anti-angiogenic, anti-proliferative and apoptotic properties in numerous cancer cells lines, acting upon multiple molecular targets [72]. Additionally, the cytotoxicity of GA is a fairly specific characteristic of this phenolic and not simply a common feature of phenolic compounds [247]. GA prevents cancer progression through its effects on COX-2, UGDH, and angiogenesis. GA competitively inhibits COX-2 by binding to its active site, and has been shown to down-regulate this enzyme in the chronic myeloid leukemia (CML) cell lines K562 and IR-K562 [248–250]. This inhibition is protective against cancer because COX-2 increases synthesis of prostaglandins, which are important in mediating tumor cell resistance [250]. In MCF-7 human breast cancer cells, GA treatment reduces viability, and inhibits UGDH activity through the non-competitive inhibition of its substrates, UDP-glucose and NAD+ [251]. UGDH catalyzes the conversion of UDP-glucose to UDP-glucuronic acid [252,253], which is a precursor of glycosaminoglycans that are involved in the progression of epithelial cancers [254,255]. GA also inhibits angiogenesis through interference with VEGF-stimulated endothelial cell MMP-2 and MMP-9 activity, as well as through inhibition of VEGFR2, eNOS, and cyclin E expression [256]. Moreover, GA inhibits endothelial migration/invasion, tube formation, cell cycle progression (G_0/G_1 arrest), and *in vivo* neovascularization in chick chorioallantoic membrane [256].

In addition to the above effects on key mechanisms in cancer progression, GA also influences cell cycle, cell death, cell proliferation and oxidative damage in various cancer types. In a prostate cancer cell line, GA's anti-cancer effects appear to be caused by the activation of ATM-Chk2. ATM-Chk2 inactivates cdc25C/C phosphatases and leads to cell cycle arrest by preventing the transition from G_2 to M phase [257].

In the human HL-60 promyelocytic leukemia cell line, GA decreases intracellular dATP and dGTP concentration suggesting that GA inhibits ribonucleotide reductase (RR), the rate-limiting enzyme in *de novo* DNA synthesis. In these cells, GA treatment inhibits progression from G0/G1 to S-phase and induces apoptosis. This is believed to be a consequence of the change in the dNTP pool, which prevents DNA synthesis in rapidly growing tumor cells [249]. GA induces apoptosis in numerous cancer cell lines through the activation of Fas, FasL, p53, regulation of Bcl-2 family proteins, and activation of caspase-mediated mechanisms [72,258,259]. Supporting these findings, *Toona sinensis* leaf extract (of which GA is a major bioactive compound) was shown to up-regulate pro-apoptotic genes TNFα, TP53BP2, and GADD45A, while down-regulating anti-apoptotic genes Survivin and cIAP1 in human oral squamous carcinoma cell lines; GA also reduced viability through a combination of apoptosis and necrosis, while normal human oral keratinocytes were not affected [94]. The balance between antioxidant and pro-oxidant activities of GA also works as a mechanism against cancer growth. In Calu-6 and A549 lung cancer cells, GA generally acts as a pro-oxidant, affecting ROS levels and potentially leading to observed mitochondrial dysfunction. GA increases the number of GSH-depleted lung cancer cells, which was reflective of increases in cell death [260]. Additionally, the inhibition of NFκB by GA is a critical anti-tumorigenic mechanism displayed by this polyphenol, NFκB being a pivotal transcription factor regulating the expression of several genes involved in cell growth, proliferation and apoptosis [72].

The studies highlighted above illustrate the cardioprotective and neuroprotective properties of GA and underscore its anti-tumorigenic attributes, implying that dietary supplementation with this polyphenol can be valuable for good health.

7. Methyl Gallate

A derivative of GA, MG is a polyphenol that has antioxidant, anti-inflammatory and anti-tumorigenic properties. The effectiveness of MG as a protective agent against oxidative stress has been shown in a wide variety of studies employing different cell types [261–264]. An *in vitro* study established MG's antioxidant properties by demonstrating its capacity to scavenge superoxide and peroxyl radicals, and protect DNA from degradation [265]. Studies from our lab have shown that MG can reduce intracellular ROS and protect the mitochondria from oxidative stress-induced damage in both PC12 cells [263] and in neonatal rat cardiomyocytes [266](in press), suggesting that this polyphenol may have valuable neuroprotective and cardioprotective effects. In both cell types, MG was able to upregulate endogenous GSH, interfere with the caspase pathway and preserve cellular DNA against stress-mediated damage, consequently decreasing cellular apoptosis and increasing viability [263,266].

In addition to its antioxidant-related benefits MG regulates immune function through its effects on arachidonic acid metabolism. Arachidonic acid is used in the synthesis of prostaglandins (PGE) and leukotrienes (LTs) by the cyclooxygenase (COX-1 and -2) and lipoxygenase (LOX) pathways [267]. The molecular products of these pathways have a broad range of physiological effects in the cardiovascular system and the immune response [267]. MG has been shown to suppress arachidonic acid metabolism through the inhibition of COX-2 and 5-LOX activities, giving it significant therapeutic value as an anti-inflammatory compound [268]. COX-2 is the predominant isoform that is upregulated during inflammation and a critical factor that controls the synthesis of PGE_2 in inflammation; PGE_2 is integral to cancer and atherosclerosis, therefore making MG-mediated inhibition of COX-2 a putative target for reducing inflammation and associated sequelae [269]. Additionally, MG is a promising candidate in immunotherapy against cancer through its anti-migratory activity against $CD4^+/CD25^+$ regulatory T cells (Tregs) and reduction of the expression of Foxp3, a Treg-specific transcription factor. Increased numbers of Tregs in tumors makes the tumor less susceptible to immune surveillance mechanisms; therefore, MG may protect against cancer through its inhibitory effects on this cell type [270,271]. The anti-cancer potential of MG is also supported by cytotoxic and anti-proliferative properties against HeLa cells, a cervical cancer cell line [246] and by its anti-proliferative and anti-migratory effect on malignant glioma cells mediated by the inhibition of Akt and ERK 1/2, and inhibiting formation of focal adhesions [272].

In summary, the potential health benefits of MG are supported by studies identifying its antioxidant, anti-inflammatory and anti-tumorigenic traits making it an attractive dietary polyphenol.

8. Challenges in Employing Polyphenols as Therapeutic Agents

Despite the evidence accumulated from epidemiological and animal studies, the health effects of polyphenol consumption remain disputable. Clinical trials employing polyphenols have yielded inconsistent outcomes, some positive but others ineffective with functional food intervention. For example, in healthy male volunteers, dietary supplementation of GTE at 710 mg/d for 3 weeks yielded no changes in CVD risk parameters other than the total:HDL cholesterol ratio [273]. Similarly, black or green tea consumption over a 4-week period (6 cups or 900 mL per day) had no effect on plasma cholesterol, antioxidant status, or triglycerides in smokers [274]. In healthy female volunteers who consumed a high linoleic acid diet, GTE intake for 4 weeks (10 cups of tea/d) decreased MDA, but no other markers of oxidative stress [275]. Further, some investigations have also indicated adverse effects of excessive polyphenols [276]. Animal studies have shown that oral intake of 5000 mg/kg/d of Pu-erh GTE for 91 days caused suppression of weight gain and led to histopathological changes in the liver; liver damage was likely due to interaction with cytochrome 450, mitochondrial damage in hepatocytes and increased lactate dehydrogenase activity all leading to accumulation of toxic metabolites in the tissue [277–279]. Hepatotoxicity has been reported with green tea dietary supplements used for weight loss in humans, with the toxicity attributed to concurrent consumption of other drugs like paracetamol, excessive uptake of EGCG by the liver, or pro-oxidant activity of EGCG in hepatocytes [278].

Furthermore, it is challenging to interpret studies with polyphenols and translate the results into the development of a useful therapeutic because differences in dietary patterns, lack of consistency in the preparations of polyphenol or doses used, and differences in genetic and environmental factors, all confound the interpretation, and can influence the outcome of intervention with functional foods. These factors make it difficult to come up with a standard recipe or a daily recommended dose that could be applied as a therapeutic: one size does not fit all [280]. Bioavailability is "a fraction of an ingested nutrient or compound that reaches the systemic circulation and the specific sites and can exert its biological action" [281]. The bioavailability of polyphenols, which are usually consumed as parts of whole food or as oral nutraceutical supplements, is influenced by a number of factors including intestinal absorption of the polyphenol, conversion to different metabolites and elimination, all of which may limit the ability of the ingested polyphenol to reach the tissue where it can elicit the desired beneficial health effects. The composition of the source of the polyphenol, and the food matrix of which it is a component are both relevant to bioavailability since polyphenols can interact with proteins or carbohydrate that can modulate their antioxidant properties; for example the addition of milk to black tea reduced its antioxidant capacity [45]. Tissue uptake of polyphenols is also variable and the kinetics of absorption vary dependent on tissue type meaning that the plasma concentration may not necessarily be reflective of tissue accumulation [45]. Polyphenol plasma concentrations also vary and are dependent on food source and amount ingested; data from 97 studies on polyphenol intake and resultant plasma concentration and urinary excretion have been reviewed by Manach *et al* in 2004 [282]. EGCG for example has poor bioavailability that has been attributed to its instability in alkaline pH, limited cellular uptake due to its hydrophobic nature, and its conversion into various metabolites that aren't as biologically active [283]. It can undergo methylation, glucuronidation or sulfation; methylation of EGCG renders it less bioactive than its non-methylated counterpart [283,284]. Interestingly this correlated with a clinical study on breast cancer patients in Los Angeles; only the women with the a low activity allele of *rs4680* encoding catechol-O-methyltransferase (COMT), an enzyme that catalyzes the methylation of EGCG (rendering it inactive), showed an inverse relationship between the risk of breast cancer and green tea consumption [109]. Finally, food processing, especially the methods used in commercial preparations, also alters the polyphenolic content and bioactivity of the foods [60]; for example brewing of tea for 7 h for preparation of commercially available drinks reduced the catechin content by 20% [285].

Extrapolating findings from *in vitro* or *in vivo* animal studies also has constraints, and potential therapeutic activities of a polyphenol observed in one model (e.g. purified polyphenols analyzed with target cells grown in controlled environments) may not translate well to humans and their complex physiological systems. For example, EGCG was found to cross the blood-brain barrier in an animal model, thus making it an attractive molecule to develop therapeutics against neurotoxicity; however discrepancies were observed when this was analyzed in human subjects [151]. Another example can be seen in an *in vivo* study investigating the antioxidant activity of polyphenol rich beverages in humans, which measured the response time to raise plasma antioxidant levels in healthy volunteers. The results of the study were inconsistent with expectations based on *in vitro* experiments, which showed that black tea displayed lower *in vitro* antioxidant capacity compared to red wine or green tea. However, when tested *in vivo* black tea produced a delayed but high response relative to green tea [198].

Conclusion

In summary, epidemiologically, polyphenol enriched diets have proven beneficial for human health. The literature reviewed here substantiates that gallate polyphenols counteract oxidative stress by acting as antioxidants and by modulating signaling molecules. Gallates mitigate ROS associated disease burden as related to CVD and neurodegeneration endorsing their therapeutic efficacy as molecules that support healthy aging. Although significant advances have been made in our comprehension of the mechanisms by which polyphenols protect human health, more research needs to be done to enhance bioavailability and preserve the bioactivity of these molecules in human subjects. To develop polyphenols as nutraceutical supplements for benefits to human health, advanced studies need to be undertaken with an emphasis on the issues of bioavailability, pharmacokinetic behavior, and combinatorial polyphenol formulations towards targeted disease(s). The pharmacokinetics of biologically active polyphenols or stable analogs thereof need to be identified, and concentrations needed for achieving health goals inferred, to aid in the investigation of nutritional interventions and establish these molecules as sentinels of human health [286].

References

[1]   Finkel, T.; Holbrook, N. Oxidants, oxidative stress and the biology of ageing. *Nature* 2000, *408*, 239–247.

[2]   Jomova, K.; Valko, M. Advances in metal-induced oxidative stress and human disease. *Toxicology* 2011, *283*, 65–87.

[3]   Eiserich, J. P.; Patel, R. P.; O'Donnell, V. B. Pathophysiology of nitric oxide and related species: free radical reactions and modification of biomolecules. *Mol. Aspects Med.* 1999, *19*, 221–357.

[4]   Schleicher, E.; Friess, U. Oxidative stress, AGE, and atherosclerosis. *Kidney Int. Suppl.* 2007, S17–26.

[5]   Valko, M.; Leibfritz, D.; Moncol, J.; Cronin, M. T. D.; Mazur, M.; Telser, J. Free radicals and antioxidants in normal physiological functions and human disease. *Int. J. Biochem. Cell Biol.* 2007, *39*, 44–84.

[6]   Ott, M.; Gogvadze, V.; Orrenius, S.; Zhivotovsky, B. Mitochondria, oxidative stress and cell death. *Apoptosis* 2007, *12*, 913–22.

[7]   Drummond, G.; Selemidis, S. Combating oxidative stress in vascular disease: NADPH oxidases as therapeutic targets. *Nat. Rev. Drug Discov.* 2011, *10*, 453–471.

[8]   Lacy, F.; Gough, D. a; Schmid-Schönbein, G. W. Role of xanthine oxidase in hydrogen peroxide production. *Free Radic. Biol. Med.* 1998, *25*, 720–7.

[9]   Paravicini, T. M.; Touyz, R. M. NADPH oxidases, reactive oxygen species, and hypertension: clinical implications and therapeutic possibilities. *Diabetes Care* 2008, *31 Suppl 2*, S170–80.

[10]   Hegab, Z.; Gibbons, S.; Neyses, L.; Mamas, M. a Role of advanced glycation end products in cardiovascular disease. *World J. Cardiol.* 2012, *4*, 90–102.

[11]   Kohen, R.; Nyska, A. Oxidation of Biological Systems: Oxidative Stress Phenomena, Antioxidants, Redox Reactions, and Methods for Their Quantification. *Toxicol. Pathol.* 2002, *30*, 620–650.

[12]   Lushchak, V. I. Glutathione homeostasis and functions: potential targets for medical interventions. *J. Amino Acids* 2012, *2012*, 736837.

[13]   Dizdaroglu, M.; Jaruga, P. Free Radical-Induced Damage to DNA: Mechanisms and Measurement. *Free Radic. Biol. Med.* 2002, *32*, 1102–1115.

[14]   Dhalla, N. S.; Temsah, R. M.; Netticadan, T. Role of oxidative stress in cardiovascular diseases. *J. Hypertens.* 2000, *18*, 655–73.

[15]   Sugamura, K. and J. F. K. J. Reactive Oxygen Species in Cardiovascular Disease. *Free Radic. Biol. Med.* 2011, *51*, 978–992.

[16]   Dhalla, N. S.; Elmoselhi, A. B.; Hata, T.; Makino, N. Status of myocardial antioxidants in ischemia-reperfusion injury. *Cardiovasc. Res.* 2000, *47*, 446–56.

[17] Hansson, G. K.; Libby, P. The immune response in atherosclerosis: a double-edged sword. *Nat. Rev. Immunol.* 2006, *6*, 508–19.

[18] Libby, P. Inflammation and cardiovascular disease mechanisms. *Am. J. Clin. Nutr.* 2006, *83*, 456S–460S.

[19] Cai, H.; Harrison, D. G. Endothelial dysfunction in cardiovascular diseases: the role of oxidant stress. *Circ. Res.* 2000, *87*, 840–4.

[20] Huo, Y.; Ley, K. F. Role of platelets in the development of atherosclerosis. *Trends Cardiovasc. Med.* 2004, *14*, 18–22.

[21] Maulik, S. K.; Kumar, S. Oxidative stress and cardiac hypertrophy: a review. *Toxicol. Mech. Methods* 2012, *22*, 359–66.

[22] Daou, G. B.; Srivastava, A. K. Reactive oxygen species mediate Endothelin-1-induced activation of ERK1/2, PKB, and Pyk2 signaling, as well as protein synthesis, in vascular smooth muscle cells. *Free Radic. Biol. Med.* 2004, *37*, 208–15.

[23] Schiffrin; EL Role of endothelin-1 in hypertension. 1999, *34*, 876–881.

[24] Williams, B. Angiotensin II and the Pathophysiology of Cardiovascular Remodeling. *Am. J. Cardiol.* 2001, *9149*.

[25] Halliwell, B. Oxidative stress and neurodegeneration: where are we now? *J. Neurochem.* 2006, *97*, 1634–58.

[26] Mariani, E.; Polidori, M. C.; Cherubini, A.; Mecocci, P. Oxidative stress in brain aging, neurodegenerative and vascular diseases: an overview. *J. Chromatogr. B. Analyt. Technol. Biomed. Life Sci.* 2005, *827*, 65–75.

[27] Freeman, L. R.; Keller, J. N. Oxidative stress and cerebral endothelial cells: regulation of the blood-brain-barrier and antioxidant based interventions. *Biochim. Biophys. Acta* 2012, *1822*, 822–829.

[28] Alikunju, S.; Abdul Muneer, P. M.; Zhang, Y.; Szlachetka, A. M.; Haorah, J. The inflammatory footprints of alcohol-induced oxidative damage in neurovascular components. *Brain. Behav. Immun.* 2011, *25 Suppl 1*, S129–36.

[29] Venkataraman, K.; Khurana, S.; Tai, T. C. Oxidative stress in aging-matters of the heart and mind. *Int. J. Mol. Sci.* 2013, *14*, 17897–925.

[30] Markesbery, W. Oxidative Stress hypothesis in Alzheimer's Disease. *Free Radic. Biol. Med.* 1997, *23*, 134–147.

[31] Maries, E.; Dass, B.; Collier, T. J.; Kordower, J. H.; Steece-Collier, K. The role of alpha-synuclein in Parkinson's disease: insights from animal models. *Nat. Rev. Neurosci.* 2003, *4*, 727–38.

[32] Harman, D. Aging: a theory based on free radical and radiation chemistry. *J. Gerontol.* 1956, *11*, 298–300.

[33] Kumar, M.; Andersen, J. Perspectives on MAO-B in aging and neurological disease. *Mol. Neurobiol.* 2004, *30*, 77–89.

[34] Ungvari, Z.; Parrado-Fernandez, C.; Csiszar, A.; De Cabo, R. Mechanisms underlying caloric restriction and lifespan regulation: implications for vascular aging. *Circ. Res.* 2008, *102*, 519–528.

[35] Ungvari, Z.; Sonntag, W. E.; Csiszar, A. Mitochondria and aging in the vascular system. *J. Mol. Med. (Berl).* 2010, *88*, 1021–1027.

[36] Oberley, L. W.; Buettner, G. R. Role of superoxide dismutase in cancer: a review. *Cancer Res.* 1979, *39*, 1141–9.

[37] Varmus, H. E. Oncogenes and transcriptional control. *Science* 1987, *238*, 1337–9.

[38] Bishop, J. The Molecular Genetics of Cancer. *Science (80-.).* 1987, *235*, 305–311.

[39] Abate, C.; Patel, L.; Rauscher, F. J.; Curran, T. Redox regulation of fos and jun DNA-binding activity in vitro. *Science* 1990, *249*, 1157–61.

[40] Klaunig, J. E.; Kamendulis, L. M. The role of oxidative stress in carcinogenesis. *Annu. Rev. Pharmacol. Toxicol.* 2004, *44*, 239–67.

[41] Valko, M.; Rhodes, C. J.; Moncol, J.; Izakovic, M.; Mazur, M. Free radicals, metals and antioxidants in oxidative stress-induced cancer. *Chem. Biol. Interact.* 2006, *160*, 1–40.

[42] Farbstein, D.; Kozak-Blickstein, A.; Levy, A. P. Antioxidant vitamins and their use in preventing cardiovascular disease. *Molecules* 2010, *15*, 8098–110.

[43] Paiva, S.; Russell, R. β Carotene and Other Carotenoids as Antioxidants. *J. Am. Coll. Nutr.* 1999, *18*, 426–433.

[44] Pandey, K. B.; Rizvi, S. I. Plant polyphenols as dietary antioxidants in human health and disease. *Oxid. Med. Cell. Longev.* 2009, *2*, 270–278.

[45] Manach, C.; Scalbert, A.; Morand, C.; Rémésy, C.; Jiménez, L. Polyphenols: food sources and bioavailability. *Am. J. Clin. Nutr.* 2004, *79*, 727–47.

[46] Khurana, S.; Piche, M.; Hollingsworth, A.; Venkataraman, K.; Tai, T. C. Oxidative stress and cardiovascular health : therapeutic potential of polyphenols. *Can. J. Physiol. Pharmacol.* 2013, *212*, 198–212.

[47] Khurana, S.; Venkataraman, K.; Hollingsworth, A.; Piche, M.; Tai, T. C. Polyphenols: benefits to the cardiovascular system in health and in aging. *Nutrients* 2013, *5*, 3779–827.

[48] Vauzour, D.; Rodriguez-Mateos, A.; Corona, G.; Oruna-Concha, M. J.; Spencer, J. P. E. Polyphenols and human health: prevention of disease and mechanisms of action. *Nutrients* 2010, *2*, 1106–1131.

[49] Arts, I. C. W.; Hollman, P. C. H. Polyphenols and disease risk in epidemiologic studies. *Am. J. Clin. Nutr.* 2005, *81*, 317S–325S.

[50] Renaud, S.; de Lorgeril, M. Wine, alcohol, platelets, and the French paradox for coronary heart disease. *Lancet* 1992, *339*, 1523–6.

[51] Ferrieres, J. The French paradox: lessons for other countries. *Heart* 2004, *90*, 107–111.

[52] Pérez-López, F. R.; Chedraui, P.; Haya, J.; Cuadros, J. L. Effects of the Mediterranean diet on longevity and age-related morbid conditions. *Maturitas* 2009, *64*, 67–79.

[53] Wilken, R.; Veena, M. S.; Wang, M. B.; Srivatsan, E. S. Curcumin: A review of anti-cancer properties and therapeutic activity in head and neck squamous cell carcinoma. *Mol. Cancer* 2011, *10*, 12.

[54] Mandel, S. A.; Amit, T.; Kalfon, L.; Reznichenko, L.; Youdim, M. B. H. Targeting multiple neurodegenerative diseases etiologies with multimodal-acting green tea catechins. *J. Nutr.* 2008, *138*, 1578S–1583S.

[55] Yang, Y. C.; Lu, F. H.; Wu, J. S.; Wu, C. H.; Chang, C. J. The protective effect of habitual tea consumption on hypertension. *Arch. Intern. Med.* 2004, *164*, 1534–1540.

[56] Geleijnse, J. M.; Launer, L. J.; Van der Kuip, D. A. M.; Hofman, A.; Witteman, J. C. M. Inverse association of tea and flavonoid intakes with incident myocardial infarction: the Rotterdam Study. *Am. J. Clin. Nutr.* 2002, *75*, 880–6.

[57] Gu, X.; Creasy, L.; Kester, A.; Zeece, M. Capillary Electrophoretic Determination of Resveratrol in Wines †. *J. Agric. Food Chem.* 1999, *47*, 3223–3227.

[58] Patil, B.; Pike, L.; Yoo, K. Variation in the quercetin content in different colored onions (Allium cepa L.). *J. Am. Soc. Hortic. Sci.* 1995, *120*, 909–913.

[59] Bonoli, M.; Bendini, A.; Cerretani, L.; Lercker, G.; Toschi, T. G. Qualitative and semiquantitative analysis of phenolic compounds in extra virgin olive oils as a function of the ripening degree of olive fruits by different analytical techniques. *J. Agric. Food Chem.* 2004, *52*, 7026–32.

[60] Howard, L. R.; Prior, R. L.; Liyanage, R.; Lay, J. O. Processing and Storage Effect on Berry Polyphenols: Challenges and Implications for Bioactive Properties. *J. Agric. Food Chem.* 2012.

[61] Kuroda, Y.; Hara, Y. Antimutagenic and anticarcinogenic activity of tea polyphenols. *Mutat. Res.* 1999, *436*, 69–97.

[62]   Balentine, D. A.; Wiseman, S. A.; Bouwens, L. C. The chemistry of tea flavonoids. *Crit. Rev. Food Sci. Nutr.* 1997, *37*, 693–704.

[63]   Sharma, V.; Rao, L. J. M. A thought on the biological activities of black tea. *Crit. Rev. Food Sci. Nutr.* 2009, *49*, 379–404.

[64]   Zuo, Y.; Chen, H.; Deng, Y. Simultaneous determination of catechins, caffeine and gallic acids in green, Oolong, black and pu-erh teas using HPLC with a photodiode array detector. *Talanta* 2002, *57*, 307–16.

[65]   Hong, J.; Smith, T. J.; Ho, C. T.; August, D. a; Yang, C. S. Effects of purified green and black tea polyphenols on cyclooxygenase- and lipoxygenase-dependent metabolism of arachidonic acid in human colon mucosa and colon tumor tissues. *Biochem. Pharmacol.* 2001, *62*, 1175–83.

[66]   Henning, S. M.; Wang, P.; Heber, D. Chemopreventive effects of tea in prostate cancer: green tea versus black tea. *Mol. Nutr. Food Res.* 2011, *55*, 905–20.

[67]   Graham, H. N. Green tea composition, consumption, and polyphenol chemistry. *Prev. Med. (Baltim).* 1992, *21*, 334–50.

[68]   Arts, I. C.; van De Putte, B.; Hollman, P. C. Catechin contents of foods commonly consumed in The Netherlands. 2. Tea, wine, fruit juices, and chocolate milk. *J. Agric. Food Chem.* 2000, *48*, 1752–7.

[69]   Bhuyan, L. P.; Sabhapondit, S.; Baruah, B. D.; Bordoloi, C.; Gogoi, R.; Bhattacharyya, P. Polyphenolic compounds and antioxidant activity of CTC black tea of North-East India. *Food Chem.* 2013, *141*, 3744–51.

[70]   Wang, Z. Y.; Huang, M. T.; Lou, Y. R.; Xie, J. G.; Reuhl, K. R.; Newmark, H. L.; Ho, C. T.; Yang, C. S.; Conney, A. H. Inhibitory effects of black tea, green tea, decaffeinated black tea, and decaffeinated green tea on ultraviolet B light-induced skin carcinogenesis in 7,12-dimethylbenz[a]anthracene-initiated SKH-1 mice. *Cancer Res.* 1994, *54*, 3428–35.

[71]   Arts, I. C. W.; van de Putte, B.; Hollman, P. C. H. Catechin Contents of Foods Commonly Consumed in The Netherlands. 1. Fruits, Vegetables, Staple Foods, and Processed Foods. *J. Agric. Food Chem.* 2000, *48*, 1746–1751.

[72]   Verma, S.; Singh, A.; Mishra, A. Gallic acid: molecular rival of cancer. *Environ. Toxicol. Pharmacol.* 2013, *35*, 473–85.

[73]   Yilmaz, Y.; Toledo, R. T. Major flavonoids in grape seeds and skins: antioxidant capacity of catechin, epicatechin, and gallic acid. *J. Agric. Food Chem.* 2004, *52*, 255–60.

[74] Häkkinen, S.; Heinonen, M. Screening of selected flavonoids and phenolic acids in 19 berries. *Food Res. Int.* 1999, *32*, 345–353.

[75] Saravanan, K.; Aradhya, S. M. Polyphenols of pseudostem of different banana cultivars and their antioxidant activities. *J. Agric. Food Chem.* 2011, *59*, 3613–23.

[76] Sellappan, S.; Akoh, C. C.; Krewer, G. Phenolic compounds and antioxidant capacity of Georgia-grown blueberries and blackberries. *J. Agric. Food Chem.* 2002, *50*, 2432–8.

[77] Huang, W.; Zhang, H.; Liu, W.; Li, C. Survey of antioxidant capacity and phenolic composition of blueberry, blackberry, and strawberry in Nanjing. *J. Zhejiang Univ. Sci. B* 2012, *13*, 94–102.

[78] Ma, J.; Luo, X.-D.; Protiva, P.; Yang, H.; Ma, C.; Basile, M. J.; Weinstein, I. B.; Kennelly, E. J. Bioactive novel polyphenols from the fruit of Manilkara zapota (Sapodilla). *J. Nat. Prod.* 2003, *66*, 983–6.

[79] Loizzo, M. R.; Said, A.; Tundis, R.; Hawas, U. W.; Rashed, K.; Menichini, F.; Frega, N. G.; Menichini, F. Antioxidant and antiproliferative activity of Diospyros lotus L. extract and isolated compounds. *Plant Foods Hum. Nutr.* 2009, *64*, 264–70.

[80] Rashed, K.; Zhang, X.; Luo, M.; Zheng, Y. Anti-HIV-1 activity of phenolic compounds isolated from Diospyros lotus fruits. 2012, *3*, 199–207.

[81] Sawant, L.; Prabhakar, B.; Mahajan, A.; Pai, N.; Pandita, N. Development and Validation of HPLC Method for Quantification of Phytoconstituents in Phyllanthus emblica. *J. Chem. Pharm. Res.* 2011, *3*, 937–944.

[82] Wang, R.; Ding, Y.; Liu, R.; Xiang, L.; Du, L. Pomegranate : Constituents , Bioactivities and Pharmacokinetics. In *Fruit, Vegetbale and Cereal Science and Biotechnology*; Global Science Books, 2010.

[83] Baliga, M. S.; Dsouza, J. J. Amla (Emblica officinalis Gaertn), a wonder berry in the treatment and prevention of cancer. *Eur. J. Cancer Prev.* 2011, *20*, 225–39.

[84] Yeh, C. T.; Yen, G. C. Effect of vegetables on human phenolsulfotransferases in relation to their antioxidant activity and total phenolics. *Free Radic. Res.* 2005, *39*, 893–904.

[85] Shahrzad, S.; Bitsch, I. Determination of some pharmacologically active phenolic acids in juices by high-performance liquid chromatography. *J. Chromatogr. A* 1996, *741*, 223–31.

[86] Goldberg, D. Catechin and epicatechin concentrations of red wines: regional and cultivar-related differences. *Am. J. Enol. Vitic.* 1998, *49*, 23–34.

[87] Ertan Anli, R.; Vural, N. Antioxidant phenolic substances of Turkish red wines from different wine regions. *Molecules* 2009, *14*, 289–97.

[88] Tian, R. R.; Pan, Q. H.; Zhan, J. C.; Li, J. M.; Wan, S. B.; Zhang, Q. H.; Huang, W. D. Comparison of phenolic acids and flavan-3-ols during wine fermentation of grapes with different harvest times. *Molecules* 2009, *14*, 827–38.

[89] Dağdelen, A.; Tümen, G.; Ozcan, M. M.; Dündar, E. Phenolics profiles of olive fruits (Olea europaea L.) and oils from Ayvalık, Domat and Gemlik varieties at different ripening stages. *Food Chem.* 2013, *136*, 41–5.

[90] Carrasco-Pancorbo, A.; Gómez-Caravaca, A. M.; Cerretani, L.; Bendini, A.; Segura-Carretero, A.; Fernández-Gutiérrez, A. A simple and rapid electrophoretic method to characterize simple phenols, lignans, complex phenols, phenolic acids, and flavonoids in extra-virgin olive oil. *J. Sep. Sci.* 2006, *29*, 2221–2233.

[91] Carrasco Pancorbo, A.; Segura Carretero, A.; Fernández Gutiérrez, A. Co-electroosmotic capillary electrophoresis determination of phenolic acids in commercial olive oil. *J. Sep. Sci.* 2005, *28*, 925–934.

[92] Chen, W.; Zhang, C.; Huang, Y.; Cheng, F.; Shen, Y.; Wang, R.; Tang, M.; Zheng, Y.; Zhao, S. The inhibiting activity of areca inflorescence extracts on human low density lipoprotein oxidation induced by cupric ion. *Int. J. Food Sci. Nutr.* 2012, *63*, 236–41.

[93] Bhandare, A. M.; Kshirsagar, A. D.; Vyawahare, N. S.; Hadambar, A. A.; Thorve, V. S. Potential analgesic, anti-inflammatory and antioxidant activities of hydroalcoholic extract of Areca catechu L. nut. *Food Chem. Toxicol.* 2010, *48*, 3412–3417.

[94] Chia, Y. C.; Rajbanshi, R.; Calhoun, C.; Chiu, R. H. Anti-neoplastic effects of gallic acid, a major component of Toona sinensis leaf extract, on oral squamous carcinoma cells. *Molecules* 2010, *15*, 8377–89.

[95] Hseu, Y. C.; Chang, W. H.; Chen, C. S.; Liao, J. W.; Huang, C. J.; Lu, F. J.; Chia, Y. C.; Hsu, H. K.; Wu, J. J.; Yang, H. L. Antioxidant activities of Toona Sinensis leaves extracts using different antioxidant models. *Food Chem. Toxicol.* 2008, *46*, 105–114.

[96] Mukherjee, P. K.; Maity, N.; Nema, N. K.; Sarkar, B. K. Bioactive compounds from natural resources against skin aging. *Phytomedicine* 2011, *19*, 64–73.

[97] Tomaino, A.; Martorana, M.; Arcoraci, T.; Monteleone, D.; Giovinazzo, C.; Saija, A. Antioxidant activity and phenolic profile of pistachio (Pistacia vera L., variety Bronte) seeds and skins. *Biochimie* 2010, *92*, 1115–22.

[98] Marzouk, M. S. A.; Moharram, F. A.; Mohamed, M. A.; Gamal-Eldeen, A. M.; Aboutabl, E. A. Anticancer and antioxidant tannins from Pimenta dioica leaves. *Z. Naturforsch. C.* 2007, *62*, 526–36.

[99] Kuriyama, S.; Shimazu, T.; Ohmori, K.; Kikuchi, N.; Nakaya, N.; Nishino, Y.; Tsubono, Y.; Tsuji, I. Green tea consumption and mortality due to cardiovascular disease, cancer, and all causes in Japan: the Ohsaki study. *JAMA* 2006, *296*, 1255–65.

[100] Li, Q.; Kakizaki, M.; Kuriyama, S.; Sone, T.; Yan, H.; Nakaya, N.; Mastuda-Ohmori, K.; Tsuji, I. Green tea consumption and lung cancer risk: the Ohsaki study. *Br. J. Cancer* 2008, *99*, 1179–84.

[101] Nagao, T.; Komine, Y.; Soga, S.; Meguro, S.; Hase, T.; Tanaka, Y.; Tokimitsu, I. Ingestion of a tea rich in catechins leads to a reduction in body fat and malondialdehyde-modified LDL in men. *Am. J. Clin. Nutr.* 2005, 122–129.

[102] Kuriyama, S.; Hozawa, A. Green tea consumption and cognitive function : a cross-sectional study from the Tsurugaya Project. *Am. J. Clin. Nutr.* 2006, 355–61.

[103] Feng, L.; Li, J.; Ng, T.; Lee, T.; Kua, E.; Zeng, Y. Tea drinking and cognitive function in oldest-old Chinese. *J. Nutr. Heal. Aging* 2012, *16*, 754–758.

[104] Hollman, P. C.; Feskens, E. J.; Katan, M. B. Tea flavonols in cardiovascular disease and cancer epidemiology. *Proc. Soc. Exp. Biol. Med.* 1999, *220*, 198–202.

[105] Yuan, J. Green tea and prevention of esophageal and lung cancers. *Mol. Nutr. Food Res.* 2011, *55*, 886–904.

[106] Yuan, J. M.; Sun, C.; Butler, L. M. Tea and cancer prevention: epidemiological studies. *Pharmacol. Res.* 2011, *64*, 123–35.

[107] Bosetti, C.; Bravi, F.; Talamini, R.; Parpinel, M.; Gnagnarella, P.; Negri, E.; Montella, M.; Lagiou, P.; Franceschi, S.; Vecchia, C. La Flavonoids and Prostate Cancer Risk : A Study in Italy Flavonoids and Prostate Cancer Risk : A Study in Italy. 2009, 37–41.

[108] Mursu, J.; Nurmi, T.; Tuomainen, T.-P.; Salonen, J. T.; Pukkala, E.; Voutilainen, S. Intake of flavonoids and risk of cancer in Finnish men: The Kuopio Ischaemic Heart Disease Risk Factor Study. *Int. J. Cancer* 2008, *123*, 660–3.

[109] Wu, A. H.; Butler, L. M. Green tea and breast cancer. *Mol. Nutr. Food Res.* 2011, *55*, 921–30.

[110] Stangl, V.; Dreger, H.; Stangl, K.; Lorenz, M. Molecular targets of tea polyphenols in the cardiovascular system. *Cardiovasc. Res.* 2007, *73*, 348–358.

[111] Lusis, A. J. Atherosclerosis. *Nature* 2000, *407*, 233–241.

[112] Ou, H. C.; Song, T. Y.; Yeh, Y. C.; Huang, C. Y.; Yang, S. F.; Chiu, T. H.; Tsai, K. L.; Chen, K. L.; Wu, Y. J.; Tsai, C. S.; Chang, L. Y.; Kuo, W. W.; Lee, S. Da EGCG protects against oxidized LDL-induced endothelial dysfunction by inhibiting LOX-1-mediated signaling. *J. Appl. Physiol.* 2010, *108*, 1745–1756.

[113] Ludwig, A.; Lorenz, M.; Grimbo, N.; Steinle, F.; Meiners, S.; Bartsch, C.; Stangl, K.; Baumann, G.; Stangl, V. The tea flavonoid epigallocatechin-3-gallate reduces cytokine-induced VCAM-1 expression and monocyte adhesion to endothelial cells. *Biochem. Biophys. Res. Commun.* 2004, *316*, 659–665.

[114] Pullikotil, P.; Chen, H.; Muniyappa, R.; Greenberg, C. C.; Yang, S.; Reiter, C. E. N.; Lee, J. W.; Chung, J. H.; Quon, M. J. Epigallocatechin gallate induces expression of heme oxygenase-1 in endothelial cells via p38 MAPK and Nrf-2 that suppresses proinflammatory actions of TNF-α. *J. Nutr. Biochem.* 2012, *23*, 1134–1145.

[115] Zheng, Y.; Toborek, M.; Hennig, B. Epigallocatechin gallate-mediated protection against tumor necrosis factor-α-induced monocyte chemoattractant protein-1 expression is heme oxygenase-1 dependent. *Metabolism.* 2010, *59*, 1528–35.

[116] Ramesh, E.; Geraldine, P.; Thomas, P. A. Regulatory effect of epigallocatechin gallate on the expression of C-reactive protein and other inflammatory markers in an experimental model of atherosclerosis. *Chem. Biol. Interact.* 2010, *183*, 125–132.

[117] Yang, J.; Han, Y.; Sun, H.; Chen, C.; He, D.; Guo, J.; Yu, C.; Jiang, B.; Zhou, L.; Zeng, C. (-)-Epigallocatechin gallate suppresses proliferation of vascular smooth muscle cells induced by high glucose by inhibition of PKC and ERK1/2 signalings. *J. Agric. Food Chem.* 2011, *59*, 11483–11490.

[118] Sartor, L.; Pezzato, E.; Dell'Aica, I.; Caniato, R.; Biggin, S.; Garbisa, S. Inhibition of matrix-proteases by polyphenols: chemical insights for anti-inflammatory and anti-invasion drug design. *Biochem. Pharmacol.* 2002, *64*, 229–237.

[119] Maeda, K.; Kuzuya, M.; Cheng, X. W.; Asai, T.; Kanda, S.; Tamaya-Mori, N.; Sasaki, T.; Shibata, T.; Iguchi, A. Green tea catechins inhibit the cultured smooth muscle cell invasion through the basement barrier. *Atherosclerosis* 2003, *166*, 23–30.

[120] Cheng, X. W.; Kuzuya, M.; Nakamura, K.; Liu, Z.; Di, Q.; Hasegawa, J.; Iwata, M.; Murohara, T.; Yokota, M.; Iguchi, A. Mechanisms of the inhibitory effect of epigallocatechin-3-gallate on cultured human vascular smooth muscle cell invasion. *Arterioscler. Thromb. Vasc. Biol.* 2005, *25*, 1864–1870.

[121] Lill, G.; Voit, S.; Schrör, K.; Weber, A. A. Complex effects of different green tea catechins on human platelets. *FEBS Lett.* 2003, *546*, 265–270.

[122] Jin, Y. R.; Im, J. H.; Park, E. S.; Cho, M. R.; Han, X. H.; Lee, J. J.; Lim, Y.; Kim, T. J.; Yun, Y. P. Antiplatelet activity of epigallocatechin gallate is mediated by the inhibition of PLC gamma2 phosphorylation, elevation of PGD2 production, and maintaining calcium-ATPase activity. *J. Cardiovasc. Pharmacol.* 2008, *51*, 45–54.

[123] Cuccioloni, M.; Mozzicafreddo, M.; Spina, M.; Tran, C. N.; Falconi, M.; Eleuteri, A. M.; Angeletti, M. Epigallocatechin-3-gallate potently inhibits the in vitro activity of hydroxy-3-methyl-glutaryl-CoA reductase. *J. Lipid Res.* 2011, *52*, 897–907.

[124] Meir, K. S.; Leitersdorf, E. Atherosclerosis in the apolipoprotein-E-deficient mouse: a decade of progress. *Arterioscler. Thromb. Vasc. Biol.* 2004, *24*, 1006–14.

[125] Miura, Y.; Chiba, T.; Tomita, I.; Koizumi, H.; Miura, S.; Umegaki, K.; Hara, Y.; Ikeda, M.; Tomita, T. Tea catechins prevent the development of atherosclerosis in apoprotein E-deficient mice. *J. Nutr.* 2001, *131*, 27–32.

[126] Milenkovic, D.; Deval, C.; Gouranton, E.; Landrier, J. F.; Scalbert, A.; Morand, C.; Mazur, A. Modulation of miRNA expression by dietary polyphenols in apoE deficient mice: a new mechanism of the action of polyphenols. *PLoS One* 2012, *7*, e29837.

[127] Kim, J. A.; Formoso, G.; Li, Y.; Potenza, M. A.; Marasciulo, F. L.; Montagnani, M.; Quon, M. J. Epigallocatechin gallate, a green tea polyphenol, mediates NO-dependent vasodilation using signaling pathways in vascular endothelium requiring reactive oxygen species and Fyn. *J. Biol. Chem.* 2007, *282*, 13736–13745.

[128] Potenza, M. A.; Marasciulo, F. L.; Tarquinio, M.; Tiravanti, E.; Colantuono, G.; Federici, A.; Kim, J. A.; Quon, M. J.; Montagnani, M. EGCG, a green tea polyphenol, improves endothelial function and

insulin sensitivity, reduces blood pressure, and protects against myocardial I/R injury in SHR. *Am. J. Physiol. Endocrinol. Metab.* 2007, *292*, E1378–87.

[129] Negishi; H; Xu; JW; Ikeda; K Black and green tea polyphenols attenuate blood pressure increases in stroke-prone spontaneously hypertensive rats. 2004, *134*, 38–42.

[130] Lorenz, M.; Wessler, S.; Follmann, E.; Michaelis, W.; Düsterhöft, T.; Baumann, G.; Stangl, K.; Stangl, V. A constituent of green tea, epigallocatechin-3-gallate, activates endothelial nitric oxide synthase by a phosphatidylinositol-3-OH-kinase-, cAMP-dependent protein kinase-, and Akt-dependent pathway and leads to endothelial-dependent vasorelaxation. *J. Biol. Chem.* 2004, *279*, 6190–5.

[131] Persson, I. A. L.; Josefsson, M.; Persson, K.; Andersson, R. G. G. Tea flavanols inhibit angiotensin-converting enzyme activity and increase nitric oxide production in human endothelial cells. *J. Pharm. Pharmacol.* 2006, *58*, 1139–44.

[132] Balasuriya, B. W. N.; Rupasinghe, H. P. V. Plant flavonoids as angiotensin converting enzyme inhibitors in regulation of hypertension. *Funct. Foods Heal. Dis.* 2011, *5*, 172–188.

[133] Nguyen Dinh Cat, A.; Touyz, R. M. A new look at the renin-angiotensin system-focusing on the vascular system. *Peptides* 2011, *32*, 2141–50.

[134] Reiter, C. E. N.; Kim, J.; Quon, M. J. Green tea polyphenol epigallocatechin gallate reduces endothelin-1 expression and secretion in vascular endothelial cells: roles for AMP-activated protein kinase, Akt, and FOXO1. *Endocrinology* 2010, *151*, 103–114.

[135] Hao, J.; Kim, C. H.; Ha, T. S.; Ahn, H. Y. Epigallocatechin-3 gallate prevents cardiac hypertrophy induced by pressure overload in rats. *J. Vet. Sci* 2007, *8*, 121–129.

[136] Sheng, R.; Gu, Z.; Xie, M.; Zhou, W.; Guo, C. EGCG inhibits cardiomyocyte apoptosis in pressure overload-induced cardiac hypertrophy and protects cardiomyocytes from oxidative stress in rats. *Acta Pharmacol. Sin.* 2007, *28*, 191–201.

[137] Sheng, R.; Gu, Z. L.; Xie, M. L. Epigallocatechin gallate, the major component of polyphenols in green tea, inhibits telomere attrition mediated cardiomyocyte apoptosis in cardiac hypertrophy. *Int. J. Cardiol.* 2011.

[138] Li, H. L.; Huang, Y.; Zhang, C. N.; Liu, G.; Wei, Y. S.; Wang, A. B.; Liu, Y. Q.; Hui, R. T.; Wei, C.; Williams, G. M.; Liu, D. P.; Liang, C. C. Epigallocathechin-3 gallate inhibits cardiac hypertrophy through

blocking reactive oxidative species-dependent and -independent signal pathways. *Free Radic. Biol. Med.* 2006, *40*, 1756–1775.

[139] Kim, C. J.; Kim, J. M. J. H.; Lee, S. R.; Jang, Y. H.; Chun, K. J. Polyphenol (-)-epigallocatechin gallate targeting myocardial reperfusion limits infarct size and improves cardiac function. *Korean J Anesthsiol* 2010, *58*, 169–175.

[140] Piao, C. S.; Kim, D. S.; Ha, K. C.; Kim, H. R.; Chae, H. J.; Chae, S. W. The Protective Effect of Epigallocatechin-3 Gallate on Ischemia/Reperfusion Injury in Isolated Rat Hearts: An ex vivo Approach. *Korean J. Physiol. Pharmacol.* 2011, *15*, 259–266.

[141] Yanagi, S.; Matsumura, K.; Marui, A.; Morishima, M.; Hyon, S. H.; Ikeda, T.; Sakata, R. Oral pretreatment with a green tea polyphenol for cardioprotection against ischemia-reperfusion injury in an isolated rat heart model. *J. Thorac. Cardiovasc. Surg.* 2011, *141*, 511–517.

[142] Townsend, P. A.; Scarabelli, T. M.; Pasini, E.; Gitti, G.; Menegazzi, M.; Suzuki, H.; Knight, R. A.; Latchman, D. S.; Stephanou, A. Epigallocatechin-3-gallate inhibits STAT-1 activation and protects cardiac myocytes from ischemia/reperfusion-induced apoptosis. *FASEB J.* 2004, *18*, 1621–1623.

[143] Duilio, C.; Ambrosio, G.; Kuppusamy, P.; DiPaula, A.; Becker, L. C.; Zweier, J. L. Neutrophils are primary source of O2 radicals during reperfusion after prolonged myocardial ischemia. *Am. J. Physiol. Heart Circ. Physiol.* 2001, *280*, H2649–57.

[144] Aneja, R.; Hake, P. W.; Burroughs, T. J.; Denenberg, A. G.; Wong, H. R.; Zingarelli, B. Epigallocatechin, a green tea polyphenol, attenuates myocardial ischemia reperfusion injury in rats. *Mol. Med.* 2004, *10*, 55–62.

[145] Takano, K.; Nakaima, K.; Nitta, M.; Shibata, F.; Nakagawa, H. Inhibitory effect of (-)-epigallocatechin 3-gallate, a polyphenol of green tea, on neutrophil chemotaxis in vitro and in vivo. *J. Agric. Food Chem.* 2004, *52*, 4571–4576.

[146] Sheng, R.; Gu, Z.; Xie, M.; Zhou, W.; Guo, C. Epigallocatechin gallate protects H9c2 cardiomyoblasts against hydrogen dioxides- induced apoptosis and telomere attrition. *Eur. J. Pharmacol.* 2010, *641*, 199–206.

[147] Weinreb, O.; Amit, T.; Mandel, S.; Youdim, M. B. H. Neuroprotective molecular mechanisms of (-)-epigallocatechin-3-gallate: a reflective outcome of its antioxidant, iron chelating and neuritogenic properties. *Genes Nutr.* 2009, *4*, 283–96.

[148] Stefani, M.; Rigacci, S. Protein folding and aggregation into amyloid: the interference by natural phenolic compounds. *Int. J. Mol. Sci.* 2013, *14*, 12411–57.

[149] Hyung, S. J.; DeToma, A. S.; Brender, J. R.; Lee, S.; Vivekanandan, S.; Kochi, A.; Choi, J. S.; Ramamoorthy, A.; Ruotolo, B. T.; Lim, M. H. Insights into antiamyloidogenic properties of the green tea extract (-)-epigallocatechin-3-gallate toward metal-associated amyloid-β species. *Proc. Natl. Acad. Sci. U. S. A.* 2013, *110*, 3743–8.

[150] Bieschke, J.; Russ, J.; Friedrich, R. P.; Ehrnhoefer, D. E.; Wobst, H.; Neugebauer, K.; Wanker, E. E. EGCG remodels mature alpha-synuclein and amyloid-beta fibrils and reduces cellular toxicity. *Proc. Natl. Acad. Sci. U. S. A.* 2010, *107*, 7710–5.

[151] Mähler, A.; Mandel, S.; Lorenz, M.; Ruegg, U.; Wanker, E. E.; Boschmann, M.; Paul, F. Epigallocatechin-3-gallate: a useful, effective and safe clinical approach for targeted prevention and individualised treatment of neurological diseases? *EPMA J.* 2013, *4*, 5.

[152] Rezai-Zadeh, K.; Shytle, D.; Sun, N.; Mori, T.; Hou, H.; Jeanniton, D.; Ehrhart, J.; Townsend, K.; Zeng, J.; Morgan, D.; Hardy, J.; Town, T.; Tan, J. Green tea epigallocatechin-3-gallate (EGCG) modulates amyloid precursor protein cleavage and reduces cerebral amyloidosis in Alzheimer transgenic mice. *J. Neurosci.* 2005, *25*, 8807–14.

[153] Rezai-Zadeh, K.; Arendash, G. W.; Hou, H.; Fernandez, F.; Jensen, M.; Runfeldt, M.; Shytle, R. D.; Tan, J. Green tea epigallocatechin-3-gallate (EGCG) reduces beta-amyloid mediated cognitive impairment and modulates tau pathology in Alzheimer transgenic mice. *Brain Res.* 2008, *1214*, 177–87.

[154] Ye, Q.; Ye, L.; Xu, X.; Huang, B.; Zhang, X.; Zhu, Y.; Chen, X. Epigallocatechin-3-gallate suppresses 1-methyl-4-phenyl-pyridine-induced oxidative stress in PC12 cells via the SIRT1/PGC-1α signaling pathway. *BMC Complement. Altern. Med.* 2012, *12*, 82.

[155] Cantó, C.; Auwerx, J. PGC-1alpha , SIRT1 and AMPK , an energy sensing network that controls energy expenditure. *Curr. Opin. Lipidol.* 2009, *20*, 98–105.

[156] Hou, R. R.; Chen, J. Z.; Chen, H.; Kang, X. G.; Li, M. G.; Wang, B. R. Neuroprotective effects of (-)-epigallocatechin-3-gallate (EGCG) on paraquat-induced apoptosis in PC12 cells. *Cell Biol. Int.* 2008, *32*, 22–30.

[157] Tai, K. K.; Truong, D. D. (-)-Epigallocatechin-3-gallate (EGCG), a green tea polyphenol, reduces dichlorodiphenyl-trichloroethane (DDT)-

induced cell death in dopaminergic SHSY-5Y cells. *Neurosci. Lett.* 2010, *482*, 183–7.

[158] Chao, J.; Lau, W. K. W.; Huie, M. J.; Ho, Y. S.; Yu, M. S.; Lai, C. S. W.; Wang, M.; Yuen, W. H.; Lam, W. H.; Chan, T. H.; Chang, R. C. C. A pro-drug of the green tea polyphenol (-)-epigallocatechin-3-gallate (EGCG) prevents differentiated SH-SY5Y cells from toxicity induced by 6-hydroxydopamine. *Neurosci. Lett.* 2010, *469*, 360–4.

[159] Choi, J.; Park, C.; Kim, D.; Cho, M.; Jin, B. Prevention of Nitric Oxide-Mediated 1-Methyl-4-Phenyl-1,2,3,6-Tetrahydropyridine- Induced Parkinson's Disease in Mice by Tea Phenolic Epigallocatechin 3-Gallate. *Neurotoxicology* 2002, *23*, 367–374.

[160] Youdim, M. B. H.; Grünblatt, E.; Levites, Y.; Maor, G.; Mandel, S. Early and late molecular events in neurodegeneration and neuroprotection in Parkinson's disease MPTP model as assessed by cDNA microarray; the role of iron. *Neurotox. Res.* 2002, *4*, 679–689.

[161] Mandel, S.; Grünblatt, E.; Maor, G.; Youdim, M. Early and late gene changes in MPTP mice model of Parkinson's disease employing cDNA microarray. *Neurochem. Res.* 2002, *27*, 1231–1243.

[162] Levites, Y.; Amit, T.; Youdim, M. B. H.; Mandel, S. Involvement of protein kinase C activation and cell survival/ cell cycle genes in green tea polyphenol (-)-epigallocatechin 3-gallate neuroprotective action. *J. Biol. Chem.* 2002, *277*, 30574–80.

[163] Karavidas, A.; Lazaros, G.; Tsiachris, D.; Pyrgakis, V. Aging and the cardiovascular system. *Hellenic J. Cardiol.* 2010, *51*, 421–7.

[164] Prince, M.; Bryce, R.; Albanese, E.; Wimo, A.; Ribeiro, W.; Ferri, C. P. The global prevalence of dementia: a systematic review and metaanalysis. *Alzheimers. Dement.* 2013, *9*, 63–75.e2.

[165] Muqtadar, H.; Testai, F. D.; Gorelick, P. B. The dementia of cardiac disease. *Curr. Cardiol. Rep.* 2012, *14*, 732–40.

[166] Newman, A. B.; Fitzpatrick, A. L.; Lopez, O.; Jackson, S.; Lyketsos, C.; Jagust, W.; Ives, D.; Dekosky, S. T.; Kuller, L. H. Dementia and Alzheimer's disease incidence in relationship to cardiovascular disease in the Cardiovascular Health Study cohort. *J. Am. Geriatr. Soc.* 2005, *53*, 1101–7.

[167] Meng, Q.; Velalar, C. N.; Ruan, R. Regulating the age-related oxidative damage, mitochondrial integrity, and antioxidative enzyme activity in Fischer 344 rats by supplementation of the antioxidant epigallocatechin-3-gallate. *Rejuvenation Res.* 2008, *11*, 649–60.

[168] Niu, Y.; Na, L.; Feng, R.; Gong, L.; Zhao, Y.; Li, Q.; Li, Y.; Sun, C. The phytochemical, EGCG, extends lifespan by reducing liver and kidney function damage and improving age-associated inflammation and oxidative stress in healthy rats. *Aging Cell* 2013, 1–9.

[169] Lin, S. M.; Wang, S. W.; Ho, S. C.; Tang, Y. L. Protective effect of green tea (-)-epigallocatechin-3-gallate against the monoamine oxidase B enzyme activity increase in adult rat brains. *Nutrition* 2010, *26*, 1195–200.

[170] Mandel, S. A.; Amit, T.; Weinreb, O.; Youdim, M. B. H. Understanding the broad-spectrum neuroprotective action profile of green tea polyphenols in aging and neurodegenerative diseases. *J. Alzheimers. Dis.* 2011, *25*, 187–208.

[171] Yang, C.; Wang, X.; Lu, G.; Picinich, S. Cancer prevention by tea: animal studies, molecular mechanisms and human relevance. *Nat. Rev. Cancer* 2009, *9*, 429–439.

[172] Schramm, L. Going Green: The Role of the Green Tea Component EGCG in Chemoprevention. *J Carcinog. Mutagen.* 2013, *4*, 34–38.

[173] Chen, L.; Zhang, H. Y. Cancer preventive mechanisms of the green tea polyphenol (-)-epigallocatechin-3-gallate. *Molecules* 2007, *12*, 946–57.

[174] Babich, H.; Schuck, A. G.; Weisburg, J. H.; Zuckerbraun, H. L. Research strategies in the study of the pro-oxidant nature of polyphenol nutraceuticals. *J. Toxicol.* 2011, *2011*, 467305.

[175] D'Archivio, M.; Santangelo, C.; Scazzocchio, B.; Varì, R.; Filesi, C.; Masella, R.; Giovannini, C. Modulatory effects of polyphenols on apoptosis induction: relevance for cancer prevention. *Int. J. Mol. Sci.* 2008, *9*, 213–28.

[176] Deka, A.; Vita, J. Tea and Cardiovascular Disease. *Pharmacol. Res.* 2011, *64*, 136–145.

[177] Sesso, H. D.; Gaziano, J. M.; Buring, J. E.; Hennekens, C. H. Coffee and tea intake and the risk of myocardial infarction. *Am. J. Epidemiol.* 1999, *149*, 162–7.

[178] Mukamal, K. J. Tea Consumption and Mortality After Acute Myocardial Infarction. *Circulation* 2002, *105*, 2476–2481.

[179] Mukamal, K. J.; Alert, M.; Maclure, M.; Muller, J. E.; Mittleman, M. A. Tea consumption and infarct-related ventricular arrhythmias: the determinants of myocardial infarction onset study. *J. Am. Coll. Nutr.* 2006, *25*, 472–9.

[180] Geleijnse, J. M.; Launer, L. J.; Hofman, A.; Pols, H. A.; Witteman, J. C. Tea flavonoids may protect against atherosclerosis: the Rotterdam Study. *Arch. Intern. Med.* 1999, *159*, 2170–4.

[181] Maron, D. J.; Lu, G. P.; Cai, N. S.; Wu, Z. G.; Li, Y. H.; Chen, H.; Zhu, J. Q.; Jin, X. J.; Wouters, B. C.; Zhao, J. Cholesterol-lowering effect of a theaflavin-enriched green tea extract: a randomized controlled trial. *Arch. Intern. Med.* 2003, *163*, 1448–53.

[182] Trautwein, E. A.; Du, Y.; Meynen, E.; Yan, X.; Wen, Y.; Wang, H.; Molhuizen, H. O. F. Purified black tea theaflavins and theaflavins/catechin supplements did not affect serum lipids in healthy individuals with mildly to moderately elevated cholesterol concentrations. *Eur. J. Nutr.* 2010, *49*, 27–35.

[183] Checkoway, H.; Powers, K.; Smith-Weller, T.; Franklin, G. M.; Longstreth, W. T.; Swanson, P. D. Parkinson's Disease Risks Associated with Cigarette Smoking, Alcohol Consumption, and Caffeine Intake. *Am. J. Epidemiol.* 2002, *155*, 732–738.

[184] Nurk, E.; Refsum, H.; Drevon, C. Intake of flavonoid-rich wine, tea, and chocolate by elderly men and women is associated with better cognitive test performance. *J. Nutr.* 2009, 120–127.

[185] Letenneur, L.; Proust-Lima, C.; Le Gouge, A.; Dartigues, J. F.; Barberger-Gateau, P. Flavonoid intake and cognitive decline over a 10-year period. *Am. J. Epidemiol.* 2007, *165*, 1364–71.

[186] Hertog, M. G.; Feskens, E. J.; Hollman, P. C.; Katan, M. B.; Kromhout, D. Dietary antioxidant flavonoids and risk of coronary heart disease: the Zutphen Elderly Study. *Lancet* 1993, *342*, 1007–11.

[187] Hertog, M.; Feskens, E.; Kromhout, D. Antioxidant flavonols and coronary heart disease risk. *Lancet* 1997, *349*, 699.

[188] Ng, T. P.; Feng, L.; Niti, M.; Kua, E. H.; Yap, K. B. Tea consumption and cognitive impairment and decline in older Chinese adults. *Am. J. Clin. Nutr.* 2008, *88*, 224–31.

[189] Hertog, M. G.; Feskens, E. J.; Hollman, P. C.; Katan, M. B.; Kromhout, D. Dietary flavonoids and cancer risk in the Zutphen Elderly Study. *Nutr. Cancer* 1994, *22*, 175–84.

[190] Goldbohm, R. A.; Hertog, M. G.; Brants, H. A.; van Poppel, G.; van den Brandt, P. A. Consumption of black tea and cancer risk: a prospective cohort study. *J. Natl. Cancer Inst.* 1996, *88*, 93–100.

[191] Geybels, M. S.; Verhage, B. A. J.; Arts, I. C. W.; van Schooten, F. J.; Goldbohm, R. A.; van den Brandt, P. A. Dietary flavonoid intake, black

tea consumption, and risk of overall and advanced stage prostate cancer. *Am. J. Epidemiol.* 2013, *177*, 1388–98.

[192] Butler, L. M.; Wu, A. H. Green and black tea in relation to gynecologic cancers. *Mol. Nutr. Food Res.* 2011, *55*, 931–40.

[193] Sun, C. L.; Yuan, J. M.; Koh, W. P.; Yu, M. C. Green tea, black tea and breast cancer risk: a meta-analysis of epidemiological studies. *Carcinogenesis* 2006, *27*, 1310–5.

[194] Wu, A. H.; Arakawa, K.; Stanczyk, F. Z.; Van Den Berg, D.; Koh, W. P.; Yu, M. C. Tea and circulating estrogen levels in postmenopausal Chinese women in Singapore. *Carcinogenesis* 2005, *26*, 976–80.

[195] Li, N.; Sun, Z.; Han, C.; Chen, J. The Chemopreventive Effects of Tea on Human Oral Precancerous Mucosa Lesions. *Exp. Biol. Med.* 1999, *220*, 218–224.

[196] Sun, C. L.; Yuan, J. M.; Koh, W. P.; Yu, M. C. Green tea, black tea and colorectal cancer risk: a meta-analysis of epidemiologic studies. *Carcinogenesis* 2006, *27*, 1301–9.

[197] Leung, L.; Su, Y.; Chen, R.; Zhang, Z. Theaflavins in black tea and catechins in green tea are equally effective antioxidants. *J. Nutr.* 2001, *1*, 2248–2251.

[198] Serafini, M.; Laranjinha, J.; Almeida, L.; Maiani, G. Inhibition of human LDL lipid peroxidation by phenol-rich beverages and their impact on plasma total antioxidant capacity in humans. *J. Nutr. Biochem.* 2000, *11*, 585–590.

[199] Feng, Q.; Torii, Y.; Uchida, K.; Nakamura, Y.; Hara, Y.; Osawa, T. Black Tea Polyphenols, Theaflavins, Prevent Cellular DNA Damage by Inhibiting Oxidative Stress and Suppressing Cytochrome P450 1A1 in Cell Cultures. *J. Agric. Food Chem.* 2002, *50*, 213–220.

[200] Vermeer, M. A.; Mulder, T. P. J.; Molhuizen, H. O. F. Theaflavins from black tea, especially theaflavin-3-gallate, reduce the incorporation of cholesterol into mixed micelles. *J. Agric. Food Chem.* 2008, *56*, 12031–6.

[201] Ikeda, I.; Yamahira, T.; Kato, M.; Ishikawa, A. Black-tea polyphenols decrease micellar solubility of cholesterol in vitro and intestinal absorption of cholesterol in rats. *J. Agric. Food Chem.* 2010, *58*, 8591–5.

[202] Loke, W. M.; Proudfoot, J. M.; Hodgson, J. M.; McKinley, A. J.; Hime, N.; Magat, M.; Stocker, R.; Croft, K. D. Specific dietary polyphenols attenuate atherosclerosis in apolipoprotein E-knockout mice by alleviating inflammation and endothelial dysfunction. *Arterioscler. Thromb. Vasc. Biol.* 2010, *30*, 749–57.

[203] Ma, H.; Huang, X.; Li, Q.; Guan, Y.; Yuan, F.; Zhang, Y. ATP-dependent potassium channels and mitochondrial permeability transition pores play roles in the cardioprotection of theaflavin in young rat. *J. Physiol. Sci.* 2011, *61*, 337–42.

[204] Cai, F.; Li, C. R.; Wu, J. L.; Chen, J. G.; Liu, C.; Min, Q.; Yu, W.; Ouyang, C. H.; Chen, J. H. Theaflavin ameliorates cerebral ischemia-reperfusion injury in rats through its anti-inflammatory effect and modulation of STAT-1. *Mediators Inflamm.* 2006, *2006*, 30490.

[205] Skrzypczak-Jankun, E.; Jankun, J. Theaflavin digallate inactivates plasminogen activator inhibitor: Could tea help in Alzheimer's disease and obesity? *Int. J. Mol. Med.* 2010, *26*, 45–50.

[206] Periz, G.; Fortini, M. E. Proteolysis in Alzheimer's disease. Can plasmin tip the balance? *EMBO Rep.* 2000, *1*, 477–8.

[207] Tucker, H. M.; Kihiko, M.; Caldwell, J. N.; Wright, S.; Kawarabayashi, T.; Price, D.; Walker, D.; Scheff, S.; McGillis, J. P.; Rydel, R. E.; Estus, S. The plasmin system is induced by and degrades amyloid-beta aggregates. *J. Neurosci.* 2000, *20*, 3937–46.

[208] Bastianetto, S.; Yao, Z. X.; Papadopoulos, V.; Quirion, R. Neuroprotective effects of green and black teas and their catechin gallate esters against beta-amyloid-induced toxicity. *Eur. J. Neurosci.* 2006, *23*, 55–64.

[209] Luo, Z.; Zhao, Y.; Wang, Y.; Yang, X.; Zhao, B. Protective effect of theaflavins on neuron against 6-hydroxydopamine-induced apoptosis in SH-SY5Y cells. *J. Clin. Biochem. Nutr.* 2012, *50*, 133–8.

[210] Anandhan, A.; Janakiraman, U.; Manivasagam, T. Theaflavin ameliorates behavioral deficits, biochemical indices and monoamine transporters expression against subacute 1-methyl-4-phenyl-1,2,3,6-tetrahydropyridine (MPTP)-induced mouse model of Parkinson's disease. *Neuroscience* 2012, *218*, 257–67.

[211] Anandhan, A.; Tamilselvam, K.; Radhiga, T.; Rao, S.; Essa, M. M.; Manivasagam, T. Theaflavin, a black tea polyphenol, protects nigral dopaminergic neurons against chronic MPTP/probenecid induced Parkinson's disease. *Brain Res.* 2012, *1433*, 104–13.

[212] Rajavelu, A.; Tulyasheva, Z.; Jaiswal, R.; Jeltsch, A.; Kuhnert, N. The inhibition of the mammalian DNA methyltransferase 3a (Dnmt3a) by dietary black tea and coffee polyphenols. *BMC Biochem.* 2011, *12*, 16.

[213] Wu, H.; Coskun, V.; Tao, J.; Xie, W.; Ge, W.; Yoshikawa, K.; Li, E.; Zhang, Y.; Sun, Y. E. Dnmt3a-dependent nonpromoter DNA

methylation facilitates transcription of neurogenic genes. *Science* 2010, *329*, 444–8.

[214] LaPlant, Q.; Vialou, V.; III, H. C. Dnmt3a regulates emotional behavior and spine plasticity in the nucleus accumbens. *Nat. Neurosci.* 2010, *13*, 1137–1143.

[215] Feng, J.; Zhou, Y.; Campbell, S. L.; Le, T.; Li, E.; Sweatt, J. D.; Alcino, J.; Fan, G. Dnmt1 and Dnmt3a are required for the maintenance of DNA methylation and synaptic function in adult forebrain neurons. *Nat. Neurosci.* 2010, *13*, 423–430.

[216] Apostolides, Z.; Balentine, D. A.; Harbowy, M. E.; Hara, Y.; Weisburger, J. H. Inhibition of PhIP mutagenicity by catechins, and by theaflavins and gallate esters. *Mutat. Res.* 1997, *389*, 167–72.

[217] Wang, Z.; Das, M.; Bickers, D.; Mukhtar, H. Interaction of epicatechins derived from green tea with rat hepatic cytochrome P-450. *Drug Metab. Dispos.* 1988, *16*, 98–103.

[218] Halder, B.; Pramanick, S.; Mukhopadhyay, S.; Giri, A. K. Inhibition of benzo[a]pyrene induced mutagenicity and genotoxicity by black tea polyphenols theaflavins and thearubigins in multiple test systems. *Food Chem. Toxicol.* 2005, *43*, 591–7.

[219] Gupta, S.; Chaudhuri, T.; Ganguly, D.; Giri, A. Anticlastogenic effects of black tea (World blend) and its two active polyphenols theaflavins and thearubigins in vivo in Swiss albino mice. *Life Sci.* 2001, *69*, 2735–44.

[220] Yang, G. Y.; Liao, J.; Li, C.; Chung, J.; Yurkow, E. J.; Ho, C. T.; Yang, C. S. Effect of black and green tea polyphenols on c-jun phosphorylation and H(2)O(2) production in transformed and non-transformed human bronchial cell lines: possible mechanisms of cell growth inhibition and apoptosis induction. *Carcinogenesis* 2000, *21*, 2035–9.

[221] Klein, R. D.; Fischer, S. M. Black tea polyphenols inhibit IGF-I-induced signaling through Akt in normal prostate epithelial cells and Du145 prostate carcinoma cells. *Carcinogenesis* 2002, *23*, 217–21.

[222] Lee, H. H.; Ho, C. T.; Lin, J. K. Theaflavin-3,3'-digallate and penta-O-galloyl-beta-D-glucose inhibit rat liver microsomal 5alpha-reductase activity and the expression of androgen receptor in LNCaP prostate cancer cells. *Carcinogenesis* 2004, *25*, 1109–18.

[223] Vartiainen, E.; Laatikainen, T.; Peltonen, M.; Juolevi, A.; Männistö, S.; Sundvall, J.; Jousilahti, P.; Salomaa, V.; Valsta, L.; Puska, P. Thirty-five-year trends in cardiovascular risk factors in Finland. *Int. J. Epidemiol.* 2010, *39*, 504–18.

[224] Rissanen, T. H.; Voutilainen, S.; Virtanen, J. K.; Venho, B.; Vanharanta, M.; Mursu, J.; Salonen, J. T. Low Intake of Fruits , Berries and Vegetables Is Associated with Excess Mortality in Men : the Kuopio Ischaemic Heart Disease Risk Factor (KIHD). *Nutr. Epidemiol.* 2003, 199–204.

[225] Iqbal, R.; Anand, S.; Ounpuu, S.; Islam, S.; Zhang, X.; Rangarajan, S.; Chifamba, J.; Al-Hinai, A.; Keltai, M.; Yusuf, S. Dietary patterns and the risk of acute myocardial infarction in 52 countries: results of the INTERHEART study. *Circulation* 2008, *118*, 1929–37.

[226] Frisardi, V.; Panza, F.; Seripa, D.; Imbimbo, B. P.; Vendemiale, G.; Pilotto, A.; Solfrizzi, V. Nutraceutical properties of Mediterranean diet and cognitive decline: possible underlying mechanisms. *J. Alzheimers. Dis.* 2010, *22*, 715–40.

[227] Bahorun, T.; Luximon-Ramma, A.; Neergheen-Bhujun, V. S.; Gunness, T. K.; Googoolye, K.; Auger, C.; Crozier, A.; Aruoma, O. I. The effect of black tea on risk factors of cardiovascular disease in a normal population. *Prev. Med. (Baltim).* 2012, *54 Suppl*, S98–102.

[228] Kubota, K.; Sumi, S.; Tojo, H.; Sumi-Inoue, Y.; I-Chin, H.; Oi, Y.; Fujita, H.; Urata, H. Improvements of mean body mass index and body weight in preobese and overweight Japanese adults with black Chinese tea (Pu-Erh) water extract. *Nutr. Res.* 2011, *31*, 421–8.

[229] Lekakis, J.; Rallidis, L. S.; Andreadou, I.; Vamvakou, G.; Kazantzoglou, G.; Magiatis, P.; Skaltsounis, A.-L.; Kremastinos, D. T. Polyphenolic compounds from red grapes acutely improve endothelial function in patients with coronary heart disease. *Eur. J. Cardiovasc. Prev. Rehabil.* 2005, *12*, 596–600.

[230] Stanely Mainzen Prince, P.; Priscilla, H.; Devika, P. T. Gallic acid prevents lysosomal damage in isoproterenol induced cardiotoxicity in Wistar rats. *Eur. J. Pharmacol.* 2009, *615*, 139–43.

[231] Yeh, C. T.; Ching, L. C.; Yen, G. C. Inducing gene expression of cardiac antioxidant enzymes by dietary phenolic acids in rats. *J. Nutr. Biochem.* 2009, *20*, 163–71.

[232] Vijaya Padma, V.; Poornima, P.; Prakash, C.; Bhavani, R. Oral treatment with gallic acid and quercetin alleviates lindane-induced cardiotoxicity in rats. *Can. J. Physiol. Pharmacol.* 2013, *91*, 134–40.

[233] Erol-Dayi, Ö.; Arda, N.; Erdem, G. Protective effects of olive oil phenolics and gallic acid on hydrogen peroxide-induced apoptosis. *Eur. J. Nutr.* 2012, *51*, 955–60.

[234] Umadevi, S.; Gopi, V.; Simna, S. P.; Parthasarathy, A.; Yousuf, S. M. J.; Elangovan, V. Studies on the cardioprotective role of gallic acid against AGE-induced cell proliferation and oxidative stress in H9C2 (2-1) cells. *Cardiovasc. Toxicol.* 2012, *12*, 304–11.

[235] Umadevi, S.; Gopi, V.; Vellaichamy, E. Inhibitory Effect of Gallic Acid on Advanced Glycation End Products Induced Up-Regulation of Inflammatory Cytokines and Matrix Proteins in H9C2 (2-1) Cells. *Cardiovasc. Toxicol.* 2013, *2*.

[236] Hsiang, C. Y.; Hseu, Y. C.; Chang, Y. C.; Kumar, K. J. S.; Ho, T. Y.; Yang, H. L. Toona sinensis and its major bioactive compound gallic acid inhibit LPS-induced inflammation in nuclear factor-κB transgenic mice as evaluated by in vivo bioluminescence imaging. *Food Chem.* 2013, *136*, 426–34.

[237] Chang, S. S.; Lee, V. S. Y.; Tseng, Y. L.; Chang, K. C.; Chen, K. B.; Chen, Y. L.; Li, C. Y. Gallic Acid Attenuates Platelet Activation and Platelet-Leukocyte Aggregation: Involving Pathways of Akt and GSK3β. *Evid. Based. Complement. Alternat. Med.* 2012, *2012*, 683872.

[238] Hsu, C.-L.; Yen, G.-C. Effect of gallic acid on high fat diet-induced dyslipidaemia, hepatosteatosis and oxidative stress in rats. *Br. J. Nutr.* 2007, *98*, 727–35.

[239] Ngamukote, S.; Mäkynen, K.; Thilawech, T.; Adisakwattana, S. Cholesterol-lowering activity of the major polyphenols in grape seed. *Molecules* 2011, *16*, 5054–61.

[240] Mansouri, M. T.; Farbood, Y.; Sameri, M. J.; Sarkaki, A.; Naghizadeh, B.; Rafeirad, M. Neuroprotective effects of oral gallic acid against oxidative stress induced by 6-hydroxydopamine in rats. *Food Chem.* 2013, *138*, 1028–33.

[241] Sameri, M.; Sarkaki, A. Motor Disorders and Impaired Electrical Power of Pallidal EEG Improved by Gallic Acid in Animal Model of Parkinson's Disease. *Pakistan J. Biol. Sci.* 2011.

[242] Mattson, M. P.; Meffert, M. K. Roles for NF-kappaB in nerve cell survival, plasticity, and disease. *Cell Death Differ.* 2006, *13*, 852–60.

[243] Kim, M. J.; Seong, A. R.; Yoo, J. Y.; Jin, C. H.; Lee, Y. H.; Kim, Y. J.; Lee, J.; Jun, W. J.; Yoon, H. G. Gallic acid, a histone acetyltransferase inhibitor, suppresses β-amyloid neurotoxicity by inhibiting microglial-mediated neuroinflammation. *Mol. Nutr. Food Res.* 2011, *55*, 1798–808.

[244] Li, L.; Ng, T. B.; Gao, W.; Li, W.; Fu, M.; Niu, S. M.; Zhao, L.; Chen, R. R.; Liu, F. Antioxidant activity of gallic acid from rose flowers in senescence accelerated mice. *Life Sci.* 2005, *77*, 230–40.

[245] Gomes, C. A.; da Cruz, T. G.; Andrade, J. L.; Milhazes, N.; Borges, F.; Marques, M. P. M. Anticancer activity of phenolic acids of natural or synthetic origin: a structure-activity study. *J. Med. Chem.* 2003, *46*, 5395–401.

[246] Fiuza, S. M.; Gomes, C.; Teixeira, L. J.; Girão da Cruz, M. T.; Cordeiro, M. N. D. S.; Milhazes, N.; Borges, F.; Marques, M. P. M. Phenolic acid derivatives with potential anticancer properties--a structure-activity relationship study. Part 1: methyl, propyl and octyl esters of caffeic and gallic acids. *Bioorg. Med. Chem.* 2004, *12*, 3581–9.

[247] Inoue, M.; Suzuki, R.; Sakaguchi, N.; Li, Z.; Takeda, T.; Ogihara, Y.; Jiang, B. Y.; Chen, Y. Selective induction of cell death in cancer cells by gallic acid. *Biol. Pharm. Bull.* 1995, *18*, 1526–30.

[248] Chandramohan Reddy, T.; Bharat Reddy, D.; Aparna, A.; Arunasree, K. M.; Gupta, G.; Achari, C.; Reddy, G. V.; Lakshmipathi, V.; Subramanyam, A.; Reddanna, P. Anti-leukemic effects of gallic acid on human leukemia K562 cells: Downregulation of COX-2, inhibition of BCR/ABL kinase and NF-κB inactivation. *Toxicol. Vitr.* 2012, *26*, 396–405.

[249] Madlener, S.; Illmer, C.; Horvath, Z.; Saiko, P.; Losert, A.; Herbacek, I.; Grusch, M.; Elford, H. L.; Krupitza, G.; Bernhaus, A.; Fritzer-Szekeres, M.; Szekeres, T. Gallic acid inhibits ribonucleotide reductase and cyclooxygenases in human HL-60 promyelocytic leukemia cells. *Cancer Lett.* 2007, *245*, 156–62.

[250] Reddy, T. C.; Aparoy, P.; Babu, N. K.; Kumar, K. A.; Kalangi, S. K.; Reddanna, P. Kinetics and docking studies of a COX-2 inhibitor isolated from Terminalia bellerica fruits. *Protein Pept. Lett.* 2010, *17*, 1251–7.

[251] Hwang, E. Y.; Huh, J.-W.; Choi, M.-M.; Choi, S. Y.; Hong, H.-N.; Cho, S.-W. Inhibitory effects of gallic acid and quercetin on UDP-glucose dehydrogenase activity. *FEBS Lett.* 2008, *582*, 3793–3797.

[252] Feingold, D. S.; Franzen, J. S. Pyridine nucleotide-linked four-electron transfer dehydrogenases. *Trends Biochem. Sci.* 1981, *6*, 103–105.

[253] Huh, J. W.; Lee, H. J.; Choi, M. M.; Yang, S. J.; Yoon, S. Y.; Kim, D. W.; Kim, S. Y.; Choi, S. Y.; Cho, S. W. Identification of a UDP-glucose-binding site of human UDP-glucose dehydrogenase by photoaffinity labeling and cassette mutagenesis. *Bioconjug. Chem.* 2005, *16*, 710–6.

[254] Auvinen, P.; Tammi, R.; Parkkinen, J.; Tammi, M.; Agren, U.; Johansson, R.; Hirvikoski, P.; Eskelinen, M.; Kosma, V. M. Hyaluronan

in peritumoral stroma and malignant cells associates with breast cancer spreading and predicts survival. *Am. J. Pathol.* 2000, *156*, 529–36.

[255] Simpson, M. A.; Wilson, C. M.; McCarthy, J. B. Inhibition of Prostate Tumor Cell Hyaluronan Synthesis Impairs Subcutaneous Growth and Vascularization in Immunocompromised Mice. *Am. J. Pathol.* 2002, *161*, 849–857.

[256] Hseu, Y. C.; Chen, S. C.; Lin, W. H.; Hung, D. Z.; Lin, M. K.; Kuo, Y. H.; Wang, M. T.; Cho, H. J.; Wang, L.; Yang, H.-L. Toona sinensis (leaf extracts) inhibit vascular endothelial growth factor (VEGF)-induced angiogenesis in vascular endothelial cells. *J. Ethnopharmacol.* 2011, *134*, 111–21.

[257] Agarwal, C.; Tyagi, A.; Agarwal, R. Gallic acid causes inactivating phosphorylation of cdc25A/cdc25C-cdc2 via ATM-Chk2 activation, leading to cell cycle arrest, and induces apoptosis in human prostate carcinoma DU145 cells. *Mol. Cancer Ther.* 2006, *5*, 3294–302.

[258] Hsu, C. L.; Lo, W. H.; Yen, G. C. Gallic acid induces apoptosis in 3T3-L1 pre-adipocytes via a Fas- and mitochondrial-mediated pathway. *J. Agric. Food Chem.* 2007, *55*, 7359–65.

[259] You, B. R.; Moon, H. J.; Han, Y. H.; Park, W. H. Gallic acid inhibits the growth of HeLa cervical cancer cells via apoptosis and/or necrosis. *Food Chem. Toxicol.* 2010, *48*, 1334–40.

[260] You, B. R.; Park, W. H. Gallic acid-induced lung cancer cell death is related to glutathione depletion as well as reactive oxygen species increase. *Toxicol. In Vitro* 2010, *24*, 1356–62.

[261] Hsieh, T. J.; Liu, T. Z.; Chia, Y. C.; Chern, C. L.; Lu, F. J.; Chuang, M. chun; Mau, S. Y.; Chen, S. H.; Syu, Y. H.; Chen, C. H. Protective effect of methyl gallate from Toona sinensis (Meliaceae) against hydrogen peroxide-induced oxidative stress and DNA damage in MDCK cells. *Food Chem. Toxicol.* 2004, *42*, 843–50.

[262] Crispo, J. A. G.; Ansell, D. R.; Piche, M.; Eibl, J. K.; Khaper, N.; Ross, G. M.; Tai, T. C. Protective effects of polyphenolic compounds on oxidative stress-induced cytotoxicity in PC12 cells. *Can. J. Physiol. Pharmacol.* 2010, *88*, 429–438.

[263] Crispo, J. A. G.; Piché, M.; Ansell, D. R.; Eibl, J. K.; Tai, I. T.; Kumar, A.; Ross, G. M.; Tai, T. C. Protective effects of methyl gallate on H2O2-induced apoptosis in PC12 cells. *Biochem. Biophys. Res. Commun.* 2010, *393*, 773–8.

[264] Whang, W. K.; Park, H. S.; Ham, I. H.; Oh, M.; Namkoong, H.; Kim, H. K.; Hwang, D. W.; Hur, S. Y.; Kim, T. E.; Park, Y. G.; Kim, J. R.; Kim,

J. W. Methyl gallate and chemicals structurally related to methyl gallate protect human umbilical vein endothelial cells from oxidative stress. *Exp. Mol. Med.* 2005, *37*, 343–52.

[265] Kaur, R.; Singh, B.; Arora, S. Amelioration of oxidative damage by Methyl gallate in different in vitro models. *Phytopharmacology* 2011, *1*, 82–94.

[266] Khurana, S.; Hollingsworth, A.; Piche, M.; Venkataraman, K.; Kumar, A.; Ross, G. M.; Tai, T. C. Anti-apoptotic actions of Methyl Gallate on Neonatal Rat Cardiac Myocytes exposed to H2O2. *Oxid. Med. Cell. Longev. in press.*

[267] Charlier, C.; Michaux, C. Dual inhibition of cyclooxygenase-2 (COX-2) and 5-lipoxygenase (5-LOX) as a new strategy to provide safer non-steroidal anti-inflammatory drugs. *Eur. J. Med. Chem.* 2003, *38*, 645–659.

[268] Kim, S. J.; Jin, M.; Lee, E.; Moon, T. C.; Quan, Z.; Yang, J. H.; Son, K. H.; Kim, K. U.; Son, J. K.; Chang, H. W. Effects of methyl gallate on arachidonic acid metabolizing enzymes: Cyclooxygenase-2 and 5-lipoxygenase in mouse bone marrow-derived mast cells. *Arch. Pharm. Res.* 2006, *29*, 874–8.

[269] Ricciotti, E.; FitzGerald, G. a Prostaglandins and inflammation. *Arterioscler. Thromb. Vasc. Biol.* 2011, *31*, 986–1000.

[270] Lee, H.; Lee, H.; Kwon, Y.; Lee, J.; Kim, J.; Shin, M. K.; Kim, S. H.; Bae, H. Methyl gallate exhibits potent antitumor activities by inhibiting tumor infiltration of CD4+CD25+ regulatory T cells. *J. Immunol.* 2010, *185*, 6698–705.

[271] Beyer, M.; Schultze, J. Regulatory T cells in cancer. *Blood* 2006, *108*, 804–811.

[272] Lee, S. H.; Kim, J. K.; Kim, D. W.; Hwang, H. S.; Eum, W. S.; Park, J.; Han, K. H.; Oh, J. S.; Choi, S. Y. Antitumor activity of methyl gallate by inhibition of focal adhesion formation and Akt phosphorylation in glioma cells. *Biochim. Biophys. Acta - Gen. Subj.* 2013, *1830*, 4017–4029.

[273] Frank, J.; George, T. W.; Lodge, J. K.; Rodriguez-Mateos, A. M.; Spencer, J. P. E.; Minihane, A. M.; Rimbach, G. Daily consumption of an aqueous green tea extract supplement does not impair liver function or alter cardiovascular disease risk biomarkers in healthy men. *J. Nutr.* 2009, *139*, 58–62.

[274] Princen, H. M. G.; van Duyvenvoorde, W.; Buytenhek, R.; Blonk, C.; Tijburg, L. B. M.; Langius, J. A. E.; Meinders, A. E.; Pijl, H. No Effect

of Consumption of Green and Black Tea on Plasma Lipid and Antioxidant Levels and on LDL Oxidation in Smokers. *Arterioscler. Thromb. Vasc. Biol.* 1998, *18*, 833–841.

[275] Freese, R.; Basu, S.; Hietanen, E.; Nair, J.; Nakachi, K.; Bartsch, H.; Mutanen, M. Green tea extract decreases plasma malondialdehyde concentration but does not affect other indicators of oxidative stress, nitric oxide production, or hemostatic factors during a high-linoleic acid diet in healthy females. *Eur. J. Nutr.* 1999, *38*, 149–57.

[276] Mennen, L. I.; Walker, R.; Bennetau-Pelissero, C.; Scalbert, A. Risks and safety of polyphenol consumption. *Am. J. Clin. Nutr.* 2005, *81*, 326S–329S.

[277] Wang, D.; Meng, J.; Xu, K.; Xiao, R.; Xu, M.; Liu, Y.; Zhao, Y.; Yao, P.; Yan, H.; Liu, L. Evaluation of oral subchronic toxicity of Pu-erh green tea (camellia sinensis var. assamica) extract in Sprague Dawley rats. *J. Ethnopharmacol.* 2012, *142*, 836–44.

[278] Mazzanti, G.; Menniti-Ippolito, F.; Moro, P. A.; Cassetti, F.; Raschetti, R.; Santuccio, C.; Mastrangelo, S. Hepatotoxicity from green tea: a review of the literature and two unpublished cases. *Eur. J. Clin. Pharmacol.* 2009, *65*, 331–41.

[279] Schmidt, M.; Schmitz, H. J.; Baumgart, A.; Guédon, D.; Netsch, M. I.; Kreuter, M. H.; Schmidlin, C. B.; Schrenk, D. Toxicity of green tea extracts and their constituents in rat hepatocytes in primary culture. *Food Chem. Toxicol.* 2005, *43*, 307–14.

[280] Espín, J. C.; García-Conesa, M. T.; Tomás-Barberán, F. A. Nutraceuticals: facts and fiction. *Phytochemistry* 2007, *68*, 2986–3008.

[281] Visioli, F.; De La Lastra, C. A.; Andres-Lacueva, C.; Aviram, M.; Calhau, C.; Cassano, A.; D'Archivio, M.; Faria, A.; Favé, G.; Fogliano, V.; Llorach, R.; Vitaglione, P.; Zoratti, M.; Edeas, M. Polyphenols and human health: a prospectus. *Crit. Rev. Food Sci. Nutr.* 2011, *51*, 524–46.

[282] Manach, C.; Williamson, G.; Morand, C.; Scalbert, A.; Rémésy, C. Bioavailability and bioefficacy of polyphenols in humans. I. Review of 97 bioavailability studies. *Am. J. Clin. Nutr.* 2005, *81*, 230S–242S.

[283] Huo, C.; Wan, S.; Lam, W.; Li, L. The challenge of developing green tea polyphenols as therapeutic agents. *Inflammopharmacology* 2008, *16*, 248–252.

[284] Landis-Piwowar, K. R.; Wan, S. B.; Wiegand, R. A.; Kuhn, D. J.; Chan, T. H.; Dou, Q. P. Methylation suppresses the proteasome-inhibitory function of green tea polyphenols. *J. Cell. Physiol.* 2007, *213*, 252–60.

[285] Chen, Z.; Zhu, Q. Y.; Tsang, D.; Huang, Y. Degradation of green tea catechins in tea drinks. *J. Agric. Food Chem.* 2001, *49*, 477–82.

[286] Kay, C. D. The future of flavonoid research. *Br. J. Nutr.* 2010, *104 Suppl* , S91–5.

In: Recent Advances in Gallate Research
Editor: Amanda L. Kinsey

ISBN: 978-1-63117-071-3
© 2014 Nova Science Publishers, Inc.

Chapter IV

Role of Gallates on the Inflammatory Process

Susana Gorzalczany* and María Laura Anzoise

Cátedra de Farmacología, Facultad de Farmacia y Bioquímica Universidad
de Buenos Aires, Buenos Aires, Argentina

Abstract

Gallic acid is a phenolic acid also known as 3,4,5-trihydroxybenzoic
acid. It is found free in plants but also as salts and esters. The last kind of
compounds is named gallates. They are widespread in nature and are
consumed as part of the human diet in significant amounts. Gallates show
an interesting biological profile and they have significant
antiinflammatory activity in preclinical assays. This review summarizes
the current knowledge on the effects of gallic acid and gallates on
inflammation, with a focus on the mechanisms involved. In this sense,
different molecular and cellular targets and radical scavenging properties
are also analyzed. On the other hand since few clinical trials have
described the relevance of gallates in human diseases related to
inflammatory process, the need for further controlled intervention trials
will be discussed.

---

* Corresponding author: E-mail: sgorza@ffyb.uba.ar.

Abbreviations

AIF	apoptosis-inducing factor
AP-1	activator protein-1
βPGG	1,2,3,4, 6 penta-O-galloyl-β-D-glucose
CCL17	chemokine (C-C motif) ligand 17
cGMP	cyclic guanosine monophosphate
COX_2	cyclooxygenase 2
CXCL9	chemokine (C-X-X motif) ligand 9
DNA	deoxyribonucleic acid
ECG	(-)epicatechin gallate
EG	ethyl gallate
EGCG	(-)-epigallocatechin 3-gallate
Endo G	endonuclease G
ERK	extracellular signal regulated kinase
GA	gallic acid
GS	7-O-galloyl-D-sedoheptulose
GSPE	grape seed-derived procyanidins
HO-1	heme oxygenase-1
HUVECs	human umbilical vein endothelial cells
ICAM-1	intercellular adhesion molecule-1
IFN	interferon
IKK	IkappaB kinase
iNOS	inducible isoform nitric oxide synthase
IL	interleukin
JNK	c-Jun NH_2 terminal kinase
Kd	dissociation constant
LPS	lipopolysaccharide
MCP-1	monocyte chemoattractant protein-1
MG	methyl gallate
MAPKs	mitogen activated protein kinases
MMPs	matrix metalloproteinases
mRNA	messenger ribonucleic acid
NF-κB	nuclear factor-kappaB
NO	nitric oxide
Nrf2	nuclear factor (erythroid-derived 2) like 2
4-OMGA	4-O-methylgallic
PG	n-propyl gallate

PGE$_2$	prostaglandin E2
RANKL	receptor activator for nuclear factor κB ligand
ROS	reactive oxygen species
STAT	signal transducer and activator of transcription
TBARs	thiobarbituric acid reactive substances
TNFα	tumor necrosis factor-α
TPA	12-O-Tetradecanoylphorbol-*13-acetate*
TXNL4B	*thioredoxin like protein 4B*
VCAM-1	vascular cell adhesion molecule-1

Introduction

Inflammation is a natural response of living organisms to the presence of internal and external substances which are recognized by the host as being "non-self" or "foreign invader", producing a cascade of events that could produce a damaged tissue. Inflammatory responses are highly heterogeneous in terms of the cell types and molecular mediators involved. Inflammation also comes in different modalities that can be classified as acute versus chronic and local versus systemic. Despite this complexity, all inflammatory responses can be broken down into four common components that align in a universal configuration of the inflammatory pathway: inflammatory inducers, sensors, mediators, and target tissues. Inflammatory inducers can be exogenous or endogenous signals. Sensor cells, such as macrophages and mast cells, detect inducers with specific receptors and respond by producing inflammatory mediators, creating a unique mediator signature for each inducer. Inflammatory mediators, act on target tissues and alter their functional states, promoting elimination of the inducers, adaptation to the noxious state, and restoration of tissue homeostasis [1, 2]. Nevertheless, uncontrolled inflammation often results in chronic diseases such as arthritis, autoimmune disorder, cancer, dementia, diabetic, neurodegeneration and vascular disease [3, 4]. The prevalence of these diseases has increased rapidly over the past decades. The underlying reasons for the intimate association of inflammation and disease are currently understood, mainly in the extreme cases when diseases are caused by a dysregulated inflammatory response, such as inflammatory tissue damage and sepsis. However, the association between inflammation and human diseases cannot be explained by dysregulation alone [5]. The limitation of current antiinflammatory therapies is acknowledged, and continuous efforts are made to improve the available treatments and find new drugs. In this sense, plants have been the basis of many traditional medicine systems throughout the world for thousands years and still remain as the main new source of structurally important chemical substances that lead to the development of innovative drugs [6, 7, 8]. The search for antiinflammatory agents isolated from medicinal plant is intensifying and different bioactive compounds have shown to modulate inflammatory responses [9, 10].

Gallic acid, an organic acid, known as 3,4,5-trihydroxybenzoic acid ($C_6H_2(OH)_3COOH$), is found widely throughout the plant kingdom [11]. A large number of plants contain high gallic acid contents, either in free form or as part of tannins. It is present in tea, red wine, fruits and medicinal plants [11, 12]. The healthy effect of grape seed-derived procyanidins (GSPE) could explain the "French paradox", an epidemiological observation that French people have a relatively low incidence of coronary heart disease, although they have diet rich in saturated fats. The composition of GSPE is known to consist largely of gallic acid besides catechin, epicatechin and procyanidin dimers and trimmers. These compounds are also present as esters linked to gallic acid in the aliphatic 3-hydroxyl group in C-ring [13]. Therefore, gallic acid could explain at least in part, the French paradox [14].

Salts and esters of gallic acid are termed gallates. Different esters derivatives can be obtained by diverse atom carbon number of the aliphatic side chain, giving them specific physicochemical characteristics, especially lipophilicity. Nevertheless, these chemical changes in the gallic molecule can modify their pharmacokinetic or pharmacodynamic properties. These compounds were named according to the atom carbon number of the side chain, such as methyl, ethyl, octadecyl gallate [15].

In addition, certain tannins are gallic acid esters of glucose and of other sugars. Some medicinal herbals contain hydrolysable tannin with five ester bonds formed between carboxylic groups of gallic acid and aliphatic hydroxyl groups of glucose core. The most studies have been conducted with 1,2,3,4, 6 penta-O-galloyl-β-D-glucose (β-PGG) due to its natural abundance, although α-anomer also exists naturally [16]. Besides, synthetic galloyl esters of sugar were obtained, and some of them, such as galloylsucroses showed a valuable antioxidant activity [17].

Furthermore, galloyl conjugated of different polyphenols, such as (-)-epigallocatechin 3-gallate (EGCG), the main polyphenol in green tea, (-)epicatechin gallate (ECG), hyperin-2''-O-gallate, astragallin-2''-O-gallate, bergenin gallate, etc. have been appreciated for their beneficial effects [18, 19].

Alkyl Gallates and Inflammation

Gallic acid (GA) is present in tea, red wine, fruits, beverages and various medicinal plants [12]. It is commonly used in different industries, as antioxidant in food, in cosmetics and in the pharmaceutical industry. *In vivo* and *in vitro* studies have provided evidence that GA possess many potential therapeutic properties, including anti-cancer, antiinflammatory, antimutagenic and antioxidant activities. It also seems to have antifungal, antiviral and antibacterial properties [12, 20, 21]. Evidence about GA antiinflammatory activity is related to its ability to inhibit myeloperoxidase release, acting as scavenger of superoxide anions [22] and inhibiting the increases in the IL-6 and IL-8 gene and protein levels induced by *Fusabacterium nucelatum* in human oral epithelial cells [23]. Also, GA treatment decreased LPS-induced nuclear factor-kappaB (NF-κB) activation in transgenic mice, suppressing the production of pro-inflammatory cytokines (TNFα and IL-1β) and the inhibition of the expression of TXNL4B, iNOS and COX_2 in RAW264.7 cells and it could be responsible of the *in vivo* activity observed by Hsiang et al. [24]. In the same sense, Reddy et al. [25, 26] described the GA as selective inhibitor of COX_2. Moreover, GA inhibited the pro-inflammatory cytokine gene expression and production of TNFα and IL-6, κB and p38 mitogen-activated protein kinase dependant in human mast cell [27]. Furthermore, GA showed a significant increase in capase-3 activity on inflammatory status of fibroblast-like synovial cells from synovial tissues of patients with rheumatoid arthritis, suggesting that GA possess a pro-apoptotic effect and it can suppress pro-inflammatory mediator expressions [28].

On the other hand, 4-O-methylgallic (4-OMGA) acid, the main metabolite of GA in rats, rabbits, chickens and humans [29], also showed anti-inflammatory activity. Lee et al. [30] investigated the functional effect of 4-OMGA in human umbilical vein endothelial cells (HUVECs) stimulated with TNF-α and described that 4-OMGA is able to inhibit the promoter activities of intercellular adhesion molecule-1 (ICAM-1), vascular cell adhesion molecule-1(VCAM-1) and the activity of NF-κB without affecting cytosolic IκB kinase (IKK) activation. Moreover, this compound exhibits an antiinflammatory activity by interfering with the formation of the NF-κB-DNA complex in the nuclei through direct and redox-sensitive interactions, suggesting that 4-OMGA may play an important role in the prevention of inflammatory responses [30, 31].

One of the alkyl gallates that it is possible to find in nature is methyl gallate (MG). It was described as the main compound from *Acacia farnesiana* [32], *Sapium sebiferum* [33], *Galla Rhois* [34], *Toona sinensis* [35]. *It was shown that MG* possesses a wide range of biological properties that include antioxidant, antiinflammatory, antimicrobial and antitumor properties [36, 37]. MG showed a significant antiinflammatory activity on the 12-O-Tetradecanoylphorbol-*13-acetate* (*TPA*) ear edema [38], inducing its dual cyclooxygenase and lipoxygenase inhibitory activity *in vitro* [39]. Due to its ability to inhibit the protein and mRNA expressions of iNOS and COX_2 and suppressed the phosphorylation of ERK1/2, the production of NO, IL-6 and IL-8 and the inflammation could be reduced [40, 23, 37].

The enhanced oxidising environment can facilitate the binding of pathogens or antigens to effector cells leading to a hyperresponsive innate immune system and since reactive oxygen species are implicated in various inflammatory disorders, it is possible to deduce that antioxidants are emerging as prophylactic and therapeutic agents [41]. The proton donating ability of MG may reflect its usefulness as free radical inhibitors or scavengers [42], so this strong antioxidant activity could be responsible, at least in part, of the antiinflammatory activity attributed for MG.

On the other hand, ethyl gallate (EG), used as a food additive, has been reported to exhibit anticancer, antimicrobial, and free radical scavenging activities [43, 44]. ICAM-1 and VCAM-1 are known cell adhesion molecules that participate in the early events of innate immune response by allowing leukocyte endothelial interaction and their subsequent migration at the site of insult. Mehla et al. [45] described that EG, the active compound of *Pisticia integerrina*, attenuated LPS induced ICAM-1 and VCAM-1 at protein and mRNA levels by blocking activator protein-1 (AP-1) transcription factors without affecting nuclear transcription factor NF-κB. Besides, EG alleviated inflammatory condition in preclinical acute lung injury model in mice, reducing neutrophils, reactive oxygen species (ROS), pro-inflammatory cytokines. Besides, EG enhanced the expression of heme oxygenase-1 (HO-1) mediated, at least in part, by Nrf2 nuclear translocation, a transcription factor that regulates the gene expression of antioxidant and detoxication enzymes [46].

Apoptosis is an orderly cellular suicide program, critical for the development and homeostasis of a multicellular organism and taking to consideration this, it is important to note that some protein families are involved in both apoptotic and inflammatory signalling [47]. It has shown that EG act on mitochondrial-dependent pathways and on caspase cascade to activate the intrinsic apoptotic pathway through expression of caspases 8, 9, and 3, apoptosis-inducing factor (AIF), and endonuclease G (Endo G), preventing various mediated injuries in *in vivo* pathological-situations[43].

Moreover, *n*-propyl gallate (PG), an ester that is also known as propyl 3,4,5-trihidroxybenzoate and it is synthesized by condensation of propanol and gallic acid. PG is used in foods, cosmetics, hair products, adhesives and lubricants due to its antioxidative properties [17, 48]. The antioxidant activity was showed in cultured cells and *in vivo* models too [49. 50]. Apart from its antioxidant activity PG produced a reduction of TPA-induce expression levels of COX_2 and PGE_2 in human THP-1 monocytes, inducing the inhibition of nuclear translocation and phosphorylation of p65. In this sense, it also reduced the phosphorylation of IκB and the activity of IκB kinase [36, 51]. In the same sense, PG induced antiinflammatory activity in *in vivo* models, such as air pouch induced by carrageenan and acetic acid-induced permeability in rodents. Besides, PG suppressed IκB-α degradation and phosphorylation of JNJ1/2 in LPS stimulated macrophage, resulting in the suppression of promoter activities of NF-κB and c-JUN [52].

Octyl and dodecyl gallates are synthetic esters of gallic acid [53]. Despite being potential allergens, they are frequently use as antioxidant additives in foods and cosmetics for their abilities to prevent the oxidation of unsaturated fats [54, 55]. Dodecyl gallate and octyl gallate are active against Gram-positive bacterias, although dodecyl gallate is active at minor concentration [56]. However, only octyl gallate showed antifungic acitivity [57]. But, as many natural compounds, dodecyl gallate is able to promote cellular oxidative stress, inducing an increase in proapoptotic (Bax) and a decrease in antiapoptotic (Bcl-2) proteins expression in B16F10 mouse melanoma cells [58]. Nevertheless, octyl gallate had no significant effect on the inflammatory responses of acute *Chlamydia pneumoniae* infection *in vivo* [59].

It is important that, alkyl gallates, including the widely used as antioxidants such as propyl, octyl, and dodecyl gallate showed that all gallates are moderate to strong contact sensitizers and dodecyl gallate was found to be the strongest one, using an experimental model of sensitization in guinea pigs. A characteristic correlation between side chain length and mean response was observed, giving a maximum of sensitization at a length of 12 carbon atoms [54, 60]. Apart from that, these kinds of gallates have a low acute toxicity and no effects were observed even at the highest dose of 5 g/kg in long-term toxicity studies in rodents. In addition, there is no evidence of a carcinogenic or mutagenic action induced by gallates. However, most of the available studies were published before 1960, so it could be useful to re-evaluate the toxicity of this kind of compounds, using modern strategies [61].

Galloylated Sugars and Inflammation

1,2,3,4,6-penta-O-galloyl-β-D-glucose (βPGG), a bioactive tannin, presents in many medicinal plants and exhibits multiple biological activities which implicate a great potential for PGG in the therapy. Tannins are secondary metabolites of plants, mostly water-soluble phenolic compounds that can precipitate alkaloids, gelatine and other proteins. Hydrolysable tannins are esters of gallic acid. GA molecules can be esterified to a core polyol, and the galloyl groups may be further esterified to form more complex structures. Gallotannins, the pollygalloyl esters of glucose, are the simplest hydrolysable tannins, βPGG is a prototypical gallotannin. Most studies have been conducted with βPGG due to its natural abundance, though the α-anomer also exists naturally. An interesting point from other polyphenolic compounds is the lack of prooxidant activity of βPGG in aqueous that support βPGG as a distinct form of gallic acid and possibly other tea polyphenolics, in term of biological activities [62].

It was described that gallotannins stimulated the TNFα and 1L-β secretion in human peripheral blood momonuclear cells and this activity is related to antitumoral action *in vivo* [63]. On the contrary, βPGG attenuated the stimulating effect of LPS [64]. LPS is a known trigger in the pathogenesis of sepsis and lipid A is the toxic component, so the therapeutic approaches for severe sepsis is currently focusing on the neutralization of LPS effect and lipid A. Genfa et al. [65] showed that βPGG directly bound to lipid A *in vitro* with a K_d of 32 μM, and protected mice from a lethal challenge by LPS. They described that the reduction of the endotoxin level induced by βPGG in rats being tightly associated with the TNFα level as well. Additionally, βPGG isolated from root of *Paeonia lactiflora* Pall, revealed that it is more potent than epigallocatechin gallate (EGCG), gallic acid, and gallacetophenone in both iNOS and COX_2 inhibitory activity in LPS-activated Raw 264.7 [66]. More studies supported the antiinflammatory effect of βPGG, Kang et al. demonstrated that βPGG treatment attenuated TNFα-induced NF-κB p65 translocation, expression levels of adhesion molecules including ICAM-1, VCAM-1 and monocyte chemoattractant protein-1 (MCP-1) in human umbilical vein endothelial cells, suggesting that βPGG suppress the vascular inflammatory process, which may be closely related with the activation of vascular NO/cGMP signaling [67]. Moreover, since inflammatory or immunological disorders can be suppressed by limiting IL-8 synthesis and/or IL-8 gene expression, Oh et al. demonstrated that the βPGG is a potent inhibitor of IL-8 gene expression and the activation of NF-κB, preventing the degradation of I-κBα [68]. Additionally, βPGG, isolated from the barks of *Juglans mandshurica* suppressed TNFα/IFNγ-induced protein and mRNA expression of CCL17 in the human keratinocyte cell line HaCaT and inhibited NF-κB activation as well as STAT1 activation in the same model. Since, CCL17 is a ligand for CCR4, which is predominantly expressed on Th2 lymphocytes into the site of inflammation, CCL17 is considered to be a pivotal mediator in the inflammatory response during the development of Th2-dominant inflammatory skin diseases such as atopic dermatitis. In this sense, pretreatment with βPGG resulted in significant reduction in expression of CXCL9, 10, and 11 in the HaCaT cells treated with IFN-γ, suggesting that βPGG might be a useful tool in therapy of skin inflammatory diseases [69].

Other gallotannins have been studied as well. 2,6-tri-O-galloyl-beta-D-allose reduced LPS-induced NO production, decreasing gene expression, production of iNOS and the activation of NF-κB in macrophages [70]. Corilagin (beta-1-O-galloyl-3,6-(R)-hexahydroxydiphenoyl-D-glucose) could significantly reduce production of pro-inflammatory cytokines and mediators TNF-α, IL-1β, IL-6, NO and reduce the activity of iNOS and COX_2 on both protein and gene level by blocking NF-κB nuclear translocation on RAW264.7 cell stimulated by LPS. Moreover, corilagin could promote release of antiinflammatory factor HO-1 on both protein and gene level and suppress the release of IL-10 [71].

In addition, 7-O-galloyl-D-sedoheptulose (GS) suppressed hepatic NF-κB, COX_2 and iNOS proteins expressions in a type 2 diabetic db/db mouse model, which could be probably the result of a reduction of ROS and TBARS in the hepatic tissue, preventing oxidative/ nitrosative stress and its related inflammatory response by attenuating the expression of NADPH oxidase subunits (NOx-4 and p22 phox) and NF-κB related protein [72].

Other Gallates

Tea is a widely consumed beverage throughout the world and reported to possess significant health promoting effects. The principal catechins found in the green tea are epicatechin (6.4%), epicatchin-3-gallate (ECG, 13.6%), epigallocatechin (EGC, 19%) and epigallocatechin-3-gallate (EGCG, 59%) and account for 30-40% of its dry weight. Structural activity with EGCG indicates the importance of structure of EGCG linked to gallic acid for its antioxidant activity [73]. EGCG inhibited the IKK activity in intestinal epithelial cells and this is correlated with the presence of the gallate group because the polyphenols lacking gallate group failed to inhibit the IKK activity [74]. Moreover, EGCG selectively inhibits the phosphorylation of c-Jun and DNA binding activity of AP-1 in human chondrocytes. The inhibition of AP-1 activity by EGCG and related tea catechins was also attributed to the gallate moiety. In addition, structural and functional analyses have identified the galloyl and hydroxyl group present at the 3'position on EGCG molecule as responsible for its strong anti-inflammatory properties in articular chondrocytes [73]. It has been suggested that catechins without a pyrogallol-type structure showed no inhibition of apoptosis [75].

It was described that EGCG inhibits IKKα and IKKβ activity in SAOS-2 cells with concomitant down-regulation of NF-κB and induction of apoptosis [76].

STAT proteins are involved in modulating cellular responses to proinflammatory cytokines such as IL-1, TNFα as well as growth factors and immunomodulatory proteins including interferon. STAT1 activation in RA synovium plays an important role in inflammation process, therefore STAT1 represents a target of anti-inflammatory drugs. In this sense, EGCG showed a potent and specific inhibitory effect on IFN-γ-elicited STAT1 activation in different human cells types without any effect on other STATs, such as STAT3 and 6.

On the other hand and taking into account that a super family of proteases called metzincins, including MMPs, are principal proteases involved in degradation of extracellular matrix macromolecules and they were found to be increased in patients with arthritis rheumatoid, the effect of EGCG, decreasing the level of MMP production and also increasing the expression of tissue inhibitors of MMP-1, might represent an useful tool for the treatment of inflammatory disease [77].

EGCG inhibits NO production by suppressing iNOS mRNA and protein expression via inhibition of NF-κB/p65, as well [78]. Additionally, EGCG exerted a marked inhibition of basal and IL-1 stimulated mitogen-activated protein kinase (MAPKs) phosphorylation in chondrocytes, suppressing RANKL induced activation of c-Jun NH(2)-terminal kinase (JNK) pathways without affecting p38 kinase and extracellular signal-regulated kinase (ERK), essential signal transduction machinery involved in the regulation of inflammation associated with gene expression.

Taking together this information EGCG may represent an excellent tool for the development of new therapeutics for inflammatory process. Although the greatest amount of research are referred to ECGG, other gallates have been studied. In this sense, it was described that a topical application of equimolar of black tea constituents (theaflavin, theaflavin-3-gallate, theaflavin-3'-gallate, and theaflavin-3,3'-digallate) strongly inhibited TPA-induced edema of mouse ears reducing the in IL-1β and IL-6 protein levels [79].

Clinical Trials

Epidemiological and intervention studies have been carried out to find out dietary patterns, foods and bioactive compounds with protective anti-inflammatory actions. The most studied compounds are polyphenols, especially isoflavone, anthocyanin, but quercetin, catechin, resveratrol and curcumin have also been investigated [80].

Although epidemiologic studies are useful for evaluation of the human health effects of long term exposure to physiologic concentrations of polyphenols, it is necessary controlled randomized clinical trials to answer the question of data from animal models and *in vitro* systems are relevant for human disease outcomes. An important phenomenon is that, after absorption, polyphenols are subject to phase II metabolism that may greatly influence their bioactivity.

Since different gallates have shown antiinflammatory and antioxidative properties, they are strong candidate for a new treatment option for patients with diseases related to inflammatory process such as inflammatory bowel disease, rheumatoid arthritis and even cancer. In spite of great amount of compounds, hardly any has been studied in clinical trials and for those studied compounds the clinical results have been controversial. For instance, the therapeutic effects of PG in combination with standard medication on patients with non-ST-elevation acute coronary syndrome and its influences on serum inflammatory marker no improvement the therapeutic effect of standard treatment [81]. Nevertheless EGCG is in better situation related to clinical trials but its efficacy in human rheumatoid arthritis using the phase-controlled trials is yet to be tested. Several phase I and phase II cancer chemoprevention trials, however, have been performed using EGCG but many issues remain to be clarified [82,83].

Conflicting epidemiological inferences and discrepancies between *in vitro* and *in vivo* studies may be due to its erratic bioavailability. Aspects concerning these facts, but also related to dose levels, administration frequency and potential side effects remain to be addressed in future clinical trials.

General Considerations

Numerous studies have been published identifying molecular mechanisms of gallate effects. Mostly evidence of efficacy has been derived from animal models and *in vitro* test. The available information let us know the potential utility of gallates for the possible treatment of diseases related to inflammatory process. Nevertheless, its use requires extensive clinical testing in order to optimize its potential use in patients. Another challenge will be to develop specific preparations of alone or associated gallates in order to deliver these compounds to the target structures, enhancing its bioavalilabitlity. The research of compounds isolated from natural source, is now in a dynamic process and they could be a novel way to improve the currently treatment for diseases relate to inflammation process.

References

[1]   Long, H. K., Llu, D. & Jusko, W. (2012). *Crit Rev Biome Eng.*, *40*, 295.
[2]   Medzhitov, R. (2010). *Cell.*, *140*, 771.
[3]   Chen, S. (2011). *Curr Drug Targets.*, *12*, 288.
[4]   Medzhitov, R. (2008). *Nature*, *454*, 428.
[5]   Okin, D. & Medzhitov, R. (2012). *Curr Biol.*, *22*, R73.
[6]   Jachak, S. M. & Saklani, A. (2007). *Curr. Sci.*, *92*, 1251.
[7]   Bellik, Y., Hammoudi, S. M., Abdellah, F., Iguer-Ouada, M. & Boukraâ, L. (2012). *Recent Pat. Inflamm. Allergy Drug Discov.*, *6*, 147.
[8]   Bellik, Y., Bourkraâ, L., Alzahrani, H., Bakhotmah, B., Abdellah, F., Hammoudi, S. & Iguer-Ouada, M. (2013). *Molecules.*, *18*, 322.
[9]   Bremner, P. & Heinrich, M. (2002). *J Pharm Pharmacol.*, *54*, 453.
[10]   Nam, N. (2006). *Mini Rev Med Chem.*, *6*, 945.

[11]   Masoud, M., Hagagg, S., Ali, A. & Nasr, N. (2012). *J Mol Struct.*, *1014*, 17.

[12]   Borde, V. U., Pangrikar, P. P. & Takle, S. U. (2011). *Recent Research in Science and Technology.*, *3*, 51.

[13]   Montagut, G., Baiges, I., Valls, J., Terra, X., del Bas, J., Vitrac, X., Richard, T., Mérillon, J., Arola, L., Blay, M., Bladé, C., Fenández Larrea, J., Pujadas, G., Salvadó, J. & Ardévol, A. (2009). *Food Chem.*, *116*, 265.

[14]   Appeldoorn, C. C., Bonnefoy, A., Lutters, B. C., Daenens, K., van Berkel, T. J., Hoylaerts, M. F. & Biessen, E. A. (2005). *Circulation.*, *111*, 106.

[15]   Locatelli, C., Filippin-Monteiro, F. & Creczynsk-Pasa, T. (2013). *Eur J Med Chem.*, *60*, 233.

[16]   Zhang, C., Pan, X., Yu, M., Jin, L. & Wu, G. (2009). *Chemical Engineering Journal.*, *209*, 464.

[17]   Dufour, C., Da Silva, E., Potier, P., Queneau, Y. & Dangles, O. (2002). *J Agr food chem.*, *50*, 3425.

[18]   Okuda, T. (2005). *Phytochemistry.*, *66*, 2012.

[19]   Quideau, S., Deffieux, D., Douat-Casassus, C. & Poységu, L. (2011). *Angewandte Chemie.*, *50*, 586.

[20]   Ow, Y. & Stupans, J. (2013). *Curr drug Metab.*, *4*, 241.

[21]   Verma, S., Singh, A. & Mishra, A. (2013). *cancer Environ toxicol pharmacol.*, *35*, 473.

[22]   Kroes, B., Van den Berg, A., Quarles van Ufford, H., van Dijk, H. & Labadie, R. (1992). *Planta Med.*, *58*, 499.

[23]   Kang, M., Jang, H., Oh, J., Yang, K., Choi, N., Lim, H. & Kim, S. (2009). *J Microbiol.*, *47*, 760.

[24]   Hsiang, C. Y., Hseu, Y. C., Chang, Y. C., Senthil Kumar, K. J., Ho, T. Y. & Yang, H. L. (2013). *Food Chem.*, *136*, 426.

[25]   Reddy, T., Aparoy, P., Babu, N., Kumar, K., Kalanagi, S. & Reddanna, P. (2010). *Protein Pept. Lett.*, *17*, 1251.

[26]   Reddy, T., Reddy, D., Aparna, A., Arunasree, K., Gupta, G., Achari, C., Reddy, G., Lakshmipathi, V., Subramanyam, A. & Reddanna, P. (2012). *Toxicol. In Vitro.*, *26*, 396.

[27]   Kim, S., Jun, C., Suk, K., Choi, B., Lim, H., Park, S., Lee, S., Shin, H., Kim, D. & Shin, T. (2006). *Toxicol sci.*, *91*, 123.

[28]   Yoon, C. H., Chung, S. J., Lee, S. W., Park, Y. B., Lee, S. K. & Park, M. C. (2013). *Joint Bone Spine*, *80*, 274.

[29] Shahrzad, S., Aoyagi, K., Winter, A., Koyama, A. & Bitsch, I. (2001). *J. Nutrition.*, *131*, 1207.

[30] Lee, G., Na, H. J., Namkoong, S., Kwon, H. J., Han, S., Ha, K. S., Kwon, Y. G., Lee, H. & Kim, Y. M. (2006). *Eur J Pharmacol.*, *551*, 143.

[31] Na, H., Lee, G., Oh, H., Jeon, K., Kwon, H., Ha, K., Lee, H., Kwon, Y. & Kim, Y. (2006). *Int Immunopharmacol.*, *6*, 1597.

[32] Sánchez, E., Heredia, N., Camacho-Corona, M. D. & García, S. (2013). *J Appl Microbiol.*, Aug 20. doi: 10.1111/jam.12328. [Epub ahead of print].

[33] Kane, C. J., Menna, J. H. & Yeh, Y. C. (1988). *Biosci Rep.*, *8*, 85.

[34] Kang, M., Oh, J., Kang, I., Hong, S. & Choi, C. (2008). *J Microbiol.*, *46*, 744.

[35] Hsieh, T., Liu, T., Chia, Y., Chern, C., Lu, F., Chuang, M., Mau, S., Chen, S., Syu, Y. & Chen, C. (2004). *Food Chem Toxicol.*, *42*, 843.

[36] Hsu, F. L., Huang, W. J., Wu, T. H., Lee, M. H., Chen, L. C., Lu, H. J., Hou, W. C. & Lin, M. H. (2012). *Int J Mol Sci.*, *13*, 6073.

[37] Lee, S. H., Kim, J. K., Kim, D. W., Hwang, H. S., Eum, W. S., Park, J. , Han, K. H., Oh, J. S. & Choi, S. Y. (2013). *Biochim Biophys Acta.*, *1830*, 4017.

[38] Gorzalczany, S., López, P., Acevedo, C. & Ferraro, G. (2011). *J Ethnopharmacol.*, *133*, 994.

[39] Kim, S. J., Jin, M., Lee, E., Moon, T. C., Quan, Z., Yang, J. H., Son, K. H., Kim, K. U., Son, J. K. & Chang, H. W. (2006). *Archives of Pharmacol Research*, *29*, 874.

[40] Chae, H. S., Kang, O. H., Choi, J. G., Oh, Y. C., Lee, Y. S., Brice, O. O., Chong, M. S., Lee, K. N., Shin, D. W. & Kwon, D. Y. (2010). *Am. J. Chin. Med.*, *38*, 973.

[41] Ratnam, D., Ankola, D., Bhardwaj, V., Sahana, D. & Kumar, M. (2006). *J control release.*, *113*, 189.

[42] Ekaprasada, M., Hazli, N., Sanusi, I. & Dachriyanus, D. (2009). *Indo. J. Chem.*, *9*, 457.

[43] Kim, W., Song, H., Choi, H., Bang, H., Choi, D. & Park, H. (2012). *Int J Mol Sc.*, *13*, 11912.

[44] Zheng, G., Xu, L., Wu, P., Xie, H., Jiang, Y., Chen, F. & Wei, X. (2009). *Food Chem.*, *116*, 433.

[45] Mehla, K., Balwani, S., Kulshreshtha, A., Nandi, D., Jaisankar, P. & Ghosh, B. (2011). *J. Ethnopharmacol.*, *137*, 1345.

[46] Mehla, K., Balwani, S., Agrawal, A. & Ghosh, B. (2013). *Biochimie.*, *95*, 2404.

[47] Park, H., Lo, Y., Lin, S., Wang, L., Yang, J. & Wu, H. (2007). *Annu. Rev. Immunol.*, *25*, 561.

[48] Capitán-Vallvey, L., Valencia, M. & Nicolás, E. A. (2003). *J Food Sci.*, *68*, 1595.

[49] Han, Y. & Park, W. (2009). *Food Chem Toxicol.*, *47*, 2531.

[50] Han, Y., Moon, H., You, B. & Park, W. (2010). *Toxicol in Vitro.*, *24*, 1183.

[51] Hsu, H. C., Lin, W. C., Chang, P. J., Hong, C. Z. & Chen, C. H. (2013). *Exp ther med.*, *5*, 964.

[52] Jung, H. J., Kim, S., Jeon, W., Kim, B., Ahn, K., Kim, K., Kim, Y., Park, E. & Lim, C. (2011). *Inflammation.*, *34*, 352.

[53] van der Meeren, H. L. (1987). *Contact Dermatitis.*, *16*, 260.

[54] García-Melgares, M. L., de la Cuadra, J., Martín, B., Laguna, C., Martínez, L. & Alegre, V. (2007). *Actas Dermosifiliogr*, *98*, 688.

[55] Kubo, I., Masuoka, N., Xiao, P. & Haraguchi, H. (2002). *J. Agric. Food Chem.*, *50*, 3533.

[56] Kubo, I., Fujita, K. I., Nihei, K. I. & Masuoka, N. (2013). *Bioorg Med Chem.*, *11*, 573.

[57] Fujita, K. I. & Kubo, I. (2002). *Intl J Food Microbiol.*, *79*, 193.

[58] De Cordova, C., Locatelli, C., Assunção, L., Mattei, B., Mascarello, A., Winter, E., Nunes, R., Yunes, R. & Creczynski-Pasa, T. (2011). *Toxicol in Vitro.*, *25*, 2025.

[59] Tömäkangas, L., Vuorela, P., Saario, E., Leinonen, M., Saikku, P. & Vuorela, H. (2005). *Biochem. Pharmacol.*, *70*, 1222.

[60] Hausen, B. & Beyer, W. (1992). *Contact Dermatitis.*, *26*, 253.

[61] Van del Heijden, C. A., Janssen, P. J. & Strik, J. J. (1986). *Chem. Toxic.*, *24*, 1067.

[62] Zhang, J., Li, L., Kim, S., Hagerman, A. & Lü, J. (2009). *Pharm. Res.*, *26*, 2066.

[63] Feldman, K. S., Sahasrabudhe, K., Smith, R. S. & Scheuchenzuber, W. J. (1999). *Bioorg Med Chem Lett.*, *5*, 985.

[64] Feldman, K. S., Sahasrabudhe, K., Lawlor, M. D., Wilson, S. L., Lang, C. H. & Scheuchenzuber, W. J. (2001). *Bioorg Med Chem Lett.*, *11*, 1813.

[65] Genfa, L., Jiang, Z., Hong, Z., Yimin, Z., Liangxi, W., Guo, W., Ming, H., Donglen, J. & Lizhao, W. (2005). *Int Immunopharmacol.*, *5*, 1007.

[66] Lee, S. J., Lee, I. S. & Mar, W. (2003). *Arch Pharm Res.*, *26*, 832.

[67] Kang, D. G., Moon, M. K., Choi, D. H., Lee, J. K., Kwon, T. O. & Lee, H. S. (2005). *Eur J Pharmacol, 524*, 111.

[68] Oh, G. S., Pae, H. O., Choi, B. M., Lee, H. S., Kim, I. K., Yun, Y. G., Kim, J. D. & Chung, H. T. (2004). *Int Immunopharmacol., 4*, 377.

[69] Ju, S. M., Song, H. Y., Lee, S. J., Seo, W. Y., Sin, D. H., Goh, A. R., Kang, Y. H., Kang, I. J., Won, M. H., Yi, J. S., Kwon, D. J., Bae, Y. S., Choi, S. Y. & Prak, J. (2009). *Biochem Biophys res commun., 387*, 115.

[70] Kim, M. S., Park, S. B., Suk, K., Kim, I. K., Kim, S. Y., Kim, J. A., Lee, S. H. & Kim, S. H. (2009). *Biol Pharm Bull, 32*, 1053.

[71] Zhao, L., Zhang, S. L., Tao, J. Y., Pang, R., Jin, F., Guo, Y. J., Dong, J. H., Ye, P., Zhao, H. Y. & Zheng, G. H. (2008). *Int Immunopharmacol., 8*, 1059.

[72] Noh, J. S., Park, C. H., Tanaka, T. & Yokozawa, T. (2012). *Biol Pharm Bull, 35*, 950.

[73] Singh, R., Akhtar, N. & Haqqi, T. M. (2010). *Life Sci., 86*, 907.

[74] Yang, F., Oz, H. S., Barve, S., de Villiers, W. J., McClain, C. J., Varilek, G. W. (2001). *Mol Pharmacol, 60*, 528.

[75] Saeki, K., Hayakawa, S., Isemura, S. & Miyase, M. (2000). *Phytochemistry, 53*, 391.

[76] Hafeez, B. B., Ahmed, S., Wang, N., Gupta, S., Zhang, A. & Haqqi, T. M. (2006). *Toxicol Appl Pharm, 216*, 11.

[77] Lee, J. H., Chung, J. H. & Cho, K. H. (2005). *J Dermatol Sci., 40*, 195.

[78] Singh, R., Ahmed, S., Malemud, C. J., Gldberg, V. M. & Haqqi, T. M. (2003). *J Orthopaed Res., 21*, 102-109.

[79] Huang, M. T., Liu, Y., Ramji, D., Lo, C. Y., Ghai, G., Dushenkov, S. & Ho, C. T. (2006). *Mol NutrFood Res., 50*, 115.

[80] Rosa, F. T., Zulet, M. A., Marchini, J. S. & Martínez, J. A. (2012). *Int J Food Sci Nutr., 63*, 749.

[81] Jiang, Y. R., Yin, H. J. & Li, L. Z. (2008). *Zhongguo Zhong Xi Yi Jie He Za Zhi., 28*, 839.

[82] Salahuddin, A. (2010). *Arthritis Res Ther., 12*, 208.

[83] Mereles, D. & Hunstein, W. (2011). *Int J Mol Sci., 12*, 5592.

In: Recent Advances in Gallate Research
Editor: Amanda L. Kinsey

ISBN: 978-1-63117-071-3
© 2014 Nova Science Publishers, Inc.

Chapter V

Influence of the Nature and Concentration of Dia - and Paramagnetic Doping Elements on Electron Structure and Electrophysical Properties of Doped Lanthanum Gallate

N. Chezhina[1], D. Korolev[1] and E. Zharikova[2]
[1]Sankt Petersburg State University, St. Petersburg, Russia
[2]Moscow State University, Moscow, Russia

Abstract

Lanthanum gallate doped with strontium or simultaneously with strontium and magnesium, the latter entering the sites of gallium in perovskite structure, opened a wide series of oxygen ionic conductors promising for energy saving technologies in the so called Solid Oxide Fuel Cells (SOFC). However, introduction of bivalent elements into lanthanum gallate, which creates vacancies in the oxygen sublattice and thus triggers the oxygen conductivity of the material, makes it rather instable to decomposition, especially at high temperatures. This circumstance made the scientists to search for some additions stabilizing perovskite structure. Such stabilizers were found to be transition elements substituting for gallium.

Taking into account the fact that doped lanthanum galates are rather diluted solid solutions we carried out a thorough study of magnetic susceptibility of a wide range of solid solutions by magnetic dilution method. This method allows the state of magnetic atoms and the exchange interactions in the structure to be determined. We varied the transition elements (Cr, Mn, Fe, Co, Ni), the ratio M:Sr(Mg), changed Sr for Ca and Ba as the doping elements, and compared the results with the magnetic dilution of transition elements in $LaGaO_3$ and $LaAlO_3$ matrices.

Two main features were found on studying the magnetic susceptibility of a large amount of solid solutions. The first is that no oxidation of transition elements was observed upon heterovalent doping of lanthanum gallate. In the case of cobalt and nickel heterovalent doping results in the changes in the spin states. The second and the most significant feature lies in the clustering of paramagnetic atoms. Clustering is stronger in lanthanum gallate than in aluminate. Upon heterovalent doping with Ca and Ba clustering increases compared to strontium doped lanthanum gallate. Introduction of magnesium into gallium sites increases clustering to the extent that the clusters behave as superparamagnetics and the susceptibility in some cases becomes field dependent. The clusters in heterovalent doped lanthanum gallate include transition element atoms, bivalent elements and vacancies in the oxygen sublattice accompanying them.

The sizes of clusters and the exchange interactions in them exert an important and ambiguous impact on electrophysical properties of doped lanthanum gallate, which must be taken into account for optimization of the composition of electron-ionic conductors.

1. Introduction

Lanthanum gallate doped with strontium or simultaneously with strontium and magnesium, and also with transition elements those latter entering the sites of gallium in perovskite structure, opened a wide series of oxygen ionic and electron-ionic conductors promising for energy saving technologies in the so called Solid Oxide Fuel Cells (SOFC).

1.1. Ionic Conductors Based on Lanthanum Gallate Doped with Bivalent Elements

Simultaneous doping of lanthanum gallate with alkaline-earth elements and magnesium makes it possible to obtain a wide spectrum of compounds with ionic conductivity. Introduction of transition elements into the gallium sites, on the whole, contributes to the appearance of electronic component of conductivity. An active search for the compositions providing for maximal ionic and (or) electronic conductivity is going on from 1994, when for the first time the ionic conductivity was found in lanthanum gallate doped with strontium, calcium, barium, and magnesium [1].

This is accounted for by practical importance of the materials based on doped lanthanum gallates in the production of solid oxide fuel cells (SOFC).

The tolerance of perovskite structure of lanthanum gallate to various substitutions allows a wide spectrum of compositions to be obtained, which have various qualitative and quantitative composition and, consequently, various properties. Doped gallates are used as a rule as electrolytes in SOFC [2-7].

In such a case the cathodes must have both electronic and ionic conductivity and the electrolytes – purely ionic. $LaGaO_3$ doped with strontium and magnesium, as an electrolyte, is now a popular subject for SOFC operating in the middle temperature region (600 - 800°C).

A large number of works is devoted to the study of the structure of lanthanum gallate and its derivatives [8-22].

The data on structural analysis are ambiguous, which is substantially determined not only by the synthetic procedure but also by the quality of starting reagents.

The study [9] is particularly remarkable, since the structure of $La_{1-x}Sr_xGa_{1-y}Mg_yO_{3-\delta}$ is determined as a function of inserted Sr and Mg: orthorhombic at $x + y < 0.25$; orthorhombic and rhombohedral at $0.25 < x + y < 0.30$; at $x + y > 0.30$, if x or $y \geq 20$ – cubic. By various data the structural phase transitions in pure and doped lanthanum gallate can occur in a wide range of temperatures [16, 18, 20-22].

The choice of strontium and magnesium as heterovalent substituents is not casual, though the greater stability of Sr and Mg doped gallate compared to Ba and Ca containing analogs was found experimentally [1]. The thermodynamic examination shows a lesser endothermic effect of the solid solution formation on introduction of Sr (138±12 kJ/mol for $La_{1-x}Sr_xGa_{1-y}Mg_yO_{3-\delta}$ and 166±12 kJ/mol for $La_{1-x}Ba_xGa_{1-y}Mg_yO_{3-\delta}$; $x > 0$, $y \leq 0.2$) or magnesium (275±37 kJ/mol for $LaGa_{1-y}Mg_yO_{3-\delta}$; $y \leq 0.2$) [23]. This suggests that Sr and Mg are the most suitable doping elements in lanthanum gallate from the elements of the II group of Periodic table.

A number of works on computer simulation are devoted to the stability of doped lanthanum gallates and their electron structure [24-26]. The data of Khan using the statistic lattice simulation method [24] are in good agreement with endothermic character of experimental values in [23].

It is interesting to note that by the data of computer simulation the formation of oxygen vacancies upon heterovalent substitution of lanthanum gallate results in its destabilization, whereas doping zirconium oxide with yttrium contributes to the stabilization of fluorite structure [23]. In Sr and Mg doped gallate the binding energy of "bivalent cation – vacancy" for a $Mg_{Ga}`|V_O$ couple was found to be -0.90 kJ/mol, for a $Sr_{La}`|V_O$ couple – -0.01 kJ/mol [25], which can be a promising factor favoring an increase in the oxygen conductivity on introduction of strontium. The data of calculations [24] are in agreement with experimental transport numbers in gallates doped with strontium and magnesium, where a decrease in the oxygen transport numbers is noted for the systems containing only strontium compared to magnesium containing solutions (t_O 0.98 for $La_{0.9}Sr_{0.1}GaO_{3-\delta}$ and 0.92 for $LaGa_{0.85}Mg_{0.15}O_{3-\delta}$ at1073 K) [27].

An attention must be paid to a serious problem upon doping lanthanum gallate with alkaline-earth metals and magnesium only – the obtained samples are not single phase. Again in this case much depends on the conditions and methods of the synthesis and also on the very precursors.

Aside from the phase of gallate many researchers found admixed phases, such as $LaSrGaO_4$ and $LaSrGa_3O_7$ [8-11, 27-38], in all cases where the solubility of strontium is exceeded or close to the limit. By the data of [1] the limit of strontium solubility in $LaGaO_3$ is 10 at%. It is interesting to note that introduction of magnesium only up to 20 at% does not result in admixture phases [28]. An excess of magnesium results in the isolation of $La_4Ga_2O_9$, $LaSrGaO_4$, and $LaSrGa_3O_7$. As a rule the quantity of admixture phases is small and attains no more than 5%. The reason for their appearance is the instability of the structure of doped gallate, which, as has been shown above, can be accounted for by thermodynamics. That means that in general from energetic point of view the emergence of oxygen vacancies is unfavorable. The admixture phases being insulating to a large extent result in a decrease in the conductivity and in a decrease in the life time of a material. In some cases the admixture compounds were not detected [39].

1.2. Electron-Ionic Conductors Based on Lanthanum Gallate

At the same time in some works the effects of stabilization of the structure of lanthanum gallate doped with Sr and (or) Mg were found upon introduction of transition element ions [40, 41]. In the studies of conductivity much attention is being given to lanthanum gallates doped aside from strontium and magnesium with transition elements [4, 27, 34, 35, 42-54]. In this case we deal with electron-ionic conductors, which are interesting not only from applied point of view, but also from the point of view of fundamental studies. The main intriguing problem in this case is the separation of electronic and ionic components of conductivity, which is sometimes a very complicated problem. For elucidating the qualitative and quantitative regularities in the systems in question the most important seems to be the knowledge of their electron structure. This includes not only the valence and spin states of the atoms, but also their mutual influence and the special features of interatomic interactions. The changes in the type of conductivity on varying the qualitative or quantitative composition of conductors is directly associated with interatomic interactions and atom states in their structure. As for now the question about the electron structure of doped lanthanum gallate remains open, being partially solved on using the quantum chemistry calculations. There is an opinion that introduction of strontium together with a transition metal into $LaGaO_3$ results in a partial transition of trivalent element into a higher valence state, usually +4 [27, 43, 44, 55] and sometimes even +5 [45].

The conclusion about the change in the valence state of a transition element is made from indirect data: a decrease in the volume of the unit cell (since cations with greater charge have a smaller ionic radius [56]) [44], or an increase in the activation energy of ionic conductivity (compared to La(Sr) Ga(Mg)$O_{3-\delta}$), which is accounted for by strong Coulomb interactions between tetravalent metal cations and oxygen ions in the $M^{4+} - O - Mg^{2+}$ или $M^{2+} - O - M^{4+}$ clusters [27]. However, such explanations are open to question since the changes in the structural parameters may be associated also with clustering and with the formation of oxygen vacancies. The conclusion about the emergence of cations with the +4 charge on introduction of Sr and Mg is questionable also because in this case the conductivity had to decrease or totally disappear, however no such phenomena are observed. Moreover, the disproportionation of trivalent cations is very unprofitable (except for Mn^{3+}) for thermodynamic reasons. There is no unambiguous data directly pointing to an increase in the charge state of transition element atoms.

These rather urgent problems require unambiguous answers. In spite of a large body of data on this topic in their great majority the studies are empirical and random. The absence of systematic approach to the study of electron-ionic conductors within the context of "composition – structure – property" hampers the interpretation of experimental results and does not permit their generalization. The data about the electron structure would allow an insight into the problem of electronic and ionic conductivity of doped lanthanum gallates.

Several problems arise in selecting the qualitative and quantitative compositions of such electron ionic conductors.

1   What is the difference between lanthanum gallate and aluminate as a matrix for electron ionic conductors, aluminate would be much less expensive?

2   What must be the ratio between dia- (Sr and/or Mg) and paramagnetic (transition metal atoms) dopants to obtain the best electrophysical characteristics?

3   Which transition element would give the maximal ionic conductivity (a material for electrolytes) and which would result in the mixed electron-ionic conductivity (a material for cathodes)?

4   What is the reason for the stabilizing effect of a transition element, if its transfer to the higher oxidation state would eliminate vacancies in the oxygen sublattice and hamper the ionic conductivity?

5   Why strontium was empirically selected as a doping element in the lanthanum sites instead of calcium or barium?

The solution of all these problems lies in the electron structure of doped lanthanum gallates.

1.3. Magnetic Dilution Method

There are now a large series of physical and chemical methods used for revealing the electron structure of inorganic compounds and oxide systems in particular. From our point of view the most universal method revealing the electron states and exchange interactions in inorganic compounds is magnetic susceptibility, in the case of solids it must be applied in the form of magnetic dilution method.

The magnetic susceptibility method had been developed in detail for coordination compounds [56, 57]. From the temperature dependencies of paramagnetic components of magnetic susceptibility and effective magnetic moments it is possible to find the valence and spin state of a paramagnetic atom in a complex compound, to describe the spin transitions, and with the help of Heisenberg – Dirack – van Vleck approach (HDVV) [57] to estimate the parameters of exchange interactions between paramagnetic atoms within clusters, even in very long chains or cyclic clusters [58, 59]. Interatomic interactions are indispensable in solids, and in addition they must be of various kinds – the interactions between nearest neighbors (short order) and along the whole crystal lattice (long order). It appears impossible to estimate the exchange interactions in magnetically concentrated solids owing to a large number of variables, saying nothing about the fact that the state of individual paramagnetic atoms remains completely obscure. Magnetic dilution method opens promising perspective in the field of studying the electron structure of solids. It consists of the study of magnetic susceptibility of diluted solid solutions of an oxide containing paramagnetic elements in an isomorphous diamagnetic matrix.

On studying a series of solid solutions with various contents of paramagnetic component by the method of static magnetic susceptibility we obtain the specific susceptibilities at 16 fixed temperatures for each solid solution within the interval 77-400 K. Then we calculate the paramagnetic components of magnetic susceptibility χ_M and effective magnetic moments μ_{eff}. As the result we have three types of dependencies.

1. The Dependence $\chi_M^{para} = F(x)$

The pattern of isotherms χ_M^{para} allows a conclusion to be derived about a prevailing character of magnetic interactions in the solid solution – antiferro- or ferromagnetic – over the whole concentration range, if the isotherm is simple (χ_M^{para} monotonously decreases or increases), or in a particular site, if it is complex and has inflection or extreme points.

2. The Dependence $\mu_{eff}^{x \to 0} = F(T)$

When extrapolating μ_{eff} to the infinite dilution ($x \to 0$) the characteristics of single paramagnetic atoms may be generally obtained, which in essence is a hypothetic idea, but the very method is important for determining the valence and spin state of paramagnetic atoms and the special features of interatomic interactions, if the effective magnetic moment deviates from the single atom value.

3. The Dependence $1/\chi_M^{para} = F(T)$

Temperature dependence of the inverse paramagnetic component of magnetic susceptibility $1/\chi_M^{para}$ provides the information about special features of interatomic interactions in the solid solution with a particular concentration.

Since the systems under our study are magnetically diluted we use the approach of diluted solution to describe the concentration dependencies of magnetic susceptibility.

The Diluted Solution Approach

A group of paramagnetic atoms (from two and more) linked by exchange interactions is further said to be a cluster from the point of view of magnetochemistry. In a series of solid solutions we can track the evolution of the cluster forms and their interactions on the basis of the examination of concentration dependencies of paramagnetic component of magnetic susceptibility.

We start on the assumption that the susceptibility χ of a system of interacting magnetic atoms in a diluted solid solution is a sum of susceptibilities of single atoms and of clusters χ_i according to their fraction a_i in the system (Equation 1). In terms of effective magnetic moments Equation 2 transforms into Equation 3, since μ_{eff} is not additive.

The fractions of clusters and single atoms are constant for each concentration of the solid solution and may be expressed as Equation 4.

$$\chi = \sum_i a_i \chi_i \tag{1}$$

$$\mu^2 = \sum_i a_i \mu_i^2 \tag{2}$$

$$\sum_j a_j = 1 \tag{3}$$

The susceptibilities of clusters can be calculated using the model of Heizenberg – Dirack – van Vleck (HDVV) [57].

Since the study includes at least 8-10 solid solutions with concentration varying from $x = 0.005 - 0.10$, the susceptibility is measured at about 16-20 fixed temperatures from 77-400 K, and in the diluted solutions the sizes of clusters rarely exceed 4 paramagnetic atoms, the number of experimental points allows a correct estimation of a_i and J_i on minimizing the function

$$\sum_i \sum_j (\chi^2_{ij\,(theory)} - \chi^2_{ij\,(experiment)})$$

,   (4)

here $\sum_i$ means summing up by all the concentrations and $\sum_j$ – summing up by all the temperatures.

Therefore we can estimate the exchange parameters and, what is more, the distribution of paramagnetic atoms in the solid solutions, which rarely obeys the statistic laws [60].

Moreover, if at the infinite dilution we do obtain single paramagnetic atoms, considering the concentration range of $x = 0 - 0.05$, where the formation of clusters containing more than two atoms is almost improbable, we receive the fraction of dimers. Using the formulae of statistical thermodynamics [60] we can calculate the mixing energy for our solid solutions as will be shown later.

The magnetic dilution method has some "drawbacks", which are the reason for its unpopularity. The first is the necessity to synthesize large series of solid solutions as close to equilibrium as possible with the aim of obtaining reproducible results (first of all necessary in the study of electro physical characteristics), which can be used in thermodynamic estimations. The second is the fact that the synthesis of solid solutions includes high temperature treatment, which results in some shifts in the composition, especially in the concentration of paramagnetic atoms. And the paramagnetic component of magnetic susceptibility is calculated per mole of metal atom, and an error in the composition, even as small as 2-3% results in the same error in calculation of χ_M.

That requires a thorough chemical analysis of obtained samples. No doubt, the study of magnetic dilution is always accompanied by X-ray and such physical methods as the electron paramagnetic (spin) resonance, and others wherever possible.

We emphasize, that electron-ionic conductors based on doped lanthanum gallate are just rather diluted by paramagnetic elements solid solutions. Therefore, the systematic study of magnetic dilution must be the method able to reveal their electron structure and answer the questions formulated above. With this aim in view a detailed study of several systems was carried out. First we undertook the study of the $La_{1-0.2x}Sr_{0.2x}M_xGa_{1-x}O_{3-\delta}$ sold solutions with various transition metals and fixed ratio M:Sr =5:1. The data obtained were compared to the systems containing no strontium and with the solid solutions based on $LaAlO_3$. The next step consisted in changing the ratio M:Sr to 2:1 and in introducing magnesium into gallium sites – $La_{1-0.5x}Sr_{0.5x}M_xGa_{1-x}O_{3-\delta}$, $LaM_xGa_{1-1.2x}Mg_{0.2x}O_{3-\delta}$, $LaM_xGa_{1-1.5x}Mg_{0.5x}O_{3-\delta}$, $La_{1-0.2x}Sr_{0.2x}M_xGa_{1-1.2x}Mg_{0.2x}O_{3-\delta}$. We also studied the solid solutions containing calcium and barium as a doping element. In a number of cases we studied the electrical properties of obtained solid solutions to correlate the data of electron structure with electrical performance.

2. Materials and Methods

All the solid solutions under study were obtained by ceramic procedure. In some cases, for example to obtain the complex solid solutions of the type of $La_{1-0.2x}Sr_{0.2x}M_xGa_{1-1.2x}Mg_{0.2x}O_{3-\delta}$ the sol-gel method was used. The starting substances were: special pure grade La_2O_3, Ga_2O_3 Mn_2O_3 and MgO (99.999%), analytical pure grade $SrCO_3$ (99.99%), NiO and CoO were obtained from analytical pure grade metal nitrates, chromium oxide – by thermal decomposition of $(NH_4)_2Cr_2O_7$. All the starting substances were checked for the absence of ferromagnetic impurities by magnetic susceptibility method.

2.1. Synthesis

The ceramic procedure included a thorough grinding of the mixture of starting oxides and carbonates in an agate mortar, pelleting, and sintering at 1450°C. The time of sintering (50 h) was determined by the data of X-ray analysis and from the measurements of magnetic susceptibility after 40, 50, and 60 h. The magnetic susceptibility remained constant after 50 h of sintering, which pointed to the fact that the distribution of dia- and paramagnetic doping elements in the lattice of $LaGaO_3$ was close to the equilibrium. The cobalt and nickel containing solid solutions were in addition sintered in flowing oxygen for 10 h, and the susceptibility being unchanged proved that the state of Co and Ni was constant.

The sol-gel method consisted of dissolving the oxide mixture in diluted HNO_3, adding citric acid and ethylene glycol to the solution neutralized to pH~7 with ammonium hydroxide. The highly dispersed powder was obtained after a slow (4°/min) decomposition of the obtained gel was pressed into pellets and sintered in air for 50 h at 1450°C. With the aim of being able to compare the data of both methods in every oxide system several samples were obtained by sol-gel method in addition to the ceramic procedure. The magnetic results coincided for both synthetic methods. The X-ray analysis was performed for every sample under study. The X-ray patterns were recorded on a Rigaku Miniflex II diffractometer, CuK_α emission. In the case of nickel containing solid solutions the anomalous thermal behavior of effective magnetic moments made us to study the temperature dependence of the structure of doped lanthanum gallate. Since the content of paramagnetic element can change during the sintering the chemical analysis of paramagnetic and diamagnetic doping elements was performed for all the solid solutions by method of atom emission spectroscopy with the inductive bonded plasma. The error of the determination of x in the solid solution formula did not exceed 3%.

2.2. Measurements of Magnetic and Electrical Characteristics

We measured the specific magnetic susceptibility of the solid solutions by Faraday method in the temperature range 77-400 K. The accuracy of relative measurements of specific magnetic susceptibility was 1%. We calculated the paramagnetic component of magnetic susceptibility. The diamagnetic corrections were introduced with regard to the susceptibility of lanthanum gallate matrix measured in the same temperature range as the samples under study. We recorded the spectra of electron paramagnetic resonance on an SEPR-2+KMYa (small-scale mobile measuring analytical complex). The operating frequency of the spectrometer was 9.29 GHz (X-diapason). The electrical properties of the solid solutions were studied by the method of impedance spectroscopy on an Impedancemeter-Z3000 in the temperature range 25-800°C and the frequencies from 1 MHz to 100 Hz.

We analyzed the impedance hodographs, separated the contributions of the volume and grain boundary components of the conductivity. The hodographs were interpreted in terms of the block approach with two equivalent electric schemes for low and high temperature regions. In all the cases we observed lower values of grain boundary component of conductivity at low temperatures and their leveling in the high temperature range. The obtained values were plotted as the dependencies of $\lg\sigma - 1/T$.

3. Results and Discussion

3.1. Lanthanum Gallate Doped with Strontium and Transition Elements with M:Sr = 5:1

Since on doping lanthanum gallate with strontium and transition elements the ratio M:Sr =5:1 is the most extensively used, we studied the solid solutions $La_{1-0.2x}Sr_{0.2x}M_xGa_{1-x}O_{3-\delta}$, varying $3d$-element – Cr, Mn, Co, Ni. The data on magnetic dilution were compared with the results for the solid solutions containing no strontium – $LaM_xGa_{1-x}O_3$.

3.1.1. Chromium Containing Systems

But first we compared the data on lanthanum gallate with lanthanum aluminate and used the chromium containing systems.

The reason was that chromium (III) is in $^4A_{2g}$ ground state, which makes the calculations within HDVV model the most unambiguous. The isotherms of paramagnetic component for both systems appeared to be alike (Figure 1a), but the plots of χ_{Cr} for gallate lie higher than for aluminate. The calculation of the fraction of dimer clusters showed (Figure 1b) that clustering in gallates is greater with a lower exchange parameter J (-12 cm^{-1} in LaGaO$_3$ vs -18 cm^{-1} in LaAlO$_3$) [70]. The calculation of the mixing energy in both matrices based on the fraction of dimer clusters [61, 62] by Equation 5:

$$\frac{\left(x - \dfrac{a_2 x}{2}\right)}{\dfrac{a_2 x}{z}\left(1 - 2x + \dfrac{a_2 x}{z}\right)} = \exp\left(-\frac{2W_{12}}{kT}\right)$$

$$(5)$$

where x is the concentration, a_2 – the fraction of dimers, W_{12} – the mixing energy of solid solution formation, z – the coordination number ($z = 6$ for perovskite), W_{12} is 12 kJ/mol for aluminate and 15 kJ/mol for gallate solid solution.

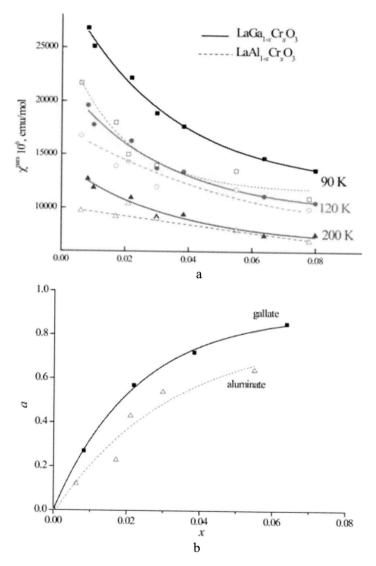

Figure 1. (*a*, *b*) The dependencies of paramagnetic components of magnetic susceptibility on chromium content on the $LaCr_xAl_{1-x}O_3$ and $LaCr_xGa_{1-x}O_3$ (*a*) and the fractions of dimer clusters in these systems (*b*).

Therefore we found that on passing from aluminate to gallate the clustering increases even without any diamagnetic heterovalent dopants. It is obvious that the enhancement of the aggregation in gallates is attributed to the increase in the covalent character of the M – O bond due to the reduced polarizing ability of gallium as compared to aluminum. The weakening of antiferromagnetic exchange is caused by the orthorhombic distortions in the gallate structure, which decrease the orbital overlapping.

The graphs for each $3d$-element in question show the isotherms of the paramagnetic term of the magnetic susceptibility $\chi_M - x$ for the solid solutions with and without strontium additives (Figure 2).

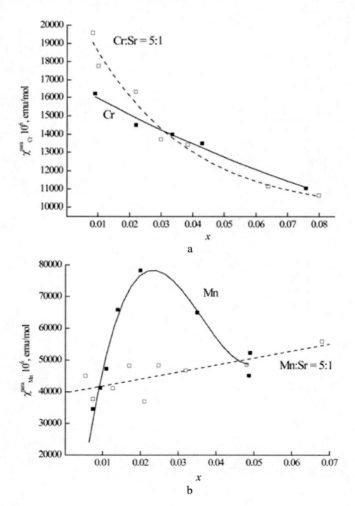

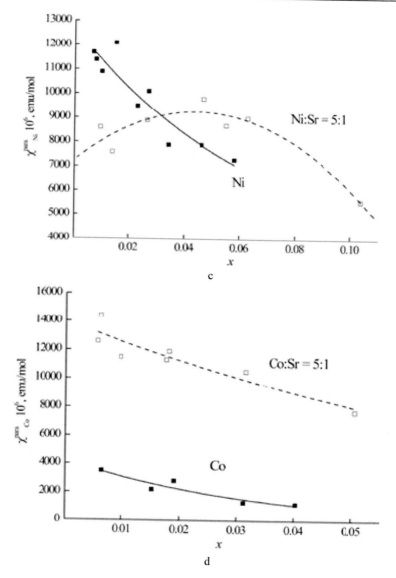

Figure 2. (*a, b, c, d*) The dependencies of paramagnetic components of magnetic susceptibility on transition metal content on the $LaM_xGa_{1-x}O_3$ and $La_{1-0.2x}Sr_{0.2x}M_xGa_{1-x}O_{3-\delta}$ for 140 K.

Except for the chromium containing samples, the isotherm patterns and the absolute values of the magnetic susceptibility significantly differ for the solid solutions $LaM_xGa_{1-x}O_3$ (M) and $La_{1-0.2x}Sr_{0.2x}M_xGa_{1-x}O_{3-\delta}$ (M:Sr = 5:1). Taking into account that the most concentrated solution contains only two Sr atoms per 98 La atoms, this circumstance is a crucial factor in the speculations on the causes of the structure stabilization.

First of all, let us look on the magnetic data for the solid solutions containing chromium. The fit of the magnetic susceptibility isotherms for the solid solutions $LaCr_xGa_{1-x}O_3$ and $La_{1-0.2x}Sr_{0.2x}M_xGa_{1-x}O_{3-\delta}$ within the entire concentration interval at $x > 0.02$ (Figure 2a) indicates that the chromium atoms are in the same state in both systems. Partial oxidation of Cr^{III} to Cr^{IV} should result in a decrease in magnetic susceptibility ($Cr^{III} - d^3$, $Cr^{IV} - d^2$), as it has been observed earlier for perovskite-like structures [63].

However, at very low concentrations of chromium the isotherm for the solid solutions containing strontium sharply goes up (over the whole temperature range). The effective magnetic moment for the infinite dilution ($x \rightarrow 0$) is higher than the spin only value for Cr(III) atom and increases with temperature.

This circumstance does not allow us to attribute it to the reduction of chromium to $Cr^{II} - {}^5E_g$ ground term. This may suggest that at infinite dilution in the systems containing strontium, disaggregation of chromium atoms is incomplete. The presence of clusters of chromium atoms at $x = 0$ indicates, first of all, that the energy of interatomic interactions in them is fairly high, more than 100 kJ/mol [64]. Emergence of such stable clusters in perovskite upon their doping with strontium along with a transition element indicates that strontium atoms are included into the clusters as, consequently, are the vacancies in the oxygen sublattice bonded with the strontium atoms. It is obvious that the appearance of clusters including transition element and strontium atoms and oxygen vacancies is responsible for the stabilization of the perovskite structure upon heterovalent doping. At this stage it appeared impossible to calculate the susceptibility of chromium containing system within the model of diluted solution. This will be done later.

3.1.2. Manganese Containing Systems

For the manganese containing systems, the extrapolation of χ_{Mn} (Figure 2b) and μ_{eff} values to infinite dilution ($x \rightarrow 0$) of the solid solutions $LaMn_xGa_{1-x}O_3$ and $La_{1-0.2x}Sr_{0.2x}Mn_xGa_{1-x}O_{3-\delta}$ gives the following values: $\mu_{eff} \sim 4.90$ BM (Mn^{III}) and $\mu_{eff} \sim 6.14$ BM, respectively [65]. For $x = 0$, μ_{eff} for the system containing Sr corresponds to the presence of only ~14% of Mn^{III} monomers and ~86% of dimers, obviously, $Mn^{II} - O - Mn^{IV}$ ($\mu_{eff} = 6.32$ BM, given $J >$ 100 cm^{-1}). The value of $\mu_{eff} \sim 8.49$ BM in the region of the maximum in the isotherm for $LaMn_xGa_{1-x}O_3$ is close to the value of μ_{eff} for the ferromagnetic tetramer $Mn^{II} - O - Mn^{IV} - O - Mn^{II} - O - Mn^{IV}$ (the ferromagnetic exchange can occur during disproportionation of Mn^{III}).

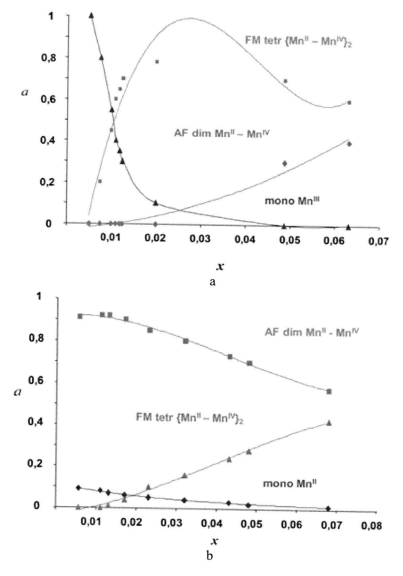

Figure 3. (a, b) Dependence of the aggregate contents on the concentration of manganese in solid solutions $LaMn_xGa_{1-x}O_3$ (a) and $La_{1-0.2x}Sr_{0.2x}Mn_xGa_{1-x}O_{3-\delta}$ (b).

Further decrease in the magnetic moment with the decreasing concentration indicates the appearance of antiferromagnetic interactions between tetramers along the axis z of of $LaGaO_3$ unit cell.

The calculation of magnetic characteristics for the $LaMn_xGa_{1-x}O_3$ system (Figure 3a) showed that the amount of tetramers with ferromagnetic exchange ($J \geq 40$ cm^{-1}) increases up to $x \sim 0.02$, with a sharp decrease in the content of dimers with $J \geq 100$ cm^{-1}. As the concentration increases, tetramers with antiferromagnetic exchange ($J \leq -30$ cm^{-1}) begin to make significant contribution.

In the case of strontium containing solid solutions, the calculation showed that the amount of monomers and dimers ($J \geq 100$ cm^{-1}) smoothly diminishes with the increase in concentration, whereas the amount of tetramers increases ($J \geq 40$ cm^{-1}) (Figure 3b).

It is obvious that the introduction of strontium into manganese containing lanthanum gallate results in the formation of very strong clusters formed from the manganese atoms and including strontium atoms and vacancies, which do not disintegrate even upon infinite dilution.

3.1.3. Cobalt Containing Systems

For the systems containing cobalt and nickel, the situation is more complicated because of a possibility of realization for these elements of high and low spin states. The non-zero values of χ_{Co} for Co^{III} and the values of effective magnetic moment at infinite dilution for nickel suggest the existence of spin equilibrium. Then, the following Equation 6 can be used for the calculation of magnetic characteristics [66, 67]:

$$\chi(T) = \frac{f_1\chi_1(T) + f_2\chi_2(T)e^{-\frac{\Delta E}{kT}}}{f_1 + f_2 e^{-\frac{\Delta E}{kT}}}, \tag{6}$$

where f_1 and f_2 represent the degree of state degeneracy with susceptibility χ_1 and χ_2, respectively, $\Delta E = E_2 - E_1$ – the energy gap between two ground states.

When χ_{Co} (Figure 2d) and μ_{eff} are extrapolated to infinite dilution, in the case of $LaCo_xGa_{1-x}O_3$ μ_{eff} increases from 1.90 to 2.43 BM, the values of μ_{eff} for $La_{1-0.2x}Sr_{0.2x}Co_xGa_{1-x}O_{3-\delta}$ are 3.32 – 3.87 BM [68]. The calculation showed that for $x = 0$ in the gallate doped with cobalt alone, only 20% of cobalt are in the spin state equilibrium $^1A_{1g} \leftrightarrow {}^5T_{2g}$, whereas 80% are in the low spin state.

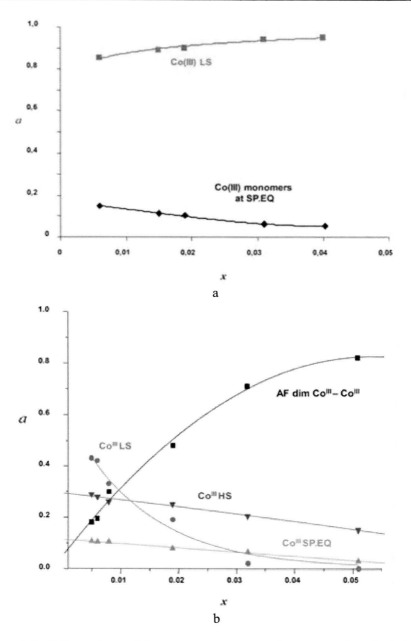

Figure 4. (*a*, *b*) Dependence of the aggregate contents on the concentration of cobalt in solid solutions $LaCo_xGa_{1-x}O_3$ (*a*) and $La_{1-0.2x}Sr_{0.2x}Co_xGa_{1-x}O_{3-\delta}$ (*b*).

For $La_{1-0.2x}Sr_{0.2x}Co_xGa_{1-x}O_{3-\delta}$ a similar calculation showed that at infinite dilution ~14% of cobalt are in the spin equilibrium, ~56% in the low spin state, and ~30% in the high spin state. The calculation of magnetic characteristics for $LaCo_xGa_{1-x}O_3$ showed the absence of high spin dimers (Figure 4a). Upon doping with strontium, as the concentration increases cobalt transforms to the high spin state and forms dimers with the exchange parameter $J \sim -80$ cm^{-1} (Figure 4b). In the ESR spectra of the solid solutions under study, only one line with $g = 4.3$ was observed, which corresponded to high spin Co^{III} [68, 69]. The introduction of strontium leads to the enhancement of clustering as well [68].

3.1.4. Nickel Containing Systems

The extrapolation of the isotherms χ_{Ni} (Figure 2c) to the infinite dilution ($x \rightarrow 0$) gives the value of $\mu_{eff} = 3.4 - 3.86$ BM for $LaNi_xGa_{1-x}O_3$. In the ESR spectra, a well resolved signal from low spin Ni^{III} with $g = 2.157$ is observed, the signal from Ni^{II} is absent. These data indicate that nickel at infinite dilution is in the spin state equilibrium. For $x = 0$, in the gallate doped with strontium some of Ni^{III} remains in the spin equilibrium, like in the pure $LaGaO_3$, whereas some (~58%) is in the low spin state. This is obviously related to Ni^{III}, which happens to be in the vicinity of Sr [71].

The calculation of exchange interactions for the gallate doped only with nickel showed that the antiferromagnetic exchange is due to the formation of dimers Ni^{III}(LS)–O–Ni^{III}(LS) ($J = -20$ cm^{-1}), rather than Ni^{III}(HS)–O–Ni^{III}(LS) (Figure 5a). When the gallate is doped with strontium, ferromagnetic dimers begin to play a major role in the exchange interactions Ni^{III}(HS)–O–Ni^{III}(LS) with $J = 10$ cm^{-1} (Figure 5b).

Thus, in the case of nickel the doping with strontium causes an increase in clusterization, as well.

The conductivity of the solid solutions in question increases as the temperature increases even in the region of low temperatures, which points to the semiconducting properties of the samples. The values of conductivity are low and depend on the content of a transition element. For the gallates doped only with a transition element, the dependence of the logarithm of specific electrical conductivity on the inverse temperature is linear and obeys Arrhenius equation. Two sections can be selected in the temperature dependencies of solid solutions containing strontium, in Arrhenius equation being valid in each of them. Different values of the activation energy for these two linear sections point to a different character (mechanism) of conductivity (Figure 6).

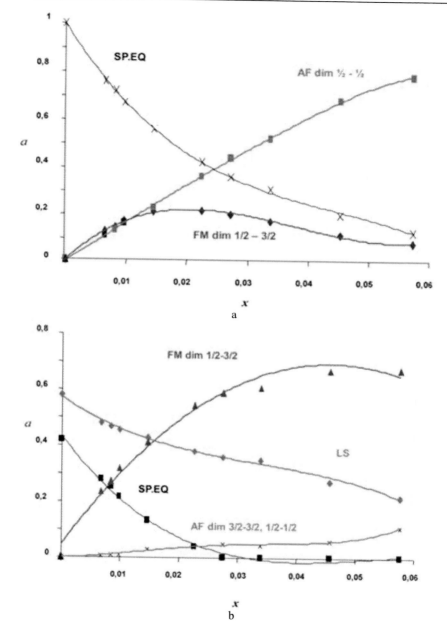

Figure 5. (*a*, *b*) Dependence of the aggregate contents on the concentration of nickel in solid solutions $LaNi_xGa_{1-x}O_3$ (*a*) and $La_{1-0.2x}Sr_{0.2x}Ni_xGa_{1-x}O_{3-\delta}$ (*b*).

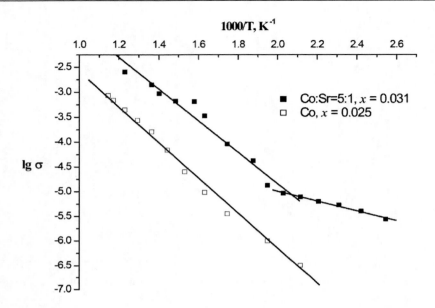

Figure 6. Dependencies of $\lg\sigma - 1/T$ for the systems with Co and Co:Sr = 5:1.

With the increase in temperature, ionic transition becomes more and more prominent. For the nickel containing systems, the conductivity became fairly high ($\lg\sigma > 0$) at $T > 500$ K.

To determine the nature of conductivity in a gallate doped with a transition element, band structure calculations (FLAPW GGA) for lanthanum gallate and lanthanum gallate in which one half of the gallium atoms was replaced with nickel ($LaGa_{0.5}Ni_{0.5}O_3$) were performed in the Institute of Solid State Chemistry of the Ural Branch of the Russian Academy of Sciences (Ekaterinburg). It was shown that the electronic conductivity in the solution appeared due to the fact that the band formed by the e_g-electrons of Ni^{III} is within the forbidden band of the pure lanthanum gallate (Figure 7a) [72]. In diluted solid solutions, this band obviously degenerates into the impurity level.

Summarizing the investigation of magnetic properties of lanthanum gallates doped with strontium and a transition element with the ratio M:Sr = 5:1, the following conclusions can be drawn. First of all, the introduction of strontium, obviously, is not associated with an increase in the oxidation state of the transition element; however, it leads to the enhancement of clusterization, with the composition of clusters and the character of exchange greatly differing for the systems containing strontium and without strontium.

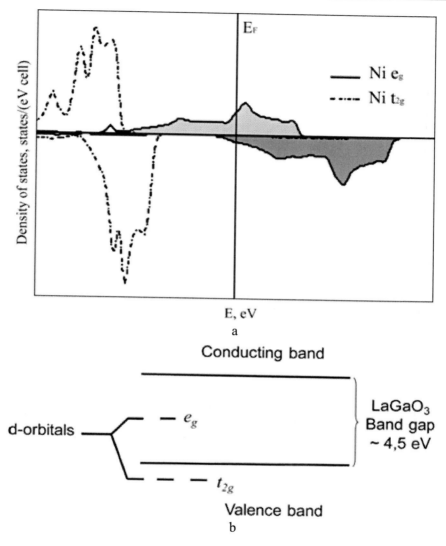

Figure 7. (*a*, *b*) Band levels for theoretical system $LaGa_{0.5}Ni_{0.5}O_3$ (*a*) and energy levels of d-orbitals and the band structure of $LaGaO_3$ (*b*).

Hence, it can be stated that strontium participates in the formation of clusters. The replacement of lanthanum with strontium results in the appearance of the oxygen vacancy in its vicinity.

By all accounts, two atoms of the *d*-element happen to be near the vacancy and strontium, forming a "cluster", which stabilizes the structure.

The band structure calculation data for lanthanum gallate doped with nickel [72] allows us to extend them to all the elements studied and schematically represent the process of gallate doping. Figure 7b shows the zones of the wide band gap semiconductor $LaGaO_3$, the d-level of the transition metal, which is split in the octahedral field, is within the forbidden band. Chromium(III) (t_{2g}^3) forms three holes in the lanthanum gallate valence band, resulting in the appearance of a weak hole conductivity. Cobalt in gallate can be in two states. The low spin cobalt with the configuration t_{2g}^6 has no free electrons. The high spin cobalt $(t_{2g}^4 e_g^2)$ in dilute solutions makes insignificant contribution to the electronic conductivity. Consequently, in the gallate doped with Sr and Co a predominantly ionic conductivity may be expected, which was confirmed experimentally. Nickel in gallate, like cobalt, is in two states: low and high spin Ni^{III}. One electron of low spin Ni^{III} $(t_{2g}^6 e_g^1)$ in the forbidden band of gallate accounts for the appearance of electronic conductivity. Manganese is entirely bound in very strong aggregates; therefore, relatively low conductivity can be expected in gallates doped with manganese. According to the data obtained (Figure 8), the conductivity of gallate with manganese without strontium turned to be even higher than with strontium.

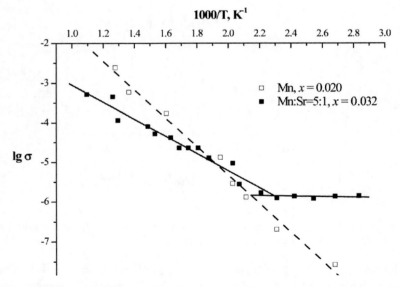

Figure 8. Dependencies $lg\sigma - 1/T$ for $LaMn_xGa_{1-x}O_3$ and $La_{1-0.2x}Sr_{0.2x}Mn_xGa_{1-x}O_{3-\delta}$ systems.

The data obtained allow us to recommend lanthanum gallate doped with strontium and nickel as a cathode for the solid oxide fuel cells due to the presence of, besides ionic, a considerable electronic conductivity. At the same time gallate doped with strontium and also with chromium and cobalt can serve as an electrolyte in the same cell, since their electronic conductivity is low, whereas the ionic (oxygen) conductivity increases in the sequence Mn < Cr < Ni < Co. Now two questions arise: 1) what happens as the fraction of strontium in the solid solutions increases; and 2) since in lanthanum gallate doped simultaneously with strontium and magnesium the ionic conductivity increases, what is the influence of magnesium or both strontium and magnesium on electron structure of doped lanthanum gallate containing also a transition element.

3.2. The Impact of the Increased Fraction of Strontium and Introduction of Magnesium on Electron Structure and Electric Properties of Doped Lanthanum Gallate

3.2.1. Chromium Containing Systems

For the system with the ratio Cr:Sr = 5:1 the isotherms of magnetic susceptibility coincided with the isotherms of the system containing no strontium starting from $x = 0.02$ [73], and for the $La_{1-0.5x}Sr_{0.5x}Cr_xGa_{1-x}O_{3-\delta}$ solid solutions the isotherms lie substantially higher (Figure 9), and at the infinite dilution the effective magnetic moment increases as the temperature increases (Figure 10).

At the infinite dilution the effective magnetic moments cannot be ascribed to the presence of single chromium atoms, no matter in which valence state it were:

Cr^{II}, d^4, ^5E_g, $\mu_{eff} \sim 4.90$ BM;
Cr^{III}, d^3, $^4A_{2g}$, $\mu_{eff} \sim 3.87$ BM;
Cr^{IV}, d^2, $^3T_{1g}$, $\mu_{eff} \sim 2.83$ BM.

An assumption naturally arises about strontium atoms and vacancies in the oxygen sublattice associated with them taking part in the formation of clusters of paramagnetic atoms in the solid solution.

In this case such clusters appear to be so strong that they do not disintegrate even at the infinite dilution, as is commonly observed in the solid solutions of isomorphous substitution, in the $LaCr_xGa_{1-x}O_3$ system [73].

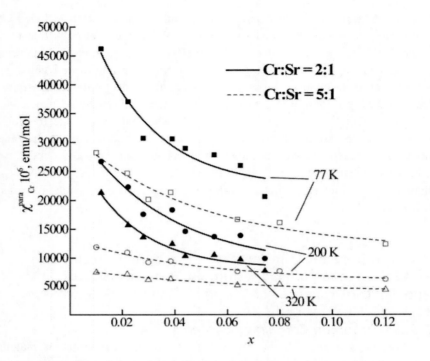

Figure 9. Concentration dependences of paramagnetic component of magnetic susceptibility calculated per 1 mole of chromium atoms for Cr:Sr = 5:1 and Cr:Sr = 2:1 systems at three temperatures.

In the doped $La_{1-0.2x}Sr_{0.2x}Cr_xGa_{1-x}O_{3-\delta}$ and $La_{1-0.5x}Sr_{0.5x}Cr_xGa_{1-x}O_{3-\delta}$ gallates we suggest the presence of single chromium atoms, antiferromagnetic Cr(III)–O–Cr(III) dimers, antiferromagnetic linear trimers, and certain large clusters with ferromagnetic exchange (clusters X), which are responsible for a non-typical temperature dependence of the effective magnetic moment at the infinite dilution (Figure 10) [73].

The final equation for calculating the theoretical susceptibilities according to the approach of diluted solution will look like:

$$\mu^2_{experim} = a_{cl\tilde{O}}\mu^2_{cl\tilde{O}} + a_{dim}\,\mu^2_{dim} + a_{trim}\mu^2_{trim} + (1 - \grave{a}_{cl\tilde{O}} - \grave{a}_{dim} - a_{trim})\mu^2_{mono} \quad (7)$$

here μ_{mono} is the spin only value of the effective magnetic moment of chromium(III), μ_{dim} and μ_{trim} were calculated for each temperature by HDVV model for two and three interacting atoms respectively [74].

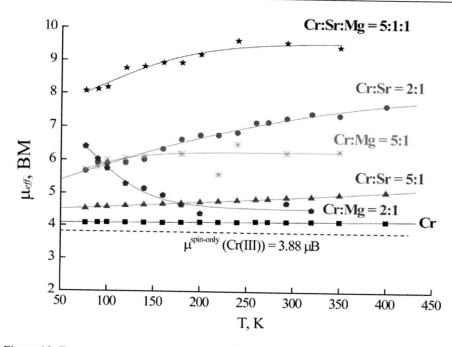

Figure 10. Temperature dependence of the effective magnetic moment at the infinite dilution for all chromium containing systems.

In this manner for an $S_1 = S_2 = 3/2$ couple with respect to $x = J_d/kT$ with $g_1 = g_2 = 2$ we obtain:

$$\mu_{dim}^2 = \frac{g^2}{2} \frac{84e^{12x} + 30e^{6x} + 6e^{2x}}{7e^{12x} + 5e^{6x} + 3e^{2x} + 1}.$$

(8)

The value of the exchange parameter J_d -12 cm^{-1} was taken from [70]. For a homonuclear trimer Cr(III)-O-Cr(III)-O-Cr(III) we have one exchange parameter J_t. The spin Hamiltonian without regard to Zeeman interaction and its eigenvalues are:

$$\hat{H} = -2J_t(\hat{S}_1 \hat{S}_2 + \hat{S}_1 \hat{S}_3)$$

(9)

$$E_t(J_t, S) = -J_t[S(S+1) - S_{23}(S_{23}+1) - S_1(S_1+1)],$$

(10)

where, according to the rules of the moment addition the total (S) and intermediate (S_{23}) spin take the values

$$S = S_1 + S_{23}, S_1 + S_{23} - 1, ..., |S_1 - S_{23}|, \tag{11a}$$

$$S_{23} = S_2 + S_3, S_2 + S_3 - 1, ..., |S_2 - S_3|. \tag{11b}$$

Using van Vleck's equation it is easy to obtain the final expression for the magnetic moment of three exchange bonded atoms $S_1 = S_2 = S_3 = 3/2$, with $g_1 = g_2 = g_3 = 2$, $y = J_t/kT$:

$$\mu_{trim}^2 = \frac{g^2}{3} \frac{247,5e^{21y}+126e^{18y}+52,5e^{15y}+141e^{12y}+52,5e^{11y}+15e^{10y}+1,5e^{7y}+15e^{6y}+52,5e^{5y}+1,5e^{3y}+15}{10e^{21y}+8e^{18y}+6e^{15y}+12e^{12y}+6e^{11y}+4e^{10y}+2e^{7y}+4e^{6y}+6e^{5y}+2e^{3y}+4} \tag{12}$$

The only difference from the case of dimers is in the fact that in the equation for the susceptibility we must sum up by the intermediate spin with the aim of taking into account the multiplicity of degeneration of the spin multiplates with the same values of the total spin.

Our calculations gave us the optimal value of the exchange parameter for the trimers J_t -20 см$^{-1}$.

Having neither the data on the structure of clusters X, nor the possibility to describe the dependence $\mu_{eff} = f(T)$ (Figure 10) with the help of HDVV model, when determining μ_{clX} we postulated that the effective magnetic moment at the infinite dilution for the system with the ratio of Cr:Sr = 2:1 is determined by clusters X only, i.e. their fraction is 1.

Then, as the calculation showed, the effective magnetic moments for the system with Cr:Sr = 5:1 is the superposition of 20% of clusters and 80% of monomers, which agrees with the difference in the ratio Cr:Sr for the systems under study. The data of calculation are given in Figure 11 *a, b*. The difference between theoretical and experimental magnetic susceptibilities for both systems does not exceed 2% (Figure 12, *a, b*).

We tried also to exclude one or other type of clusters – monomers, antiferromagnetic dimers or trimers, but this resulted in a substantial discrepancy between the data of theory and experiment (up to 7%), hence we concluded that the model of the structure of the solid solution we advanced is the most plausible [75].

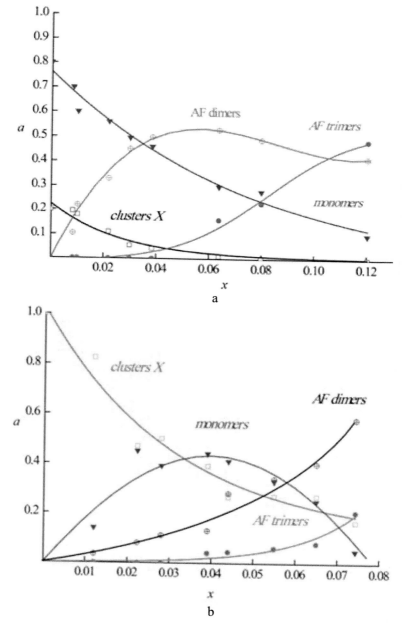

Figure 11. (*a, b*) Plots of the fractions of clusters and single atoms vs chromium concentration for the systems with various strontium content – $La_{1-0.2x}Sr_{0.2x}Cr_xGa_{1-x}O_{3-\delta}$ (*a*), $La_{1-0.5x}Sr_{0.5x}Cr_xGa_{1-x}O_{3-\delta}$ (*b*).

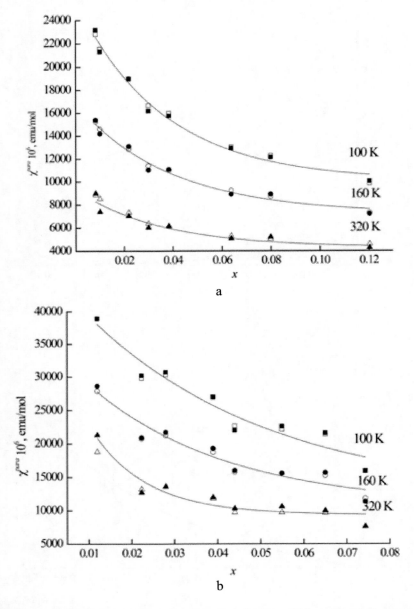

Figure 12. (*a*, *b*) Calculated (open symbol) and experimental (closed symbol) para-magnetic components of magnetic susceptibility: $La_{1-0.2x}Sr_{0.2x}Cr_xGa_{1-x}O_{3-\delta}$ (*a*) и $La_{1-0.5x}Sr_{0.5x}Cr_xGa_{1-x}O_{3-\delta}$ (b) for three temperatures.

Attention is drawn to some special features of the changes in the cluster fractions. For the solutions containing no strontium we have a typical pattern of antiferromagnetic dilution – as the concentration of a paramagnetic component increases, the fraction of monomers decreases monotonously, the fraction of antiferromagnetic dimers and trimers increases. As we introduce strontium in the ratio Cr:Sr = 5:1 the clusters X with competing antiferro- and ferromagnetic exchange appear along with monomers and dimers. Their fraction decreases as the chromium concentration in the solution increases (the same is true for monomers) (Figure 11 a). An increase in the content of strontium to the ratio Cr:Sr = 2:1 results in a relative increase in the fraction of clusters X and in a nonmonotonous change in the fraction of monomers in the solid solution (maximum at $x \sim 0.045$). As in two previous cases, as the concentration of chromium in the solution increases, the fraction of dimers and trimers increases (Figure 11 b). Such a trend has a sufficiently simple explanation.

1. The interval $0 < x < 0.045$. If at the infinite dilution ($x \to 0$) there remain only ferromagnetic clusters (Figure 12), taking into account the ratio Cr:Sr = 2:1 there will be a deficit of strontium atoms to form a real oxygen vacancy. Hence a "half" of a vacancy remains in the oxygen site, i.e. it must be an electron:

$$SrO + La_{La}^{x} + 1/2\,O_O^{x} \to Sr_{La}^{'} + 1/2V_O^{\bullet\bullet} + 1/2La_2O_3 ,$$

which can exist either in a couple with a "hole" $h^{+} \leftrightarrow \bar{e}$ of the type of Wannier-Mott exciton. As the quantity of strontium increases, the situation arises, when two strontium atoms are in the close vicinity, which results in the formation of an oxygen vacancy:

$$2SrO + 2La_{La}^{x} + O_O^{x} \to 2Sr_{La}^{'} + V_O^{\bullet\bullet} + La_2O_3 .$$

In this case a vacancy located between chromium atoms disrupts the integrity of the superexchange channel, which results in one of the chromium atoms ceases to take part in the exchange and behaves as a monomer. At the same time this decreases the relative number of clusters X. The fraction of dimers is insignificant in this region and comprises $\sim 10\%$ for $x \sim 0.045$.

2. The interval $0.045 < x < 0.075$. At the critical concentration ($x \sim 0.045$), when the fraction of monomers is maximal, the conditions are created for their further unimpeded aggregation not only into dimers, but also into trimers, their number monotonously increasing starting from $x \sim 0.045$. At this concentration the influence of strontium (by the formation of oxygen vacancies) becomes minimal, since the fraction of clusters X is small and remains almost constant up to $x = 0.075$.

As the result the fraction of antiferromagnetic dimers and trimers abruptly increases with regular decrease in the fraction of monomers, just as in the case of diluting typical antiferromagnets.

It is interesting that for the $La_{1-0.5x}Sr_{0.5x}Cr_xGa_{1-x}O_{3-\delta}$ solid solution the deviations from Curie-Weiss law are observed, which are typical for ferrimagnets. The bend in the plot of $1/\chi_{Cr}$ vs T shows itself in the region of low temperatures and becomes greater as the concentration of chromium increases (Figure 13).

The calculations of magnetization also point to the presence of highly nuclear clusters, their behavior having much in common with the behavior of super paramagnetic particles.

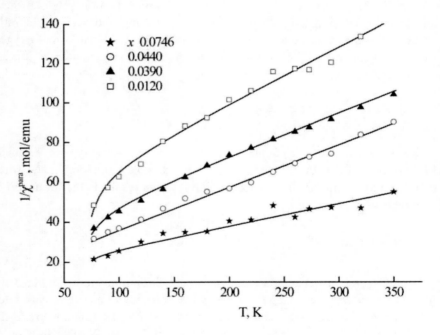

Figure 13. Plot of $1/\chi - T$ for $La_{1-0.5x}Sr_{0.5x}Cr_xGa_{1-x}O_{3-\delta}$.

The following requirements arise from the determination of super paramagnetic state for the experimental corroboration of its presence in the system under study: first, the absence of hysteresis in the magnetization curve, second, the superposition of magnetization curves obtained at various temperatures and plotted as M - H/T (Figure 14) [76-78]. The second requirement is not extended to the cases, when it appears impossible to neglect the interactions between super paramagnetic particles. In our case for diluted solutions we can state with certainty that there can be no interactions between such particles.

We can examine the character of magnetization at low temperatures with the help of the plots H/M - M^2 we considered Belov – Arrott plots (Figure15) [79].

The plots $H/M = f(M^2)$ must be linear and crossing the axis of ordinates at positive α for $T > T_c$ and at negative α for $T < T_c$. Zero value of the thermodynamic coefficient (α) corresponds to the temperature of magnetic ordering. In our case for all the compositions $\alpha > 0$ at low temperatures, which unambiguously points to the absence of spontaneous magnetization and, consequently, of long order magnetic order in the solid solutions.

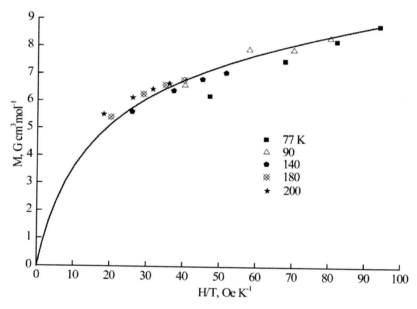

Figure 14. Superposition of magnetization curves for the Cr:Sr = 2:1 system $x = 0.0223$ at various temperatures and magnetic field strength.

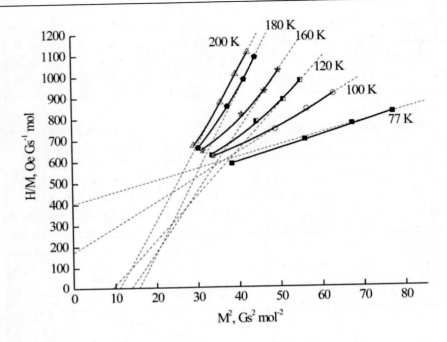

Figure 15. Belov – Arrott plots for the Cr:Sr = 2:1 solid solution, $x = 0.0223$.

Using the concept of superparamagnetism [80] we can estimate the average sizes of clusters and describe their magnetic properties [81, 82].

In the small fields just like for atomic paramagnetism we can write the equation for Langevin's function, which in a limiting case will turn into Curie – Weiss Equation 13.

$$\chi = M/H = M_0 M_s / 3k(T - \omega M_0 M_s / 3k) = C/(T - \Theta') , \qquad (13)$$

where M_0 – the magnetization of a cluster is determined by Equation 14:

$$M_0 = I_0 \int v G(v) dv = I_0 v_{av}, \qquad (14)$$

here v_{av} is an average size of the cluster, ω – the constant of intercluster interaction.

According to Equations 13 and 14 the calculation formula for determination of the sizes of ordered micro regions is the following (Equation 15):

$$r = \left\{ \frac{9kCM}{4\pi M_S I_o \rho} \right\}^{1/3}$$

(15)

where M is the molecular weight; ρ – the sample density. We used for our calculation the theoretical density taken as 4.23 g/cm^3.

We also used in our calculations a theoretical value of magnetization of saturation of a cluster substance $I_0 = 16700$ Gs·cm^3·mol^{-1}, which was determined by Equation 16:

$$I_0 = n\mu_B N_A,$$

(16)

where n – the number of electrons on a paramagnetic centre, μ_B – Bohr magneton, N_A – Avogadro number.

This estimation of the sizes of highly nuclear clusters is, of course, sufficiently rough, but it gives $r \approx 1 - 2$ nm.

A similar tendency, i.e. the dependence of susceptibility on magnetic field is observed for the whole series of the solid solutions. The obtained dependencies are similar for the solid solutions with various concentrations; hence we give them for one concentration only. In all the diluted solutions the hysteresis loop is absent. For more concentrated solutions coercive forces are small and do not exceed 0.12 Gs·cm^3·g^{-1}. All these facts allow us to consider the clusters formed in the system with Cr:Sr = 2:1 as super paramagnetic.

As we add to strontium as a doping element magnesium with the ratio Cr:Sr:Mg = 5:1:1 La$_{1-0.2x}$Sr$_{0.2x}$Cr$_x$Ga$_{1-1.2x}$Mg$_{0.2x}$O$_{3-\delta}$, the susceptibility isotherms appear to lie even higher than for the system with Cr:Sr = 2:1 described above (Figure 16).

Taking into account the fact that Mg occupies the sites of Cr and Ga rather than lanthanum as strontium does we had to suggest that other clusters with even stronger ferromagnetic exchange are formed in this system – clusters Y presumably containing the atoms of Cr, Mg, and accompanying vacancies (Figure 10).

In our HDVV calculations we took into consideration single chromium atoms, antiferromagnetic dimers, antiferromagnetic linear trimers, clusters X [74], and a new type of clusters – clusters Y.

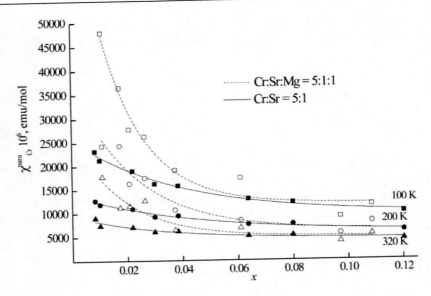

Figure 16. Concentration dependences of paramagnetic component of magnetic susceptibility calculated per 1 mole of chromium atoms for Cr:Sr:Mg = 5:1:1 and Cr:Sr = 2:1 systems at three temperatures.

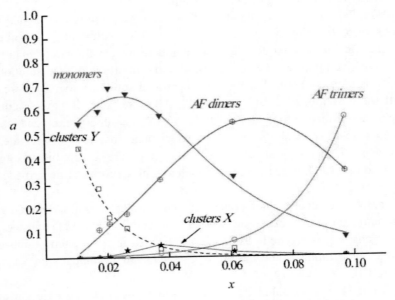

Figure 17. Plots of the fractions of clusters and single atoms vs chromium concentration for the $La_{1-0.2x}Sr_{0.2x}Cr_xMg_{0.2x}Ga_{1-1.2x}O_{3-\delta}$ system.

The influence of magnesium on the number of various clusters of chromium atoms can be traced upon comparing the concentration dependences of the cluster fractions for Cr:Sr:Mg = 5:1:1 systems (Figure 17).

The special features of the changes in the cluster fractions depend both on qualitative and quantitative composition of the system. For the solutions containing neither strontium nor magnesium, LaCr$_x$Ga$_{1-x}$O$_3$, we have a typical pattern of the dilution of antiferromagnets – as the concentration of paramagnetic component increases, the fraction of monomers decreases, the fraction of antiferromagnetic dimers increases [70].

The introduction of chromium and strontium into lanthanum gallate with the ratio Cr:Sr = 5:1 results in clusters X apart from monomers, dimers, and increasing fraction of trimers. These clusters X have no less than 4 paramagnetic atoms, are somehow associated with the vacancies in the sublattice of oxygen, and have a distinct ferromagnetic component in the exchange. The introduction of magnesium in addition to strontium results in some other clusters – clusters Y even greater than clusters X. Both types of clusters are preserved at the infinite dilution, but their fraction decreases as the concentration increases. This points again to the fact that strontium atoms and vacancies associated with them are included into these clusters with a strong bonding. We can assume that as concentration increases, the additional chromium atoms become located near the vacancies thus behaving like monomers, their fraction increasing as the concentration increases. Then the dimer and trimer clusters appear with antiferromagnetic exchange.

For the systems containing only magnesium as a diamagnetic doping element we also find the field dependent susceptibility over the whole temperature range (Figure 18). And again the magnetization vs H/T curves and positive coefficients α point to the absence of spontaneous magnetization, thus suggesting super paramagnetic behavior of the systems with Cr:Mg = 5:1 and Cr:Mg = 2:1. An estimation of the sizes of clusters (clusters Y) give $r \sim 1.1 - 1.5$ nm. The values of μ_{eff} and their temperature dependencies at the infinite dilution (Figure 10) point to the presence of clusters and the absence of chromium atoms in a higher oxidation state. Magnesium as well as strontium may give rise to oxygen vacancies and electrons at the sites of vacancies [83].

$$MgO + Ga_{Ga}^\times + 1/2\, O_O^\times \rightarrow Mg_{Ga}^{'} + 1/2\, V_O^{\bullet\bullet} + 1/2\, Ga_2O_3, \quad 1/2\, V_O^{\bullet\bullet} \equiv e$$

Migration of electrons from one paramagnetic site to another must result in a strong ferromagnetism, which we observe at the infinite dilution.

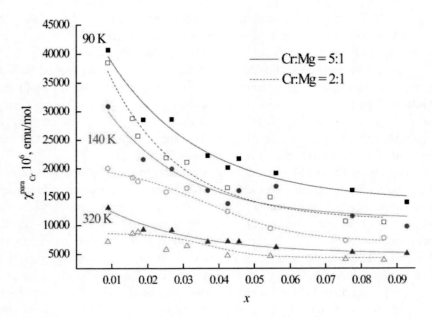

Figure 18. Plots of magnetic susceptibility vs x for the $LaCr_xGa_{1-1.2x}Mg_{0.2x}O_{3-\delta}$ (Cr: Mg=5:1) and $LaCr_xGa_{1-1.5x}Mg_{0.5x}O_{3-\delta}$ (Cr:Sr=2:1) systems.

The special features of the systems under study are directly associated with both qualitative and quantitative composition. A variation of one parameter only (concentration or the nature of the substituent) results in irreversible changes in the system as a whole, which are associated with complex and manifold interactions between separate atoms and their aggregates.

Let us see how this concept works in other transition element containing systems.

3.2.2. Nickel Containing $La_{1-0.5x}Sr_{0.5x}Ni_xGa_{1-x}O_{3-\delta}$, $LaNi_xGa_{1-1.2x}Mg_{0.2x}O_{3-\delta}$ and $LaNi_xGa_{1-1.5x}Mg_{0.5x}O_{3-\delta}$ Systems

Magnetochemical behavior of these systems has a lot in common, hence we shall consider them in one paragraph. A similarity in the behavior shows itself in a similar character of the isotherms of paramagnetic component of magnetic susceptibility. For the systems with the ratios Ni:Sr = 2:1, Ni:Mg = 5:1, and Ni:Mg = 2:1 the susceptibility monotonously increases in the region of small nickel concentrations and is almost constant in a more concentrated region (Figures 19, 20).

A comparison between these systems and the system with Ni:Sr = 5:1 shows two substantial differences: first, in the systems with magnesium and with greater quantity of strontium local extremes are absent over the whole concentration interval, whereas in the system with Ni:Sr = 5:1 a distinct maximum is observed at $x \sim 0.045$, second, the susceptibilities are essentially smaller than for Ni:Sr = 5:1.

As has been shown earlier [71], for the system with Ni:Sr = 5:1 the effective magnetic moments at the infinite dilution were described as a superposition of effective magnetic moments of low spin nickel(III) and of nickel(III) in the state of spin equilibrium.

On the basis of the ideas about mutual influence of dia- and paramagnetic atoms in the Ni:Sr = 2:1, Ni:Mg = 5:1, and Ni:Mg = 2:1 systems we can expect some shift in the spin equilibrium resulting in an increase in the quantity of low spin nickel(III).

We emphasize that for the Ni:Mg = 5:1 system such a tendency is typical owing to magnesium atoms being located in gallium sites of perovskite structure in distinction to strontium, therefore its depolarizing effect on nickel atoms must be stronger.

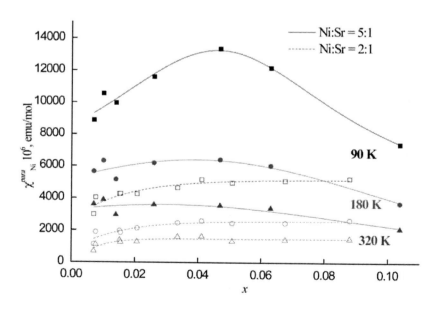

Figure 19. Plot of paramagnetic components of magnetic susceptibility vs nickel content for the systems with Ni:Sr = 5:1 and Ni:Sr = 2:1 at three temperatures.

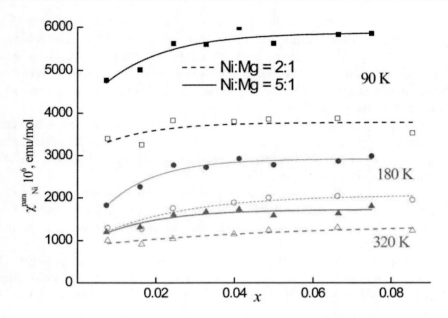

Figure 20. Plot of paramagnetic components of magnetic susceptibility vs nickel content for the systems with Ni:Mg = 5:1 and Ni:Mg = 2:1 at three temperatures.

Let us try to make sense of such an unconventional behavior of these three systems based on lanthanum gallate examining the possible cases of interatomic interactions and various valence states of nickel.

1. *The formation of Ni^{IV} in the quantity equivalent to the quantity of introduced heterovalent substituent.*

Such a situation is possible taking into account the opinions published by this moment in literature [27, 55, 84, 85]. Looking at Figure 21 we see that the values of μ_{eff} at the infinite dilution are much lower than 1.8 BM typical for low spin isolated atoms of Ni^{III}.

Assuming that these low values are associated with some fraction of diamagnetic particles [Ni^{IV} must be low spin] we find that the fraction of Ni^{IV} in all these three systems varies between 50 and 70%, which is impossible in terms of the mole ration of nickel and a substituent.

2. *Disproportioning of Ni^{III}.* We can address ourselves to the process of disproportionation resulting in two forms – Ni^{IV} and Ni^{II}, for Ni^{II} the diamagnetic state being not excluded in the square planar surrounding, when oxygen vacancies are in axial position.

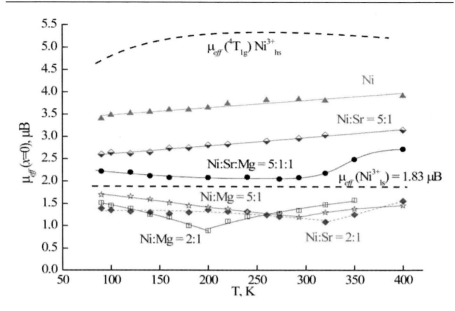

Figure 21. Temperature dependence of the effective magnetic moments at infinite dilution for all the nickel containing systems.

The idea of disproportioning is interesting since, at first sight, it can adequately account for the local maxima in the plots $1/\chi_{Ni} - T$, which appear at very low concentrations of the dopant (Figure 22 a, b, c).

For all three cases we have two anomalies in the temperature dependencies in the region of $T \sim 180$ and 300 K. One of them, about 180 K may be accounted for by the transfer $Ni^{II}_{dia} \rightarrow Ni^{II}_{para}$. However, an attempt to represent the effective magnetic moments at the infinite dilution as a superposition of the moments of nickel (II, III, IV) and possible clusters of the type $Ni^{III}(LS)-Ni^{II}$ does not agree with the experimental data. In this case it is worth while to note that in the EPR spectra only one wide line was observed attributed to the clusters of low spin Ni^{III}.

Possible location of nickel and doping diamagnetic atoms in the case of nickel disproportionation in the solid solutions.

After receiving the data on thermal X-ray for the Ni:Sr = 2:1, Ni:Mg = 5:1, and Ni:Mg = 2:1 systems (Figure 23) the hypothesis of disproportioning appears even less convincing, since in the range 320-330 K an abrupt phase transition occurs. This transition is temperature reversible and is the reason for one of the anomalies in the plots of inverse susceptibility vs temperature for diluted solid solutions.

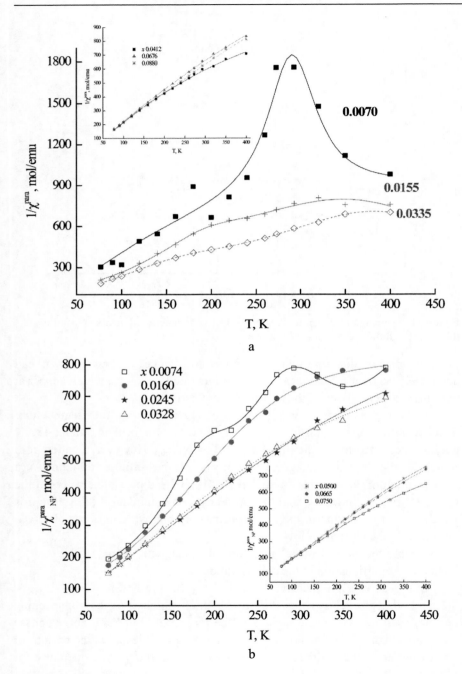

Figure 22. (Continued).

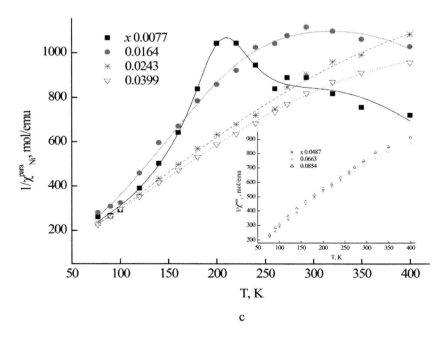

c

Figure 22. Plots of inverse susceptibility vs temperature for various systems and concentrations of the solid solutions : (*a*) Ni:Sr = 2:1 (in the insert – *x* = 0.0412; 0.0676; 0.0880); (*b*) Ni:Mg = 5:1 (in the insert – *x* = 0.0500; 0.0665; 0.0750); (*c*) Ni:Mg = 2:1 (in the insert – *x* = 0.0483; 0.0663; 0.0854).

We must bear in mind the fact that for more concentrated samples the anomalies also exist, but their absence in the plots must be associated with an increase in the fractions of low dimension clusters (as it was in chromium containing systems), which results in averaging of the susceptibility.

This structural transition from rhombohedral to orthorhombic syngony [86] occurs as the temperature increases and can result in an additional low spin nickel atoms appearing in the solution or in an increase in the crystal field splitting.

3. *Formation of high-nuclearity clusters.* To develop our ideas about this topic we must recall the situation with chromium containing systems, where we observed an increase in clustering of paramagnetic atoms as the concentration of heterovalent diamagnetic substituents in lanthanum gallate increased. Clustering is attested by non typical dependencies of effective magnetic moment at the infinite dilution, which cannot be described in terms of the theory of isotropic exchange of Heizenberg-Dirack-van-Vleck.

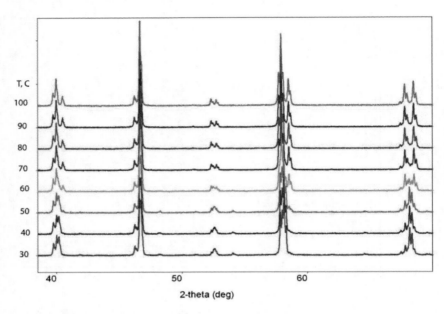

Figure 23. Thermal X-ray patterns of the samples Ni:Sr = 2:1 ($x = 0.0122$) and Ni:Sr:Mg = 5:1:1, ($x = 0.0531$).

In this case, judging from the absolute values of magnetic moment (Figure 21) in all the compositions the ferromagnetic component of the exchange exceeds the antiferromagnetic component, and we observe an abrupt increase in μ_{eff}. This may be accounted for by the fact that the distortions of the surrounding of chromium atoms resulting from the presence of vacancies of heterovalent dopants decreases the overlapping between t_{2g}-orbitals of Cr^{III} and p-orbitals of oxygen, thus decreasing the antiferromagnetic component in the exchange. Ferromagnetic exchange is not associated with orbital overlapping.

As opposed to Cr^{III}, Ni^{III} in any spin state has e_g-electrons. It is just these d_{z2} and d_{x2-y2} orbitals directly overlap with p-orbitals of oxygen atoms, and as a consequence, a strong antiferromagnetic exchange results.

Therefore, we can suggest with certainty that at the infinite dilution for nickel containing systems, where the effective magnetic moment is much lower than 1.83 BM and the character of their temperature dependence is also non typical, there are clusters of high nuclearity with competing antiferro- and ferromagnetic exchange, but antiferromagnetic component appears to prevail, thus substantially decreasing the effective magnetic moments.

3.2.2.1. Nickel Containing $La_{1-0.2x}Sr_{0.2x}Ni_xMg_{0.2x}Ga_{1-1.2x}O_{3-\delta}$ System

This system differs from all the nickel containing solid solutions. From temperature dependence of effective magnetic moment at the infinite dilution we can see that the character of the dependence is non monotonous. There is a moderate decrease in μ_{eff} from 2.4 to 2.1 BM in the temperature range 77-300 K and an abrupt increase after 300 K. This anomaly is associated with the structural phase transition mentioned above (Figure 24).

In this system the effective magnetic moments seem to be well described by the ideas about the existence of single Ni^{III} atoms. However the situation is more complicated. We deal with clusters of high nuclearity, but in distinction to the systems with Ni:Sr = 2:1, Ni:Mg = 5:1 (2:1) upon simultaneous introduction of strontium and magnesium ferromagnetic exchange channels begin to play greater role thus increasing the effective magnetic moment. A similar situation was observed for the Cr:Sr:Mg = 5:1:1 system, where we observed the greatest magnetic moments of all the system under study.

By and large, as the concentration of nickel increases, the greater number of antiferromagnetic dimers of low spin nickel are formed, which determines the shape of isotherms in Figure 24.

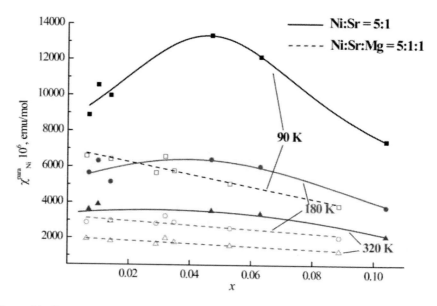

Figure 24. Concentration dependence of paramagnetic component of magnetic susceptibility for the Ni:Sr = 5:1 and Ni:Sr:Mg = 5:1:1 systems at three temperatures.

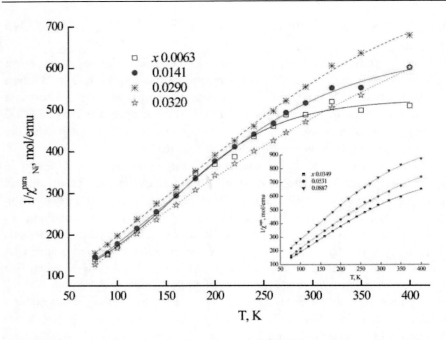

Figure 25. Plots of inverse susceptibility vs temperature for $La_{1-0.2x}Sr_{0.2x}Ni_xGa_{1-1.2x}$ $Mg_{0.2x}O_{3-\delta}$ for various concentrations (in the insert for $x = 0.0349; 0.0531; 0.0887$).

We observe no local maxima in the dependence of inverse susceptibility on temperature, only the deviations from Curie – Weiss law at high temperatures typical for temperature independent paramagnetism (Figure 25).

3.2.3. Systems $LaCo_xMg_{0.2x}Ga_{1-1.2x}O_{3-\delta}$ and $LaCo_xMg_{0.5x}Ga_{1-1.5x}O_{3-\delta}$

An interesting feature of these systems is the dependence of susceptibility on the magnetic field strength for the whole concentration interval. Such a phenomenon we observed upon magnetic dilution of lanthanum gallate containing chromium, magnesium and(or) strontium (see 3.2.1 and [74, 75, 83]). This dependence testifies for the presence of highly nuclear clusters of paramagnetic atoms in magnetically diluted systems rather than for long magnetic order.

As has been shown earlier for chromium containing systems, the sizes of clusters attain 1-1.5 nm, i.e. they contain no less than 20 paramagnetic atoms. Moreover, the examination of magnetization suggests a super paramagnetic behavior of our systems.

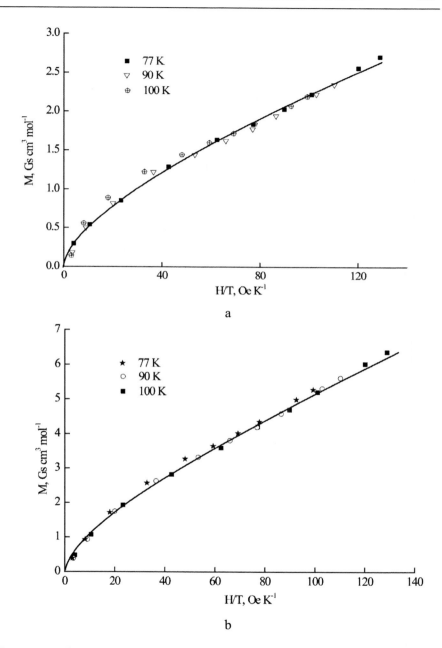

Figure 26. (*a*, *b*) Plots of molar magnetization vs *H/T* for LaCo$_x$Mg$_{0.2x}$Ga$_{1-1.2x}$O$_3$: (*a*) *x* = 0.0165; (*b*) *x* =0.0845.

From Figure 26 (*a*, *b*), where the dependence of molar magnetization on H/T is given, it is seen that the magnetizations at various temperatures and fields coincide. This is one of two requirements of superparamagnetism.

Belov – Arrott plots testifies for the absence of spontaneous magnetization in our systems, since the thermodynamic coefficient α is positive everywhere (Figure 27 *a*, *b*).

Therefore we may assume that in these systems as in chromium containing systems there exist the clusters of high nuclearity.

To calculate the paramagnetic component of magnetic susceptibility we used the values of specific susceptibility extrapolated to infinitely high field strength ($1/H = 0$). The inverse paramagnetic component vs temperature were plotted for the Co:Mg=5:1 and Co:Mg=2:1 systems respectively (Figures 28 (*a*, *b*)).

These dependencies demonstrate a deviation from Curie-Weiss law at low and at high temperatures. The deviations at high temperatures are typical for a contribution of temperature independent paramagnetism, most probably Pauli paramagnetism of conductivity electrons, since it increases as the cobalt concentration increases in the solid solutions, i.e. as the concentration of e_g electrons in the forbidden band of lanthanum gallate increases.

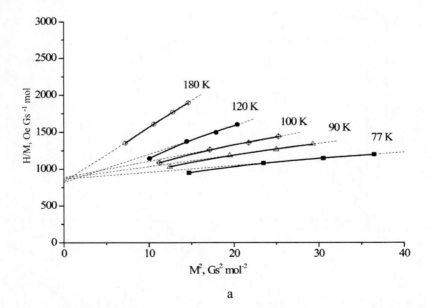

Figure 27. (Continued).

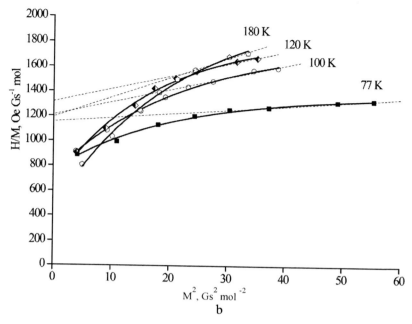

b

Figure 27. (*a, b*) Belov – Arrott plots for (*a*) LaCo$_x$Mg$_{0.2x}$Ga$_{1-1.2x}$O$_3$ x = 0.0165; (*b*) La Co$_x$Mg$_{0.5x}$Ga$_{1-1.5x}$O$_3$: (*a*) x = 0.0359.

The deviations of the dependencies from Curie – Weiss law at low temperatures seem to be determined by the character of exchange interactions between cobalt atoms and are typical for ferrimagnets. This is the first indication to a certain competition of ferro- and antiferromagnetic exchange interactions with those first prevailing.

Concentration dependencies of paramagnetic component and temperature dependencies of the effective magnetic moment are given in Figures 29 and 30 respectively.

The isotherms of paramagnetic susceptibility show that the exchange interactions in our solid solutions are antiferromagnetic. But it must be emphasized that the isotherms lie essentially higher than for the samples containing no magnesium and the higher, the higher is magnesium content in the system.

Temperature dependencies of the effective magnetic moment extrapolated to the infinite dilution and their comparison with the LaCo$_x$Ga$_{1-x}$O$_3$ and La$_{1-0.2x}$Sr$_{0.2x}$Co$_x$Ga$_{1-x}$O$_3$ systems described earlier are the most interesting for conclusions about the states of cobalt atoms and exchange interactions between them.

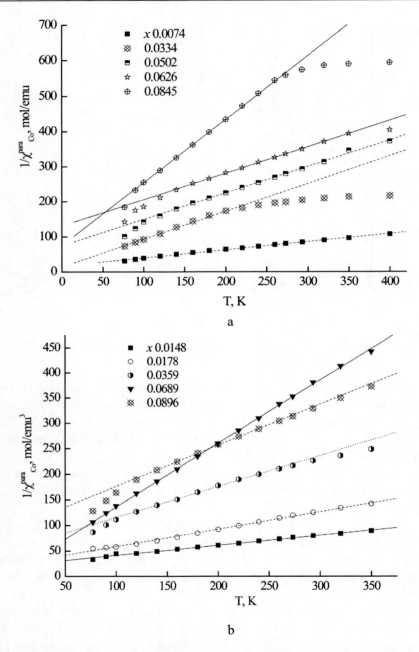

Figure 28. (*a*, *b*) Temperature dependence of inverse paramagnetic susceptibility for (*a*) $LaCo_xMg_{0.2x}Ga_{1-1.2x}O_3$ and (*b*) $LaCo_xMg_{0.5x}Ga_{1-1.5x}O_3$.

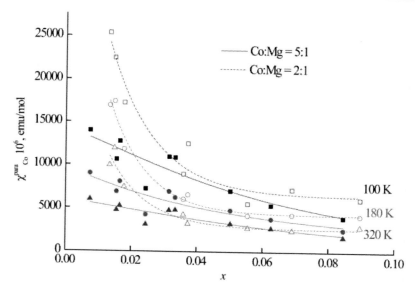

Figure 29. Concentration dependencies of paramagnetic component of magnetic susceptibility for $LaCo_xMg_{0,2x}Ga_{1-1,2x}O_3$ and $LaCo_xMg_{0,5x}Ga_{1-1,5x}O_3$ at three temperatures.

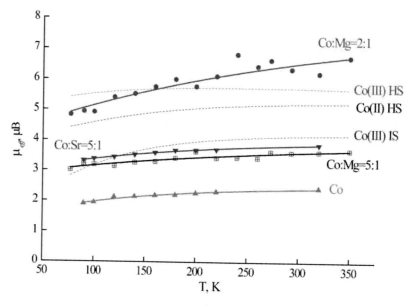

Figure 30. Temperature dependencies of the effective magnetic moment at the infinite dilution for various cobalt containing lanthanum gallate systems.

In Figure 30 the theoretical dependencies of magnetic moments for single cobalt atoms in the oxidation states 2 and 3 are given and also the dependencies for Co^{III} in various spin states.

The matter is that for Co^{III} in an octahedron of oxygen atoms three ground states can exist: $S = 0$, $^1A_{1g}$ – low spin, $S = 2$, $^5T_{2g}$ – high spin, and given substantial distortions in the nearest surrounding, which can be expected in our systems due to the vacancies and larger magnesium atoms in the same sites as cobalt, the state with the intermediate spin $S = 1$, $^3T_{1g}$ [65].

As is seen from Figure 30, for the system with Co:Mg = 2:1 the effective magnetic moment cannot be described as belonging to single cobalt atoms, no matter in which valence state there were. Its values lie higher, especially at high temperatures.

For the systems with Co:Mg = 5:1 the effective magnetic moments lie lower and almost coincide with the values obtained for the systems containing strontium (Sec. 3.1.3). Those latter were described as belonging to single cobalt atoms partially in the low spin state and partially in the state of spin equilibrium (low spin – high spin). However we cannot describe the systems with magnesium using the same approach, since there is the dependence of susceptibility on the field strength.

The dependence of susceptibility on the field strength appears as the result of the solid solution synthesis, but is not the result of introducing some ferromagnetic admixtures. A similar dependence was observed for the $La_{1-0.2x}Sr_{0.2x}Cr_xGa_{1-1.2x}Mg_{0.2x}O_{3-\delta}$ solid solutions (Sec. 3.2.1). therefore it is an integral property of our systems.

This means that in our solid solutions with the ratio Co:Mg = 2:1, where it is evident, and even with the ratio Co:Mg = 5:1 at the infinite dilution sufficiently large clusters of cobalt atoms are preserved, the interaction between them being predominantly ferromagnetic with a certain contribution of antiferromagnetic exchange.

These clusters must contain also magnesium atoms and vacancies in the oxygen sublattice accompanying them.

For cobalt atoms such a situation may be associated with the fact that in the vicinity of magnesium atoms and vacancies inevitably appear the distortions in the cobalt surrounding resulting in its transfer to the state with the intermediate spin. The neighboring cobalt atoms appear to be high spin and the exchange between two such neighbors appear to be ferromagnetic.

3.3. Lanthanum Gallate Doped with Chromium and Calcium or Barium

We studied lanthanum gallate doped with chromium, but as a diamagnetic doping element were taken calcium or barium – $La_{1-0.2x}A_{0.2x}Cr_xGa_{1-x}O_{3-\delta}$ where A = Ca or Ba. The isotherms of paramagnetic component of magnetic susceptibility appear to lie higher than the isotherms for strontium containing systems.

In the plots of inverse susceptibilities vs temperature the deviations from Curie – Weiss law are observed at low temperature pointing to the ferromagnetic behavior of these systems, just as we met for magnesium containing systems and for the increased strontium content. The effective magnetic moments extrapolated to the infinite dilution are given in Figure 31.

It is seen that we have the increased magnetic moments for both calcium and strontium containing systems, which, together with the temperature dependencies of inverse susceptibility, points to the presence of clusters with competing ferro- and antiferromagnetic exchange, ferromagnetic exchange prevailing.

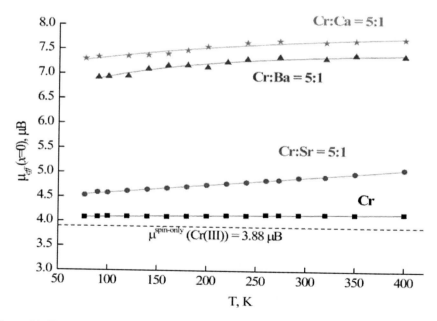

Figure 31. Temperature dependencies of the effective magnetic moment at the infinite dilution for $La_{1-0.2x}A_{0.2x}Cr_xGa_{1-x}O_{3-\delta}$ (A = Ca or Ba) systems.

The reasons for such a nonmonotonous behavior of the solid solutions upon varying the diamagnetic heterovalent doping element seem to be the following. On passing along the series Ca – Sr – Ba the size of A atom in the solid solution formula $La_{1-0.2x}A_{0.2x}Cr_xGa_{1-x}O_{3-\delta}$ increases, therefore the ionicity of A-O bond also increases, thus decreasing the ionicity of Cr-O bond. An increased covalence of the Cr-O bond results in an increased overlapping of d-orbitals with p-orbitals of oxygen. This last circumstance must result in an increase in antiferromagnetic exchange and enhancement of clustering in barium containing systems. In contrast to this in calcium containing systems, where Cr-O bond has a more ionic character, clustering must be lower, but the exchange may substantially more ferromagnetic, which shows itself in greater effective magnetic moments. This means that we have two factors acting in opposite directions.

We may suggest with certainty that it is in the case of strontium an optimal relationship between the size of clusters and sufficiently strong ferromagnetic exchange is achieved, which is responsible for the stability of the system as a whole. This seems to be the reason for using strontium as a diamagnetic doping element in SOFC.

3.4. Conductivity in the Systems with Magnesium and an Increased Content of Strontium

3.4.1. Chromium Containing Systems

For all the systems under study given low concentrations of the doping elements a break is observed in the plots lg $\sigma - T^{-1}$. The activation energy changes, which testifies for a change in the mechanism of the charge transfer: at low temperatures the electronic component of conductivity prevails, at high temperature the ionic conductivity switches on. An example for chromium containing systems is given in Figure 32. According to the data of thermal X-ray analysis this break is not associated with any polymorphic transformations and structural transitions.

An abrupt change in the mechanism of the charge transfer is observed in all cases for the most diluted solutions, since only in this concentration range the main role in conductivity is played by the highly nuclear clusters of chromium atoms including the oxygen vacancies in their composition. Coulomb field of clusters undoubtedly determine the whole energetics of the process of charge transfer for ionic conductivity (the typical energy for oxygen ion migration is 0.70 eV).

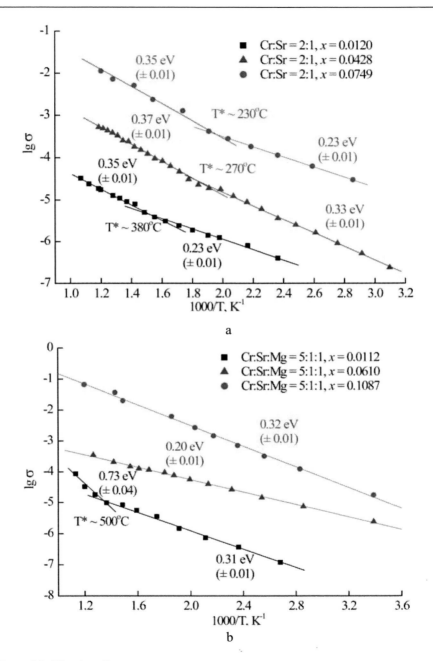

Figure 32. (Continued).

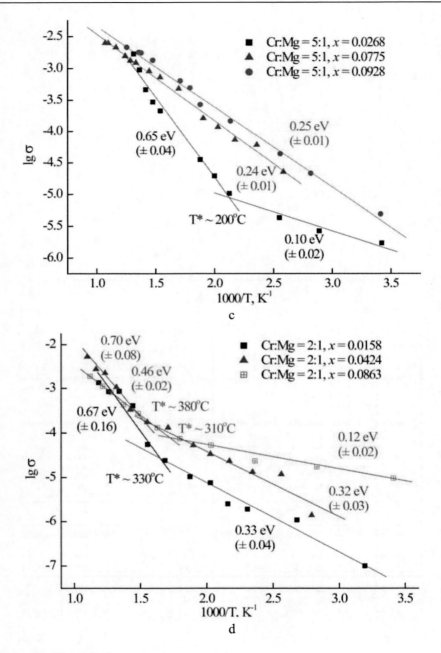

Figure 32. (Continued).

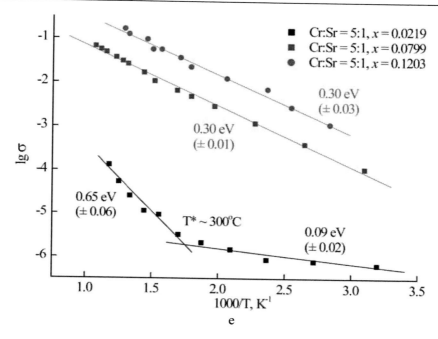

Figure 32. (*a*, *b*, *c*, *d*, *e*) Plots of logarithm of the total conductivity vs inverse temperature for various chromium containing systems and various concentrations of the solid solutions.

3.4.2. Nickel Containing Systems

The conductivity of nickel containing systems is similar, thus we show only the general patterns (Figure 33).

In most cases as the concentration of the substituents increases, no changes in the activation energy occur, which seems to be associated with various disordering of vacancies in the matrix of lanthanum gallate.

On the basis of obtained dependencies we plotted the isotherms of conductivity (Figure 34). Their run shows that the systems with the ratio M:Sr(Mg) = 5:1 have maximal conductivity. And what is more, from two systems M:Sr = 5:1 and M:Mg = 5:1, the conductivity of chromium containing solid solution is greater.

The reason seems to lie in the fact that magnesium is located in gallium sites and clustering in magnesium containing systems is higher than for the systems containing strontium. The conductivity of nickel containing systems appears to be higher than that of corresponding chromium containing systems, which is accounted for by the difference in the electron structure of transition elements- the fact discussed above.

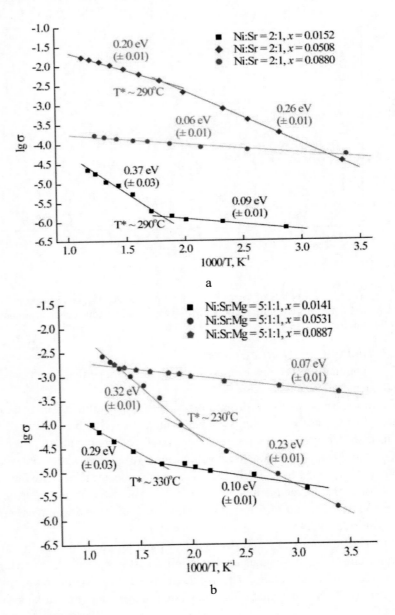

Figure 33. (Continued).

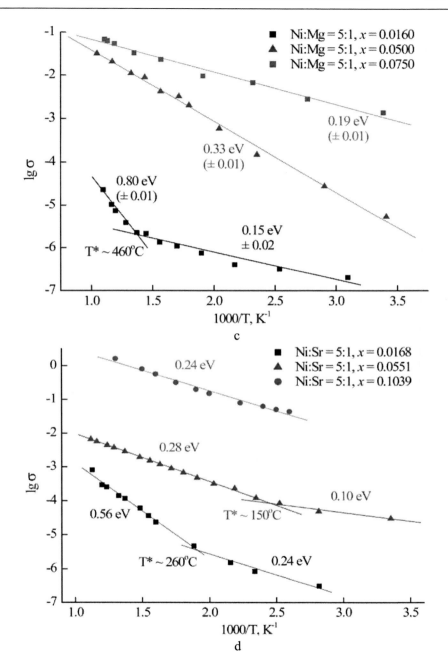

Figure 33. (Continued).

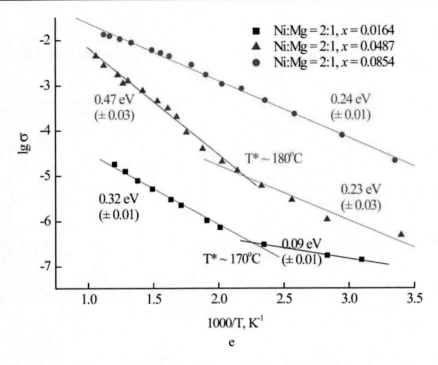

e

Figure 33. (*a*, *b*, *c*, *d*, *e*) Plots of logarithm of the total conductivity vs inverse temperature for various nickel containing systems and various concentrations of the solid solutions.

Conclusion

A detailed study of electron structure of a series of systems brings about the concept of the role of clustering both in the stability and in electrophysical performance of doped lanthanum gallate.

First, clustering in lanthanum gallate appears to be greater than in aluminate, which could be accounted for by the fact that aluminum being essentially smaller results in strong tensions in the lattice on introduction of larger elements.

Introduction of strontium rapidly results in the formation of K_2NiF_4 type structure – $LaSrAlO_4$. Small size of oxygen octahedra prevents clustering of 3*d*-elements $r(Al^{3+})_{VI} = 0.530$ Å, $r(Cr^{3+})_{VI} = 0.615$ Å, whereas $r(Ga^{3+})_{VI} = 0.620$ Å [87].

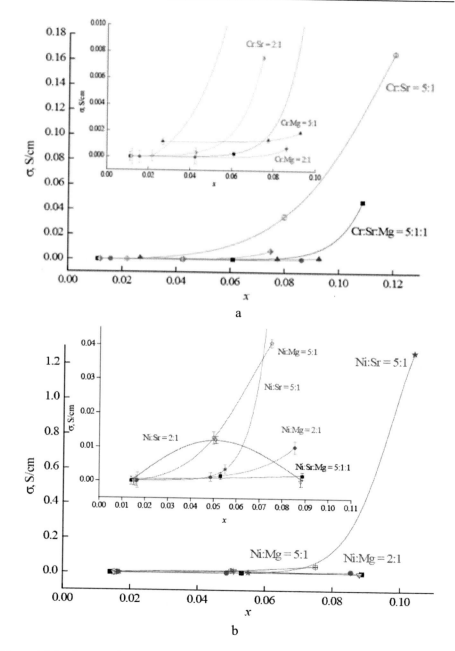

Figure 34. Isotherms of conductivity for chromium and nickel systems with various concentration of strontium and (or) magnesium.

The study of magnetic characteristics and electrophysical performance of the lanthanum gallate doped with 3d-elements and heterovalent substituents (Sr, Mg) revealed the following. Introduction of greater than 5:1 quantity of strontium relative to the transition element and introduction of magnesium result in some changes in the electron structure of these solids – the clusters of high nuclearity are formed ($n > 20$) from transition metal atoms. The character of the exchange within clusters is determined by the electron structure of a transition element.

A correlation between the quantity of introduced doping element, its nature and magnetic characteristics of the systems accounts for the fact that the formation of clusters includes both sublattices – cationic and anionic, hence the clusters include magnetic atoms, diamagnetic heterovalent dopants and vacancies accompanying them.

The isotherms of conductivity also point to a correlation for all the systems under study: an increase in the concentration of heterovalent substituent results in a decrease in the conductivity, which can be associated with the vacancies being blocked within the high nuclear clusters.

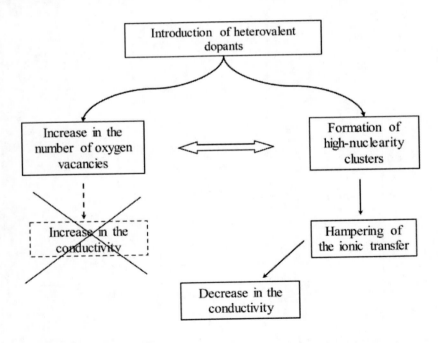

Scheme 1. Influence of heterovalent substitution on the conductivity of doped lanthanum gallate.

Therefore, the formation of a certain quantity of clusters of paramagnetic atoms is necessary for stabilization of the defect structure of lanthanum gallate. However an increase in their sizes and fraction results in a decrease in the conductivity, which may be accounted for by the influence of Coulomb field of a cluster on the process of oxygen ion migration (Scheme 1).

This study allows the theoretical basis to be found for the ratio M:Sr(Mg) = 5:1, which according to the published data is often used in practice.

References

[1]   Ishihara, T., Matsuda, H. and Takita, Y., *J. Am. Chem. Soc.*, 116, 3801 (1994).

[2]   Kuroda, K., Hashimoto, I., Adachi, K., Akikusa, J., Tamou, Y., Komada, N., Ishihara, T., and Takita, Y., *Solid State Ionics*, 132, 199 (2000).

[3]   Du, Y. and Sammes, N. M., *J. Eur. Ceram. Soc.,*, 21, 727 (2001).

[4]   Enoki, M., Yan, J., Matsumoto, H., and Ishihara, T., *Solid State Ionics*, 177, 2053 (2006).

[5]   Ishihara, T., Tabuchi, J., Ishikawa, S., Yan, J., Enoki, M., and Matsumoto, H., *Solid State Ionics*, 177, 1949 (2006).

[6]   Jacobson, A. J., *Chem. Mater.,* 22, 660 (2010).

[7]   Skinner, S. J. and Kilner, J. A., *Materials Today*, 30–37 (2003).

[8]   Kajitani, M., Matsuda, M., Hoshikawa, A., Oikawa, K., Torii, S., Kamiyama, T., Izumi, F., and Miyake, M., *Chem. Mater.,* 15, 3468 (2003).

[9]   Tas, A. C., Majewski, P. J. and Aldinger, F., *J. Am. Ceram. Soc.,* 83(12), 2954 (2000).

[10]   Datta, P., Majewski, P. and Aldinger, F., *J. Alloys Compd.,* 438, 232 (2007).

[11]   Zheng, F., Bordia, R. K. and Pederson, L. R., *Mater. Res. Bull.,* 39, 141 (2004).

[12]   Jasiolek, G. and Dabkowska, H., *J. Less Common Met.,* 160, 79–84 (1990).

[13]   Wang, Y., Liu, X., Yao, G.-D., Liebermann, R. C., and Dudley, M., *Mater. Sci. Eng.,* A132, 13 (1991).

[14]   Kobayashi, J., Tazoh, Y., Sasaura, M., and Miyazawa, S. *J. Mater. Res.,* 6(1), 97 (1991).

[15] Marti, W., Fischer, P., Altorfer, F., Scheel, H. J., and Tadin, M., *J. Phys.: Condens. Matter,* 6, 127–135 (1994).

[16] Slater, P. R., Irvine, J. T. S., Ishihara, T., and Takita, Y., *Solid State Ionics,* 107, 319 (1998).

[17] Slater, P. R., Irvine, J. T. S., Ishihara, T., and Takita, Y., *vol. SOFC-VI,* 387 (1998).

[18] Slater, P. R., Irvine, J. T. S., Ishihara, T., and Takita, Y., *J. Solid State Chem.,* 139, 135 (1998).

[19] Majewski, P., Rozumek, M., Tas, C., and Aldinger, F., *J. Electroceram.,* 8, 65 (2002).

[20] Feng, M. and Goodenough, J. B., *Eur. J. Solid State Inorg. Chem.,* 31, 663. (1994).

[21] Lerch, M., Boysen, H. and Hansen, T., *J. Phys. Chem. Solids,* 62, 445 (2001).

[22] Wang, W. L. and Lu, H. Y., *Phys. Chem. Miner.,* 33(7), 435 (2006).

[23] Cheng, J. and Navrotsky, A., *J. Solid State Chem.,* 177, 126 (2004).

[24] Khan, M. S., Islam, M. S. and Bates, D. R., *J. Phys. Chem. B,* 102, 3099 (1998).

[25] Islam, M. S., *Solid State Ionics,* 154–155, 75–85 (2002).

[26] Malavasi, L., Fisher, C. A. J. and Islam, M. S., *Chem. Soc. Rev.,* 39, 4370 (2010).

[27] Kharton, V. V., Viskup, A. P., Yaremchenko, A. A., Baker, R. T., Gharbage, B., Mather, G. C., Figueiredo, F. M., Naumovich, E. N., and Marques, F. M. B., *Solid State Ionics,* 132, 119 (2000).

[28] Stevenson, J. W., Armstrong, T. R., Pederson, L. R., Li, J., Lewinsohn, C. A., Baskaran, S. *Solid State Ionics,* 113, 571 (1998).

[29] Polini, R., Pamio, A. and Traversa, E., *J. Eur. Ceram. Soc.,* 24, 1365 (2004).

[30] Li, Z.-C., Zhang, H., Bergman, B., and Zou, X., *J. Eur. Ceram. Soc.,* 26, 2357 (2006).

[31] Shi, M., Xu, Y., Liu, A., Liu, N., Wang, C., Majewski, P., and Aldinger, F., *Mater. Chem. Phys.,* 114, 43 (2009).

[32] Datta, P., Majewski, P. and Aldinger, F., *Mater. Chem. Phys.,* 102, 240 (2007).

[33] Huang, K. and Goodenough, J. B., *J. Solid State Chem.,* 136, 274 (1998).

[34] Long, N. J., Lecarpentier, F. and Tuller, H. L., *J. Electroceram.,* 399 (1999).

[35] Trofimenko, N. and Ullmann, H., *Solid State Ionics,* 118, 215 (1999).

[36] Li, S. and Bergman, B., *J. Eur. Ceram. Soc.,* 29(6), 1139 (2009).

[37] Maglia, F., Anselmi-Tamburini, U., Chiodelli, G., Camurlu, H. E., Dapiaggi, M., and Munir, Z. A., *Solid State Ionics,* 180, 36 (2009).

[38] Huang, K., Tichy, R. S. and Goodenough, J. B., *J. Am. Ceram. Soc.,* 81, 2565 (1998).

[39] Pathak, S., Steinmetz, D., Kuebler, J., Payzant, E. A., and Orlovskaya, N., *Ceram. Int.,* 35, 1235 (2009).

[40] Ha, S. B., Choa, Y. H., Kang, Y. C., Lee, J.-H., and Lee, J.-H., *J. Eur. Ceram. Soc.,* 30, 2593 (2010).

[41] Hsieh, F.-F., Okinaka, N. and Akiyama, T., *J. Alloys Compd.,* 484(1-2), 747 (2009).

[42] Ullmann, H. and Trofimenko, N., *Solid State Ionics,* 119, 1–8 (1999).

[43] Baker, R. T., Gharbage, B. and Marques, F. M. B., *J. Eur. Ceram. Soc.,* 18, 105 (1998).

[44] Politova, E. D., Stefanovich, S. Yu., Aleksandrovskii, V. V., Kaleva, G. M., Mosunov, A. V., Avetisov, A. K., Sung, J. S., Choo, K. Y., and Kim, T. H., *Phys. Stat. Sol. (c),* 2(1), 196 (2005).

[45] Politova, E. D., Aleksandrovskii, V. V., Kaleva, G. M., Mosunov, A. V., Suvorkin, S. V., Zaitsev, S. V., Sung, J. S., Choo, K. Y., and Kim, T. H., *Solid State Ionics,* 177, 1779 (2006).

[46] Trofimenko, N., Ullmann, H. *Solid State Ionics,* 124, 263 (1999).

[47] Ishihara, T., Ishikawa, S., Hosoi, K., Nishiguchi, H., Takita, Y. *Solid State Ionics* 175, 319 (2004).

[48] Colomer, M. T. and Kilner, J. A. *Solid State Ionics,* 182, 76-81 (2011).

[49] Ishihara, T., Akbay, T., Furutani, H., and Takita, Y. *Solid State Ionics,* 113–115, 585 (1998).

[50] Ishihara, T., Ishikawa, S., Ando, M., Nishiguchi, H., and Takita, Y. *Solid State Ionics* 173, 9 (2004).

[51] Glowacki, M., Runka, T., Domukhovski, V., Diduszko, R., Mirkowska, M., Berkowski, M., and Dabrowski, B. *J. Alloys Compd.* 509, 1756 (2011).

[52] Ishihara, T., Yamada, T., Arikawa, H., Nishiguchi, H., and Takita, Y. *Solid State Ionics,* 135, 631 (2000).

[53] Yashima, M., Nomura, K., Kageyama, H., Miyazaki, Y., Chitose, N., and Adachi, K., *Chem. Phys. Lett.,* 380, 391 (2003).

[54] Mori, K., Onodera, Y., Kiyanagi, R., Richardson, J. W., Itoh, K., Sugiyama, M., Kamiyama, T., and Fukunaga, T., *Nucl. Instr. Met. Phys. Res. A,* 600, 328 (2009).

[55] Yaremchenko, A. A., Shaula, A. L., Logvinovich, D. I., Kharton, V. V., Kovalevsky, A. V., Naumovich, E. N., Frade, J. R., and Marques, F. M. B., *Mater. Chem. Phys.* 82, 684 (2003).

[56] Mabbs, F. E. and Machin, D. J. *Magnetism and Transition Metal Complexes,* London: Chapman and Hall, NY, 1973.

[57] Rakitin, Yu. V., Kalinnikov, V. T., *Modern Magnetochemistry*, Sankt-Petersburg: Nauka, 1994.

[58] Fisher, M. E., *Amer. J. Phys.* 2(5), 640 (1964).

[59] Rakitin, Yu. V., Starodub, O. R., Rakitina, V. M., Kalinnikov, V. T., and Novotortsev, V. M. *Rus. J. Inorg. Chem.*, 50(8), 1314 (2005).

[60] Smirnova, N. A., *Methods of statistical Thermodynamics in physical Chemistry,* Moscow: Izd. Vyssh. Shkola, (1973) (in Russian).

[61] Kozheurov, V. A. *Statistical Thermodynamics.* Moscow: Metallurgia, (1975). (in Russian).

[62] Chezhina, N. V., Bobrysheva, N. P. and Zvereva, I. A. The prospects of magnetic dilution method for studying polycrystalline compounds of transition metals. In: *Problems of modern chemistry of coordination compounds.* Ed. A. B. Nikol'skii. Sankt-Petersburg: Izd. SPbGU. 1992. Issue 10. 175. (in Russian)

[63] Zvereva, I., Zueva, F., Archaimbault, M., Crespin, J., Choisnet, J., and Lecomte, L. *Mater. Chem. Phys.* 48, 103 (1997).

[64] Brach, B. Ya., Bobrysheva, N. P., Reznitskii, L. A., and Chezhina, N. V., *Bull. St. Petersburg Univ.* 22, 109 (1979).

[65] Chezhina, N. V., Zharikova, E. V. and Sidorova, N. Yu., *Russ. J. Gen. Chem.* 80, 207 (2010).

[66] Kalinnikov, V. T. and Rakitin, Yu. V., *Introduction to Magneto-chemistry. Method of Static Magnetic Susceptibility*, Nauka, Moscow, 1980. (in Russian).

[67] Martin, R. L. and White, A. N., In: *Transition Metal Chemistry* 4, Dekker, New York, 1968, p. 113.

[68] Chezhina, N. V., Zharikova, E. V. and Knyazev, M. N., *Russ. J. Gen. Chem.* 80, 2399 (2010).

[69] Kharton, V. V., Viskup, A. P., Naumovich, E. N., and Lapchuk, N. M., *Solid State Ionics*, , 104, 67 (1997).

[70] Chezhina, N. V., Zolotukhina, N. V. and Bodritskaya, E. V., *Russ. J. Gen. Chem.*, 75, 1167 (2005).

[71] Chezhina, N. V., Bodritskaya, E. V. and Zhuk, N. A., *Russ. J. Gen. Chem.* 78, 1127 (2008).

[72] Chezhina, N. V., Bodritskaya, E. V., Zhuk, N. A., Bannikov, V. V., Shein, I. R., and Ivanovskii, A. L., *Physics of Solid State* 50, 2231 (2008).

[73] Chezhina, N. V., Korolev, D. A., Sukharzhevskii, S. M., and Glumov, O. V. *Russ. J. Gen. Chem.*, 80(5), 745 (20100.

[74] Korolev, D. A., Chezhina, N. V. *Russ. J. Gen. Chem.*, 81 (10), 206 (2011).

[75] Korolev, D. A., Chezhina, N. V. and Lytkina, Zh. A., *Russ. J. Gen. Chem.*, 84 (3), 360 (2012).

[76] Ishikawa, Y., *J. Phys. Soc. Japan*, 17, 1835 (1962).

[77] Ishikawa, Y., *J. Phys. Soc. Japan*, 17,1877 (1962).

[78] Bajpai, A., Banerjee, A., *Phys. Rev. B*, 62, 8996 (2000).

[79] Belov, K. P. *Magnetic Transformations* Izd. GIFML, Moscow. 1959 (in Russian).

[80] Bean, C. P., Livingston, J. D., *J. Appl. Phys.*, 10, 120S (1959).

[81] Kellerman, D. G., Gorshkov, V. S. and Karelina, V. V., *Russ. J. Inorg. Chem.*, 44 (7), 1078, (1999).

[82] Kellerman, D. G., Shalaeva, E. V. and Gusev, A. I., *Physics of Solid State*, 46 (9), 1633 (2004).

[83] Chezhina, N. V. and Korolev, D. A., *Russ. J. Gen. Chem.*, 84 (3), 353 (2012).

[84] Naumovich, E. N., Kharton, V. V., Yaremchenko, A. A., Patrakeev, M. V., Kellerman, D. G., Logvinovich, D. I., Kozhevnikov, V. L. *Phys. Rev. B*, 74, 064105 (2006).

[85] Yaremchenko, A. A., Kharton, V. V., Naumovich, E. N., Shestakov, D. I., Chukharev, V. F., Kovalevsky, A. V., Shaula, A. L., Patrakeev, M. V., Frade, J. R., and Marques, F. M. B. *Solid State Ionics,* 177, 549 (2006).

[86] Howard, C. J. and Kennedy, B. J. *J. Phys.: Cond. Mat.*, 11 (6), 3229 (1999).

[87] Shannon, R. D. and Prewitt, C. T. *Acta. Cryst. B.*, 25, 925 (1969).

In: Recent Advances in Gallate Research
Editor: Amanda L. Kinsey

ISBN: 978-1-63117-071-3
© 2014 Nova Science Publishers, Inc.

Chapter VI

Therapeutic Potential of Gallic Acid and Its Derivatives: A Review

M. Shalini, T. Kalaivani and C. Rajasekaran*

School of Bio Sciences and Technology, VIT University,
Vellore, Tamilnadu, India

Abstract

Gallates, salt or ester of gallic acid (GA) are found widely in plants as phenolic compounds. Many forms of gallates are available in plants namely, epigallocatechin-3-gallate (EGCG), epicatechin-3-gallate (ECG), epigallocatechin (EGC), GA, ethyl gallate (EG), methyl gallate, propyl gallate, gallocatechin and theaflavin-3-gallate to name a few. Among these compounds, EGCG, GA and EG have attracted many researchers around the world for their antioxidant, anticancer, antidiabetic, anti-arthritic, anti-HIV and neuroprotective properties. Food sources of each compound vary from fruits, nuts, green tea and carob flour for EGCG; blueberries, apples, flax seeds, oak bark, walnut, green tea and watercress for GA; and walnuts, *Terminalia chebula* and *T. myriocarpa* for EG. The

* Corresponding author: Dr. T. Kalaivani, Assistant Professor (Senior), School of Bio Sciences and Technology, VIT University, Vellore – 632014, Tamilnadu, India. E-mail: tkvani72@gmail.com

efficacy of these individual compounds varies based on their chemical structures and bioavailability in circulation. There are numerous reports available on their sole therapeutic properties using cell lines and animal models. In addition, these compounds are also reported to be used as a sensitizer or as an adjuvant to enhance the cytotoxic potential of some anticancer drugs. In this article, we have compared and compiled the beneficial effects of these compounds against major diseases like cancer, diabetes, inflammation, free radical generation and neurodegeneration using cell line, animal and human system. Compilation of the previous work carried out so far could form a basis for future research work related to identifying the mechanism behind each pharmaceutical property. Moreover, this review will give an insight in reasoning the differences in action of these compounds based on their structure-activity relationship, pharmacology and toxicology.

1. Introduction

Gallates are salts and esters of GA and represents a large number of phenolic secondary metabolites from plants. Different forms of gallate are available in plants namely: EGCG, ECG, EGC, GA, EG, methyl gallate, propyl gallate and theaflavin-3-gallate from green tea, walnuts and fruits etc. EGCG has a broad range of medicinal properties including its specificity in inhibiting the cancer cell proliferation. It also appears to protect against other health threats including cardiovascular disease. GA and its derivatives also possess similar properties in different cancer cell lines studied. GA was also established as a standard for the quantification of total phenolics from plants. While EGCG and GA are gaining their entry into clinical trials and have a diverse range of industrial uses such as food, pharmaceutical and cosmetic industry.

EG is also finding its way in research as a promising antioxidant candidate, against hydrogen peroxide signaling in septic shock. EG has arrived a lot of importance in the field of anticancer research due to its prooxidant nature in cancer cells. This article deals with the various pharmacological actions of these structurally related compounds in different cell lines and animal models.

2. Chemistry, Absorption and Metabolism of EGCG

EGCG is the most abundant catechin in green tea (*Camellia sinensis* L. Ktze. (Theaceae)). Many researchers have reported the beneficial effects of EGCG, such as prevention of low density lipoprotein (LDL) oxidation and oxidative damage to deoxyribonucleic acid (DNA). Its beneficial effects may be attributable to its chemical structure. The recently documented structure-function relationship of EGCG include, the pyrogallol-type structure for apoptosis and and the galloyl moiety for the suppression of fatty-acid synthase leading to cytotoxicity in cancer cells (Saeki et al., 2000; Ishii et al., 2011; Wang et al., 2003).

The pharmacokinetics parameters play an important role in selecting the dose and its frequency of intervention. Absorption of EGCG occurs in the small intestinal mucosa and passed into the large intestine where it undergoes further degradation by the local microbiota such as *Enterobacter aerogenes*, *Raoultella planticola*, *Klebsiella pneumonia* subsp. *pneumonia* and *Bifidobacterium longum* subsp. *infantis*. The products formed were analyzed with time by high performance liquid chromatography (HPLC) or liquid chromatography-mass spectrometry (LC-MS) and identified by nuclear magnetic resonance (NMR) analysis (Takagaki & Nanjo, 2010).

There are only few reports available on the effects of EGCG at its physiological concentrations. Ullmann et al., (2003) have examined the safety, tolerability, and pharmacokinetic properties of a single dose of EGCG ranging from 50 mg to 1600 mg. Only at oral doses of more than 1 gm of EGCG, at least 1 μM maximal plasma EGCG concentrations were observed (1600 mg dose, maximum concentration (Cmax) = 3392 ng/ml, range: 130–3392 ng/ml). Though many reports mention its low bioavailability in the plasma, a variation does exist in its half-life as 2-3.4h or 5h (Lee et al., 2002; Mohr & Yang, ; Yang et al., 1999). Another study states that EGCG displayed a different pharmacokinetic behavior when it was given to rats in the decaffeinated green tea (DGT), in comparison to the pure EGCG. When administered i.g., EGCG in DGT form showed a 3.6-fold higher absorption rate constant (Ka) than the pure EGCG. Based on the area under the curve (AUC) and the concentration maximum (Cmax) produced by per unit of EGCG, DGT seems to deliver EGCG into the bloodstream more effectively than the pure EGCG. Since catechins are more capable to bind with proteins, it can be attributed to other tea components present in DGT competing for the binding of plasma and tissue proteins. The molecular basis for this absorption difference is not found yet and is important to understand its pharmacokinetics for future cancer prevention studies.

EGCG was found to metabolize rapidly in the liver leading to a decreased bioavailability in the plasma (Swezey et al., 2003). After oral absorption, metabolism occurs by any one of the three process of conjugation such as methylation, sulfation or glucuronidation (Scalbert & Willianson, 2000; Ohigashi, 2000). Methylation decreases the hydrophilicity of EGCG and undergoes sulfation or glucuronidation for rapid elimination of the methylated product from the body. This process is mediated by the liver cytosolic enzyme catechol-O-methyltransferase. The level of methylation can vary based on the functional polymorphisms in the enzyme (Scalbert & Willianson, 2000).

2.1. Pharmacological Actions of EGCG

2.1.1. Antioxidant Activity

The antioxidant property of EGCG is mainly attributed to the phenolic groups present that are sensitive to oxidation generating quinones. This activity is further enhanced by the presence of the trihydroxyl structure in the D ring (Mukhtar & Ahmad, 2000; Lambert & Elias, 2010). EGCG inhibit the deleterious oxidation reaction involved in the lipid peroxidation process by hydrogen atom transfer mechanism (HAT). Peroxyl radicals abstract hydrogen atoms from unoxidized lipid substrate leading to a chain reaction. This reaction is slowed down in the presence of phenolic antioxidants (Joshua & Elias, 2010). The strong free radical scavenging and metal chelation property has been attributed to the dihydroxy and trihydroxy groups present in EGCG (Higdon & Frei, 2003; Yang et al., 2002).

Being an antioxidant EGCG was tested against a number of diseases *in vitro* and *in vivo*. One study has suggested the role of EGCG-mediated induction of some endogenous antioxidants like hemeoxygenase-1 and superoxide dismutase (SOD) in human mammary epithelial cells. The expression was reduced by the small-interfering RNA (siRNA)-mediated disruption of nuclear factor 2 (Nrf2) (Na & Surh, 2008).

EGCG pretreatment to Wistar rats for a period of 2 weeks exposed to the cooking oil fumes for 30 min has decreased the 4-hydroxynonenal (4-HNE) and ROS levels in the alveolar lavage fluid. The fumes generated are associated with lung diseases including cancer (Yang et al., 2009). Similarly, the cytosolic glutathione S tranferase (GST) activity was found to increase in

Wistar rats treated with 2% green tea solution for 4 weeks. In another study, the senescence mediated redox imbalance was analyzed in rats after green tea administration. It was found that, EGCG administration to rats for 30 days at a dose of 100 mg/kg body weight per day orally showed a 50% reduction of lipid peroxides and 39% of protein carbonyls formation in aged rats when compared to young rats (Kumaran et al., 2009). The rejuvenating potential of green tea extract has combated the age-associated macromolecular damage in rat cardiac tissue (Srividhya et al., 2008). The antioxidant property of EGCG has made the compound desirable in a number of diseases by either suppressing or preventing the diseases like, cancer, diabetes, neurodegeneration and inflammation.

2.1.2. Anticancer Activity

As mentioned earlier, EGCG has many health beneficial effects. Among all the activities reported, it was found to play a major role in cancer chemoprevention and treatment (Nakazato et al., 2005; Lambert & Elias, 2010). Epidemiological studies conducted in the past decade from different parts of the world provide evidence on the anticancer effect of EGCG. In Shangai (China), a significant reduction in the stomach cancer risk was observed among the green tea drinkers (Yu et al., 1995). Moreover, the prostate cancer incidence in China was also found to be the lowest in the world who consume green tea on a regular basis (Gupta et al., 1999). In order to study the mechanism of action of EGCG against cancer, the normal cells were transformed into cancer cells by chemical induction (Hu et al., 1995) and the oncogene transformation (Chung et al., 1999 & Ahn et al., 1999). Recently, the anticancer property has been well documented in the brain (Das, 2009), prostrate (Hsieh et al., 2009 & Bettuzzi et al., 2006) cervical (Qiao et al., 2009) and bladder (Philips et al., 2009) cancer cells. Studies conducted in both cell lines and animal models have shown a specific inhibition of Bcl-xL an anti-apoptotic protein (Leone et al., 2003). It was also reported that, EGCG not only act as a sole cancer preventing agent but also was found to act as an adjuvant by improving the anticancer potential of some other anticancer compounds like Panaxadiol against the human colorectal cancer cells (Du et al., 2012). It was also being shown to reduce various cancer risk in animal or bioassay systems studied (Katiyar & Mukhtar, 1996; Kohlmeier, 1997; Lin et al., 1999; Okabe et al., 1999; Lu et al., 1998).

From the previous reports we also understand the prooxidant mechanism of cytotoxicity of EGCG was more prominent in cancer cells. In one study, the maximum neuroprotection was offered to pheochromocytoma 12 cells (PC 12, pheochromocytoma from the rat adrenal medulla) treated with low concentrations of EGCG in the presence of a superoxide generating agent, paraquat (PQ). But when the concentration of EGCG was increased to 200 mM, a reduction in cell viability was observed indicating a biphasic mode of action proportional to the concentration dependent window of pharmacological action. While the antioxidant property exhibited at low concentrations of EGCG has a valid neuroprotective action against the oxidative stress, it is also worth directing its prooxidant nature at high concentrations in treating cancer (Gupta et al., 2003; Nishikawa et al., 2006). Similar biphasic phenomena have been reported in few standard antioxidant compounds like vitamin C (Halliwell, 1996), R-apomorphine (Gassen et al., 1998), and dopamine (Weinreb et al., 2003). Another mechanism of EGCG induced apoptosis was determined by the increasing levels of H_2O_2 in cancer cell lines such as human lung adenocarcinoma (H661) and Ha-ras gene transformed human bronchial cells (21BES). Apoptosis elicitation was prevented when catalase was added exogenously indicating the mechanism of H_2O_2 induced apoptosis.

A note should be made based on the various reports that, EGCG is the most effective apoptosis inducing agent in green tea (Azam et al., 2004). One mechanism of apoptosis induction was studied in PC-9 (human lung cancer cell) cells by NFκB inactivation leading to the down regulation of NFκB induced kinase expression (Aggarwal & Shishodia, 2006; Fujiki et al., 2001). Similarly, in HepG2 cells, EGCG was shown to stimulate apoptosis by inhibiting the cell cycle progression at its G1 phase (Shankar et al., 2007). Recent reports also demonstrate that EGCG induces cancer cell growth arrest at G1 stage of cell cycle by regulating the cyclin D1, cyclin-dependent kinases (CDK), CDK4, CDK6, p27/K1P1 and p21/WAF1/C1P1 induced apoptosis mediated by ROS generation and caspases 3 and 9 activation (Shankar et al., 2007). These multiple mechanisms of apoptosis induction and cell growth inhibition makes the compound useful for chemoprevention studies.

2.1.3. Anti-Inflammatory Activity

EGCG has been demonstrated to fight against inflammation related to pathological conditions. Kim et al., (2006) has reported the inhibitory action of EGCG against IL-8 (interleukin) production involved in the respiratory inflammation. IL-8 is also reported to be involved in the promotion of ROS by recruiting the neutrophils. The mechanism of blocking IL-1β induced NF-κB activation by reducing IκB phosphorylation has also been explained with EGCG. Simultaneously, inhibition of IL-1β induced matrix metalloproteinase (MMP-2) activity in synovial fibroblasts has been reported *in vitro* (Ahmed et al., 2006). Another study also showed a decreased production of IL-1β-induced IL-6 and MMP-1 and 3 in the synovial fibroblast cells (Ahmed et al., 2008 & Yun et al., 2008).

In the past decade few research work was carried out to find the benefits offered by EGCG to block gp120 (Williamson et al., 2006; Hamza & Zhan, 2006; Yamaguchi et al., 2002). Li et al., (2011) has reported the suppression of HIV-1$_{IIIB}$ and HIV-2$_{EHO}$ infection in HeLa-CD4-LTR-β-gal cells. The mechanism of suppression was found to be due to an allosteric reverse transcriptase inhibition. It was also found to possess a synergistic inhibition with AZT (3'-azido-3'-deoxythymidine).

2.1.4. Anti-Diabetic Potential

A wide research has been carried out to find the activity of EGCG against diabetes. Various models have been used for this purpose. Studies conducted with rat and human β-cells suggested the role of EGCG in controlling the expression of genes involved in glycolysis and gluconeogenesis. Wolfram et al., (2006), found that EGCG at 50 and 100 μM has down regulated the glucose-6-phosphatase gene and fatty acid synthase gene involved in gluconeogenesis and fatty acid synthesis respectively in rat insulin-responsive H411E hepatoma cells in a dose-dependent fashion. This down regulation could therefore make EGCG useful in the glucose metabolism by promoting the fat oxidation process in humans. Zhang et al., (2004) has also tested the ability of EGCG to protect the human islets in the presence of green tea extract (0-500 μg/ml). The ratio of BAX/Bcl-2 was found to be less when compared to the control indicating the culture recovery rate by precluding islets from apoptosis (Hara et al., 2007).

In rats, EGCG was found to be active in normalizing the blood glucose levels by improving the insulin sensitivity and thereby increasing the plasma insulin concentration in 3 weeks time. Additionally, the reduction in body weight and food intake were also observed in hypertensive rats fed with 200 mg/kg of EGCG per day. Potenza et al., (2007), has also noticed a reduced systolic blood pressure with improved plasma adiponectin and cardiac function pointing towards the ability of EGCG to alleviate multiple metabolic syndromes.

Epidemiological studies carried out from Europe and America showed a decreased risk of diabetes in people whose coffee intake is high (Rosengren et al., 2007; Salazar-Martinez et al., 2004; Van Dam & Feskens, 2002). Another study regarding the tea consumption and type2 diabetes in Japan with 17,000 healthy subjects showed a positive correlation of decreased diabetes risk with high intake of green tea (Iso et al., 2006). In addition to this long-term study, a short-term study was conducted in Japanese subjects where consumption of green tea before the oral glucose load has significantly lowered the blood glucose levels indicating the role of EGCG in controlling the postprandial hyperglycemia (Tsuneki et al., 2004).

2.1.5. Neuroprotective Agent

Several reports suggest that EGCG can protect neurons from the damage mediated by neurotoxins, ischemia, hypoxia, and serum withdrawal among other things (Han, 2003; Levites et al., 2001; Lee et al., 2003; Wei et al., 2004; Mandel et al., 2003; Guo et al., 2005). The ability of EGCG to chelate metal ions, such as iron and copper, may contribute to their antioxidant/ neuroprotective action by inhibiting the transition metal-catalyzed free radical formation. As a natural chelator, it was reported to decrease the accumulation of iron which is a major process involved in the instances of neurodegenerative diseases (Weinbreb et al., 2009; Bai et al., 2012). This ability of EGCG may be due to the inhibition of transition metal-catalyzed free radical formation. The O-diphenolic groups in the B ring, and the keto structure 4-keto, 3-hydroxy or 4-keto and 5-hydroxy in the C ring of the flavonols attach to the transition metal ions (Thompson, 1976 & Acker et al., 1996).

EGCG exhibits its neuroprotective effects in a variety of *in vitro* paradigms. It has been shown to selectively protect the cultured rat cerebellar granule neurons (CGNs) from oxidative stress (Schroeder et al., 2009). Moreover, EGCG was also reported to protect the SH-SY5Y human neuroblastoma cells against amyloid precursor protein (APP), 3-hydroxykynurenine or 6-hydroxydopamine (6-OHDA) induced toxicity (Levites et al., 2002; Jeong et al., 2004; Avramovich-Tirosh et al., 2007). EGCG was also reported to reduce and rescue then β-amyloid-induced toxicity in hippocampal neurons and the primary dopamine neurons from 1-methyl-4-phenylpyridinium (MPP+) toxicity (Choi et al., 2007; Bastianetto et al., 2006; Stull et al., 2002).

A study conducted in mice also shows the efficacy of EGCG against *N*-methyl-4-phenyl-1,2,3,6-tetrahydropyridine (MPTP) - induced dopaminergic neurodegeneration in mice (Levites et al., 2001). Choi et al., (2002) also reported a similar effect of EGCG on nNOS inhibition in the substantia nigra. EGCG was found to be protective against focal and global brain ischemia in aged rats (Park et al., 2009; Sutherland et al., 2006; Sutherland et al., 2005). Oral administration of EGCG to Swedish mutant amyloid precursor protein

(APPsw) overexpressing transgenic mice have substantially decreased the amyloid plaque burden and reduced the cognitive impairment (Rezai-Zadeh et al., 2008).

In addition to its neuroprotective action EGCG being a neutraceutical antioxidant was reported to preserve the survival of neuronal cells in cell line and animal models of neurodegeneration (Kelsey et al., 2010). The principal mechanism of action of EGCG could probably be due to its antioxidant activity; however, the activation of specific protein kinase pathways also appears to play a significant role in the neuroprotective action of this phenolic compound. Thus, EGCG exerts a significant neuroprotective effect against a wide range of oxidative insults in a multitude of neuronal cell systems.

Several clinical trials have been initiated for its neuroprotective action in which, EGCG is currently being tested in Phase II trials for parkinson's disease (PD) (Xuanwu Hospital, Beijing, China) and early stage Alzheimer's disease (AD) (Charite University, Berlin, Germany). Clinical trials have also been conducted with EGCG for the treatment of intellectual impairment in patients with Down Syndrome and Fragile X (Staff, 2013).

3. Gallic Acid

GA, an endogenous product found in free or bound forms plants (Ma et al., 2003; Singh et al., 2004; Shahrzad & Bitsch, 1996). It is widely used as a food additive to prevent oxidation. GA and its derivatives are found to possess pharmacological actions including free radical scavenging and induction of apoptosis in cancer cells (Dwibedy, 1999; Saeki et al., 2000). No-observed adverse effect level (NOAEL) of GA was reported to be 120 mg/kg/day for F334 rats and 1000 mg/kg for mice (Heijden et al., 1986; Niho et al., 2001).

3.1. Metabolism

4-Omethylgallic acid (4-OMGA) has been reported as a major metabolite of GA in rabbits, rats, chickens and humans (Zong et al., 1999; Potter & Fuller, 1968; Watanabe & Oshima, 1965; Shahrzad & Bitsch, 1998). The major metabolites of GA are found to be the products of methylation (unconjugated and conjugated 4-OMGA and 2-OMGA), decarboxylation (unconjugated and conjugated pyrogallol, 4-O-methylpyrogallol), and dehydroxylation (resorcinol). A study reports that when GA was supplied as tea to one group and as acidium gallicum tablets to the other group, the rate of absorption and elimination was calculated using their mean half-lives and mean maximum concentrations in plasma respectively. The study showed no difference in its bioavailability when taken as a tea or in the form of a tablet.

3.2. Pharmacological Actions

3.2.1. Neuroprotection

Oxidative stress is implicated in neurodegenerative diseases related to free radical mediated reactions. Oxidation of dopamine generates loads of ROS leading to the neuronal damage exhibited by apoptosis or necrosis (Fahn & Cohen, 1992; Beal, 1995; Jenner & Olanow, 1998; Igosheva et al., 2005; Qi et al., 2005). GA as a natural antioxidant was explored for its structure-activity relationship in a well defined system in liposomes and neuron protective effect against 6-OHDA induced stress in human SH-SY5Y cells. It was found that GA could improve the cell viability, intracellular GSH level, maintenance of nuclear morphology, ROS reduction and Ca^{2+} influx (Qi et al., 2005).

3.2.2. Cardioprotection

Myocardial infarction (MI) is a clinical syndrome which is followed by various pathophysiological and biochemical changes like lipid peroxidation, hyperglycemia, hyperlipidemia etc. Much evidence suggests that free radicals and active oxygen species derived from molecular oxygen (superoxide, hydrogen peroxide, and hydroxyl radical) contribute to the tissue injury which accompanies myocardial ischemia and reperfusion (McCord, 1988). In agreement with this, the GA was tested for its protection to the heart by preventing the lipid peroxidation and scavenging of superoxide and hydroxyl radicals (Jadon et al., 2007). Based on this property, another study was conducted to confirm its protection of the heart against isoproterenol (ISO)-induced damage in rats. The improved antioxidant status was behind the scene protecting the heart maintaining its function and integrity (Biemond et al., 1986). The interaction of GA to lipid membranes was also reported to be a principle determining factor for its antioxidant action.

3.2.3. Chemopreventive Effect

ROS generation is found to be involved in various diseases. Recent evidence indicates its role in carcinogenic processes (Fang et al., 2005).

Alteration in the balance between oxidant and antioxidant status occur in cancer tissues (Saroja et al., 1999). It is a known fact that phenolic hydroxyls act as potent scavengers against the free radicals (Son & Lewis, 2002). In connection to this, GA contains 3 hydroxyl groups and thus prove to be an effective antioxidant against free radicals. Anticancer study normally involves the mutation to happen with a chemical procarcinogen through elicitation of free radicals.

In one report, cancer has been initiated in rats by 1,2-dimethylhydrazine (DMH) resulting in more lipid peroxidation and less antioxidant status. Supplementation of GA in these rats has normalized the rats to a balanced antioxidant state thereby preventing the cancer progression and death (Giftson et al., 2010).

It was worth noticing the efficacy of GA on colon carcinogenesis inhibition boosted by its antioxidative action. The suppression of preneoplastic GST-P induction in rats. When GA was fed to these rats in the diet for a period of 6 weeks after the diethylnitrosamine administration, its chemopreventive action was also reported.

GA from chestnut bark (*Juglans mandshurica* Maxim. Cortex) is used as an ingredient in Chinese medicine for treating the chronic hepatitis or hepatocarcinoma. Various cell lines were used to understand the specific anticancer action of GA on normal cells and P388D1, HL-60RG, HeLa, dRLh-84, PLC/PRF/5 and KB cancer cells. GA was found to be non-toxic to the normal cells till 100 µg/ml but was highly toxic to the other cancer cells. This anticancer action was found to be similar when compared with EG and tannic acid.

3.2.4. Antidiabetic Activity

Streptozotocin induced diabetogenic activity was reported mainly by the oxygen free radicals induction and thereby damaging the pancreas (Halliwell & Gutteridge, 1985). Supplementation of the non-toxic free radical scavengers or antioxidants were reported to facilitate the regeneration of β-cells and the protection of pancreatic islets against the cytotoxic effects of streptozotocin (Coskun et al., 2005).

Parameters like blood glucose, plasma insulin, total haemoglobin, glycosylated haemoglobin, carbohydrate metabolic enzymes, pancreatic lipid peroxidation and antioxidants were estimated in the diabetic rats. The protection offered by GA (10 mg and 20 mg/kg) on pancreas against streptozotocin (STZ) induction and against 2, 2′-azinobis-(3-ethyl-benzothiazoline-6-sulfonic acid) (ABTS) radicals showed an effective antidiabetic activity along with antihyperglycaemic, antilipidperoxidative and antioxidant effects in diabetic model system. The activity of hepatic hexokinase was reduced and the activities of hepatic glucose-6-phosphatase and fructose-1, 6-bis phosphatase were increased in streptozotocin induced diabetic rats compared to normal control rats (Punithavathi et al., 2011).

4. Ethyl Gallate

EG is the ethyl ester of GA and used as an antioxidant in food (Hall et al., 1996; Monagas et al., 2005; Zhang et al., 2009). The source of this naturally occurring phenolic compound include, red wine, walnuts and other plant species. Many reports validate the presence of EG through HPLC chromatography. EG can be produced from GA and ethanol under laboratory conditions (Weetall, 1985). As discussed earlier, phenolics are the potent antioxidants and act as good hydrogen donors thereby scavenging the ROS and reactive nitrogen species (RNS) formed in the physiological system (Pereira et al., 2009). Metal chelation was also found to play an important role in its antioxidant property.

4.1. Anticancer Activity

In our previous report, we have demonstrated several *in vitro* assays to evaluate the possible antioxidant mechanisms like free radical scavenging, cytotoxic, and hemolytic activities of EG isolated from *Acacia nilotica* (L.) wild. Ex. Delile subsp. *indica* (Benth.) Brenan. From the results obtained, we concluded that the compound possesses no hemolytic activity against the rat or human erythrocytes but was cytotoxic to HeLa cancer cells in a dose-dependent mode indicating its cell specific action (Kalaivani et al., 2011). Another study also suggests that EG can induce apoptosis through mitochondrial-mediated pathway in HL-60 cells (Kim et al., 2012). It was confirmed by the release of cytochrome c, endonuclease G, apoptosis-inducing factor (AIF) and by the upregulation of Bax, a pro-apoptotic protein through western blotting analysis. In addition, EG has also enhanced the expression of caspases-3, 8, 9 and Bcl-2 interacting domain (Bid) activating the death receptor-dependent pathway. Methanolic fruit extract of *Terminalia chebula* was reported to be cytotoxic against the cancer cells like, human breast cancer cells (MCF), human prostate cancer cells (PC-3) and human osteosarcoma cells (HOS-1) by thymidine incorporation and coulter counting method. Cell viability was determined by the adenosine triphosphate (ATP) estimation and cell death by flow cytometry and Hoechst DNA staining. In all the cell lines used, a dose-dependent mode of growth inhibition through apoptosis was observed at low concentrations and by necrosis at higher concentrations of the extract. EG was found to be one of the major constituent present in the crude extract of *T. chebula* along with GA, luteolin, terminalia and tannic acid.

4.2. Against Septic Shock

EG was recently discovered to be an alternative class of vasopressors against septic shock for the maintenance of tissue perfusion in the face of hypotension (Gotes et al., 2012). The study was performed in dogs infused with *Pseudomonas aeruginosa* sepsis until the mean arterial pressure was decreased to ~60 mm Hg followed by the administration of EG and norepinephrine, a standard. Measurement of stroke work, serum creatinine, urine output and serum troponin T were done. EG was found to lower the heart rate, troponin T and high urine output when compared to the standard by inhibiting the hydrogen peroxide signaling pathway.

4.3. Anti-Inflammatory Action

Another study was conducted to know whether gallates can inhibit the cytokine-induced activation of nuclear factor κB (NF-κB) to reduce the expression of endothelial-leukocyte adhesion molecules in cultured human umbilical vein endothelial cells (HUVECs) (Murase et al., 1999). To their surprise, EG pretreated cells significantly suppressed the interleukin-1α (IL-1α) or tumor necrosis factor-α (TNF-α) induced mRNA, cell-surface expression of intercellular adhesion molecule 1 (ICAM-1), vascular cell adhesion molecule 1 (VCAM-1) and E-selectin.

Both immunoblot assay and gel shift assay were conducted to demonstrate the anti-inflammatory property of gallates in the prevention of atherosclerosis and anti-inflammatory responses *in vivo*.

4.4. Brain Preservative

Apart from the above described pharmacological properties, EG has also been reported as a better preservative of neutrophils. It is because of this property EG was attempted in the processing of ganglia through osmium-EG procedure (OEG) in comparison to the silver impregnation methods (Leise & Mulloney, 1986). Though both methods were observed to trace large neuronal tracts and regional specializations that were undetected from the silver preparations, EG was found to be better in identifying their characteristics.

Summary, Conclusion and Future Prospects

Phenolic compounds are secondary metabolites showing diverse structures based on a common phenolic ring. They are distributed widely in the plant kingdom. Most of the compounds possess pharmaceutical properties. Most of the currently available modern medicines are expensive, toxic and less effective in treating diseases. Hence, in this article we have reviewed the various pharmacological aspects of EGCG, GA and EG providing a base for future research in tables 1, 2 and 3.

Several clinical advantages of EGCG over the available traditional anti-cancer drugs include it to be less expensive for isolation, administration through oral mode, easy availability as tea worldwide, its non-toxic action of healthy cells and its acceptable safety profile (Sartippour et al., 2002; Hastak et al., 2003; Singh et al., 2011). At present the data on clinical trials are improving based on these health benefits especially for cancer chemoprevention and treatment studies. A large cohort study has proved EGCG as a potent drug for cancer onset delay or its recurrence in breast cancer patients (Fujiki et al., 1999). It was also found to be effective in patients with HPV-infected cervical lesions (Ahn et al., 2003). Collective findings on neuroprotection indicates that EGCG may be a viable therapeutic candidate against the chronic neurodegenerative diseases such as AD, PD or Huntington's. Thus the diverse therapeutic action of EGCG and the wider research involved from various parts of the world for its cell signaling mechanism or other pathway targeted actions will make the compound available over the counter for major diseases in the near future.

Table 1. Summarized pharmacological properties and mechanism of Epigallocatechin-3-gallate

Epigallocatechin-3-gallate (EGCG)	Mechanism of action
Anticancer property	↑ROS generation ↑H_2O_2 generation ↓Cell cycle progression at G1 phase (Cyclin dependent kinases 6 and 4, cyclin D1, Casapases 3 and 9) Suppress Bcl-xL (anti-apoptotic protein)
Antidiabetic activity	↓Glucose-6-phosphatase ↓Fatty acid synthase Controls Bax/Bcl-2 ratio for islet regeneration
Neuroprotection	↑Metal chelation Protection against APP, 6-OHDA, β-amyloid, MPP+ ↓Amyloid plaque burden
Anti-inflammatory property	↓IL-8 involved in inflammation ↓ROS Blocks IL-1β induced NF-κB, IL-6, MMP-1 and MMP-3 activation
Antioxidant activity	↑Endogenous antioxidants – hemoxygenase-1 and SOD ↑GST ↓ROS ↓Lipid peroxides and protein carbonyls

ROS-reactive oxygen species; H_2O_2-hydrogen peroxide; NF-nuclear factor; SOD-superoxide dismutase; GST-glutathione-s-transferase; MMP-matrix metalloproteinase; IL-interleukin; APP-amyloid precursor protein; OHDA-hydroxydopamine; MPP-1-methyl-4-phenylpyridinium.

Taking EG into account, though reports are very few, it has been proved to be a strong antioxidant with cell specific cytotoxic action against cancer cells. The mechanism of cancer growth inhibition was determined through apoptosis even at low concentrations indicating its capability in treating the cancer cells thereby showing a direction for future anticancer research. N_G-methyl-$_L$-arginine hydrochloride, a standard nitric oxide inhibitor could not improve the survival rate in patients with septic shock under clinical trial study. This failure was compensated when EG showed better activity when compared to other available treatments. Still, further work need to be carried out to determine the NO formation or metabolism.

Table 2. Summarized pharmacological effects of Gallic acid and its mechanisms

Gallic acid (GA)	Mechanism of action
Neuroprotection	↑ROS production ↓GSH ↑Ca^{2+} influx Maintains cell viability and morphology
Cardioprotection	↑Antioxidants ↓LPO ↓SOD and OH radicals Maintains the function and integrity of heart
Anticancer effect	↑Antioxidant status ↓Lipid peroxidation ↑Cancer cytotoxicity
Antidiabetic activity	Protects pancreas ↑B-cell regeneration ↓OFR

ROS-reactive oxygen species; GSH-reduced glutathione; Ca-calcium; LPO-lipid peroxidation; SOD-superoxide dismutase; OH-hydroxyl radicals; OFR-oxygen free radicals.

Table 3. Summarized pharmacological effects of Ethyl gallate and its mechanisms

Ethyl gallate (EG)	Mechanism of action
Anticancer effect	↑Antioxidant status ↑ROS production ↑Upregulation of Bax protein for apoptosis
Septic shock	↓Heart rate ↓Troponin T ↓Inhibit H_2O_2 signaling pathway
Anti-inflammatory activity	↓Leukocyte adhesion molecules through cytokine-induced NF-κB activation ↓IL-1α and TNF-α

ROS-reactive oxygen species; H_2O_2-Hydrogen peroxide; NF-nuclear factor; IL-interleukin, TNF-tumor necrosis factor.

We in our previous report have also mentioned that the compound will be an important source for the food and pharmacological industries with respect to the use of the compound as an antioxidant and a health-related drugs.

Over the past few years, numerous patents have been filed and published relating to the scientific advances in the use of green tea and its phenolic compounds like EGCG, GA and EG. Considering all the aspects of research, gallates and their derivatives or analogs could be developed into future drugs for chemoprevention, chemosensitization and cancer interception.

References

Aggarwal, BB; Shishodia, S. Molecular targets of dietary agents for prevention and therapy of cancer. *Biochemical Pharmacology*, 2006, 71, 1397-421.

Ahmed, S; Marotte, H; Kwan, K; Ruth, JH; Campbell, PL; Rabquer, BJ. Epigallocatechin-3-gallate inhibits IL-6 synthesis and suppresses trans signaling by enhancing solublegp130 production. *Proceedings of National Academy of Sciences. U S A*, 2008, 105, 14692-14697.

Ahmed, S; Pakozdi, A; Koch, AE. Regulation of interleukin-1beta-induced chemokine production and matrix metalloproteinase 2 activation by epigallocatechin-3-gallate in rheumatoid arthritis synovial fibroblasts. *Arthritis and Rheumatism*, 2006, 54, 2393-2401.

Ahn, HY; Hadizadeh, KR; Seul, C; Yun, YP; Vetter, H; Sachinidis, A. Epigallocathechin-3-gallate selectively inhibits the PDGF-BB-induced intracellular signaling transduction pathway in vascular smooth muscle cells and inhibits transformation of *sis*-transfected NIH 3T3 fibroblasts and human glioblastoma cells. *Molecular Biology of the Cell*, 1999, 10, 1093-1104.

Ahn, WS; Yoo, J; Huh, SW; Kim, CK; Lee, JM; Namkoong, SE. Protective effects of green tea extracts (polyphenon E and EGCG) on human cervical lesions. *European Journal of Cancer Prevention*, 2003, 12, 383-390.

Avramovich-Tirosh, Y; Reznichenko, L; Mit, T; Zheng, H; Fridkin, M; Weinreb, O; Mandel, S; Youdim, MB. Neurorescue activity, APP regulation and amyloid-beta peptide reduction by novel multi-functional brain permeable iron- chelating- antioxidants, M-30 and green tea polyphenol, EGCG. *Current Alzheimer Research*, 2007, 4, 403-411.

Azam, S; Hadi, N; Khan, NU; Hadi, SM. Prooxidant property of green tea polyphenols epicatechin and epigallocatechin-3-gallate: implications for anticancer properties. *Toxicology in Vitro*, 2004, 18, 555-561.

Bai, Y; Yanyan, W; Maoquan, L; Xueqing, X; Min, S; Huansheng, T. Green tea epigallocatechin-3-gallate (EGCG) promotes neural progenitor cell proliferation and sonic hedgehog pathway activation during adult hippocampal neurogenesis. *Molecular Nutrition & Food Research*, 2012, 56, 1292.

Bastianetto, S; Yao, ZX; Papadopoulos, V; Quirion, R. Neuroprotective effects of green and black teas and their catechin gallate esters against beta-amyloid-induced toxicity. *European Journal of Neuroscience*, 2006, 23, 55-64.

Beal, MF. Aging, energy and oxidative stress in neurodegenerative diseases. *Annals of Neurology*, 1995, 38, 357-366.

Bettuzzi, S; Brausi, M; Rizzi, F; Peracchia, G; Corti, A. Chemoprevention of Human Prostate Cancer by Oral Administration of green Tea Catechins in Volunteers with High-Grade Prostate Intraepithelial Neoplasia: A Preliminary Report from a One-Year Proof-of-Principle Study. *American Association for Cancer Research*, 2006, 66, 1234-1240.

Biemond, P; Swaak, AJ; Beindroff, CM; Koster, JM. Superoxide dependent and independent mechanisms of iron mobilization from ferritin by xanthine oxidase; implications for oxygen radical induced tissue, destruction during ischemia and inflammation. *Biochemical Journal*, 1986, 239, 169-173.

Choi, JY; Park, CS; Kim, DJ; Cho, MH; Jin, BK; Pie, JE. Prevention of nitric oxide-mediated 1-methyl-4-phenyl-1,2,3,6-tetrahydropyridine-induced Parkinson's disease in mice by tea phenolic epigallocatechin 3-gallate. *Neurotoxicology,* 2007, 23, 367-374.

Choi, YT; Jung, CH; Lee, SR; Bae, JH; Baek, WK; Suh, MH; Park, J; Park, CW; Suh, SI. The green tea polyphenol (-)-epigallocatechin gallate attenuates beta-amyloid-induced neurotoxicity in cultured hippocampal neurons. *Life Sciences*, 2001, 70, 603-614.

Chung, JY; Huang, C; Meng, X; Dong, Z; Yang, CS. Inhibition of activator protein 1activity and cell growth by purified green tea and black tea polyphenols in H-*ras* transformed cells: structure-activity relationship and mechanisms involved. *Cancer Research*, 1999, 59, 4610-4617.

Coskun, O; Kanter, M; Korkmaz, A; Oter, S. Quercetin, a flavonoid antioxidant, prevents and protects streptozotocin-induced oxidative stress and beta-cell damage in rat pancreas. *Pharmacological Research*, 2005, 51, 117-123.

Das, A; Banik, NL; Ray, SK. Flavonoids activated caspases for apoptosis in human glioblastoma T98G and U87MG cells but not in human normal astrocytes. *Cancer*, 2009, 116, 164-176.

Du, GJ; Wang, CZ; Qi, LW; Zhang, ZY; Calway, T; He, TC; Du, W; Yuan, CS. The synergistic apoptotic interaction of panaxadiol and epigallocatechin gallate in human colorectal cancer cells. *Phytotherapy Research*. 2012, 22, 272-277.

Dwibedy, P; Dey, GR; Naik, DB; Kishore, K; Moorthy, PN. Pulse radiolysis studies on redox reaction of gallic acid: one electron oxidation of gallic acid by hallic acid OH adduct. *Physical Chemistry Chemical Physics*, 1999, 1, 1915-1918.

Fahn, S; Cohen, G. The oxidant stress hypothesis in Parkinson's disease: evidence supporting it. *Annals of Neurology*, 1992, 32, 804-812.

Fang, YZ; Yang, S; Wu, G. Free radicals, antioxidants, and nutrition. *Nutrition*, 2005, 18, 872-879.

Fujiki, H; Suganuma, M; Okabe, S; Sueoka, E; Sueoka, N; Fujimoto, N. Cancer prevention with green tea and monitoring by a new biomarker, hnRNP B1. *Mutation Research*, 2001, 299-304.

Fujiki, H; Suganuma, M; Okabe, S; Sueoka, E; Suga, K; Imai, K. Mechanistic findings of green tea as cancer preventive for humans. *Proceedings of the Society Experimental Biology and Medicine*, 1999, 220, 225-228.

Gassen, M; Gross, A; Youdim, MB. Apomorphine enantiomers protect cultured pheochromocytoma (PC12) cells from oxidative stress induced by H_2O_2 and 6-hydroxydopamine. *Movement Disorders*, 1998, 13, 242-248.

Giftson, SJ; Jayanthi, S; Nalini, N. Chemopreventive efficacy of gallic acid, an antioxidant and anticarcinogenic polyphenol, against 1,2-dimethyl hydrazine induced rat colon carcinogenesis. *Investigational New Drugs*, 2010, 28, 251-259.

Gotes, J; Kasian, K; Jacobs, H; Cheng, ZQ; Mink, SN. Benefits of ethyl gallate versus norepinephrine in the treatment of cardiovascular collapse in *Pseudomonas aeruginosa* septic shock in dogs. *Critical Care Medicine*, 2012, 40, 560-572.

Guo, S; Bezard, E; Zhao, B. Protective effect of green tea polyphenols on the SH-SY5Y cells against 6-OHDA induced apoptosis through ROS-NO pathway. *Free Radic Biology and Medicine*, 2005, 39, 682-695.

Gupta, S; Ahmad, N; Mukhtar, H. Prostate cancer chemoprevention by green tea. Urologic Oncology: *Seminars and Original Investigations*, 1999, 17, 70-76.

Gupta, S; Hussain, T; Mukhtar, H. Molecular pathway for epigallocatechin-3-gallate-induced cell cycle arrest and apoptosis of human prostate carcinoma cells. *Archives of Biochemistry and Biophysics*, 2003, 410, 177-185.

Hall, G; Le, TTT; Stanford, JB; Sugden, JK. Hydroxyl radical scavenging by ethyl gallate and related compounds: a method for rapid evaluation. *Pharmaceutica Acta Helvetiae*, 1996, 71, 221-224.

Halliwell, B; Gutteridge, JMC. Free Radicals in Biology and Medicine1st ed.Clarendon Press, Oxford. 1985.

Halliwell, B; Vitamin, C. Antioxidant or pro-oxidant *in vivo*? *Free Radical Research*, 1996, 25, 439-454.

Hamza, A; Zhan, CG. How can (-)-epigallocatechin gallate from green tea prevent HIV-1 infection? Mechanistic insights from computational modeling and the implication for rational design of anti-HIV-1 entry inhibitors. *The Journal of Physical Chemistry*, 2006, 110, 2910–2917.

Han, MK. Epigallocatechin gallate, a constituent of green tea, suppresses cytokine-induced pancreatic beta-cell damage. *Experimental and Molecular Medicine*, 2003, 35, 136-139.

Hara, Y; Fujino, M; Takeuchi, M; Li, XK. Green-tea polyphenol (-)-epigallocatechin-3-gallate provides resistance to apoptosis in isolated islets. *Journal of Hepatobiliary Pancreatic Surgery*, 2007, 14, 493-497.

Hastak, K; Gupta, S; Ahmad, N; Agarwal, MK; Agarwal, ML; Mukhtar, H. Role of p53 and NF-kappaB in epigallocatechin-3-gallate-induced apoptosis of LNCaP cells. *Oncogene*, 2003, 22, 4851-4859.

Heijden, VDCA; Janssen, PJ; Strik, JJ. Toxicology of gallates: a review and evaluation. *Food and Chemical Toxicology*, 1986, 24, 1067-1070.

Higdon, JV; Frei, B. Tea catechins and polyphenols: health effects, metabolism, and antioxidant functions. *Critial Reviews in Food Science and Nutrition*, 2003, 43, 89-143.

Hsieh, TC; Wu, JM. Targeting CWR22Rv1 prostate cancer cell proliferation and gene expression by combinations of the phytochemicals EGCG, genistein, and quercetin. *Anticancer Research,* 2009, 29, 4025-4032.

Hu, G; Han, C; Chen, J. Inhibition of oncogene expression by green tea and (_)-epigallocatechin gallate in mice. *Nutrition and Cancer*, 1995, 24, 203-209.

Igosheva, N; Lorz, C; O'Conner, E; Glover, V; Mehmer, H. Isatin, an endogenous monoamine oxide inhibitor, triggers a dose- and time-dependent switch from apoptosis to necrosis in human neuroblastoma cells. *Neurochemistry Interntional*, 2005, 47, 216-224.

Iso, H; Date, C; Wakai, K; Fukui, M; Tamakoshi, A. The relationship between green tea and total caffeine intake and risk for self-reported type 2 diabetes among Japanese adults. *Ann. Intern. Med.*, 2006, 144, 554-562.

Jadon, A; Bhadauria, M; Shukla, S. Protective effect of *Termanalia belerica* Roxb. and gallic aid against carbon tetrachloride induced damage in albino rats. *Journal of Ethnopharmacology*, 2007, 109, 214-218.

Jenner, P; Olanow, CW. Understanding cell death in Parkinson's disease. *Annals of Neurology*, 1998, 44, 72-84.

Jeong, JH; Kim, HJ; Lee, TJ; Kim, MK; Park, ES; Choi, BS. Epigallocatechin 3-gallate attenuates neuronal damage induced by 3-hydroxykynurenine. *Toxicology*, 2004, *195*, 53-60.

Kalaivani, T; Rajasekaran, C; Mathew, L. Free radical scavenging, cytotoxic, and hemolytic activities of an active antioxidant compound ethyl gallate from leaves of *Acacia nilotica* (L.) wild. Ex. Delile subsp. Indica (Benth.) Brenan. *Journal of Food Science*, 2011, 76, 144-149.

Katiyar, SK; Mukhtar, H. Tea consumption and cancer. *World Review of Nutriton and Dietetics*, 1996, 79: 154-184.

Kelsey, NA; Wilkins, HM; Linseman, DA. Nutraceutical Antioxidants as Novel Neuroprotective Agents. *Molecules*, 2010, 15, 7792-7814.

Kim, IB; Kim, DY; Lee, SJ; Sun, MJ; Lee, MS; Li, H. Inhibition of IL-8 production by green tea polyphenols in human nasal fibroblasts and A549 epithelial cells. *Biological and Pharmaceutical Bulletin*, 2006, 29, 1120-1125.

Kim, WH; Song, HO; Choi, HJ; Bang, HI, Choi, DY; Park, H. Ethyl Gallate Induces Apoptosis of HL-60 Cells by Promoting the Expression of Caspases-8, -9, -3, Apoptosis-Inducing Factor and Endonuclease G. *Internatinal Journal of Molecular Science*, 2012, 13, 11912-11922.

Kohlmeier, L. Has the tea been ruined? *British Journal of Nutrition*, 1997, 78, 1-3.

Kumaran, VS; Arulmathi; Kalaiselvi, P. Senescence mediated redox imbalance in cardiac tissue: Antioxidant rejuvenating potential of green tea. *Nutrition,* 2009, 25, 847-854.

Lambert, JD; Elias, RJ. The antioxidant and pro-oxidant activities of green tea polyphenols: a role in cancer prevention. *Archives in Biochemistry and Biophysics,* 2010, 501, 65-72.

Lee, MJ; Maliakal, P; Chen, L; Meng, X; Bondoc, FY; Prabhu, S; Lambert, G; Mohr, S; Yang, CS. Pharmacokinetics of tea catechins after ingestion of green tea and (-)-epigallocatechin-3-gallate by humans: formation of different metabolites and individual variability. *Cancer Epidemiology Biomarkers and Prevntion*, 2002, 11, 1025-1032.

Lee, SY; Kim, CY; Lee, JJ; Jung, JG; Lee, SR. Effects of delayed administration of (_)-epigallocatechin gallate, a green tea polyphenol on the changes in polyamine levels and neuronal damage after transient forebrain ischemia in gerbils. *Brain Research Bulletin*, 2003, 61, 399-406.

Leise, EM; Mulloney, B. The osmium-ethyl gallate procedure is superior to silver impregnations for mapping neuronal pathways. *Brain Research,* 1986, 367, 265-272.

Leone, M; Zhai, D; Sareth, S; Kitada, S; Reed, JC; Pellecchia, M. Cancer prevention by tea polyphenols is linked to their direct inhibition of antiapoptotic Bcl-2-family proteins. *Cancer Research*, 2003, 63, 8118-8121.

Levites, Y.; Amit, T.; Youdim, M.B.; Mandel, S. Involvement of protein kinase C activation and cell survival/ cell cycle genes in green tea polyphenol (-)-epigallocatechin 3-gallate neuroprotective action. *Journal of Biological Chemistry*. 2002, *277*, 30574-30580.

Levites, Y; Weinreb, O; Maor, G; Youdim, MB; Mandel, S. Green tea polyphenol (_)-epigallocatechin-3-gallate prevents N-methyl-4-phenyl-1,2,3,6-tetrahydropyridine-induced dopaminergic neurodegeneration. *Journal of Neurochemistry*, 2001,78, 1073-1082.

Li, S; Hattori, T; Kodama, EN. Epigallocatechin gallate inhibits the HIV reverse transcription step. *Antiviral chemistry and chemotherapy*, 2011, 21, 239-243.

Lin, JK; Liang, YC; Lin-Shiau, SY. Cancer chemoprevention by tea polyphones through mitotic signal transduction blockade. *Biochemical Pharmacology,* 1999, 58, 911-915.

Lu, LH; Lee, SS; Huang, HC. Epigallocatechin suppression of proliferation of vascular smooth muscle cells: correlation with c-*jun* and JNK. *British Journal of Pharmacology*, 1998, 124, 1227–1237.

Ma, J; Luo, XD; Protiva, P; Yang, H; Ma, C; Basile, MJ; Weinstein, IB; Kennely, EJ. Bioactive novel polyphenols from the fruit of *Manilkara zapota* (Sapodilla), *Journal of Natural Products*, 2003, 7, 983-986.

Mandel, S; Reznichenko, L; Amit, T; Youdim, MB. Green tea polyphenol (_)-epigallocatechin-3-gallate protects rat PC12 cells from apoptosis induced by serum withdrawal independent of P13-Akt pathway. *Neurotoxicity Research*, 2003, 5, 419-424.

Martinez, SE; Willett, WC; Ascherio, A; Manson, JE; Leitzmann, MF; Stampfer, MJ; Hu, FB. Coffee consumption and risk for type 2 diabetes mellitus. *Annls of Internal Medicine*, 2004, 140, 1-8.

McCord, JM. Free radicals and myocardial ischemia: overview. *Free Radical Biology and Medicine*, 1988, 4, 9-14.

Mohr, S; Yang, CS. Pharmacokinetics of tea catechins after ingestion of green tea and (-)-epigallocatechin-3-gallate by humans: formation of different metabolites and individual variability. *Cancer Epidemiology Biomarkers and Prevention* 11:1025-1032.

Monagas, M; Suarez, R; Gomez-Cordoves, C; Bartolome, B. Simultaneous determination of nonanthocyanin phenolic compounds in red wines by HPLC-DAD/ESI-MS. *American Journal of Enology and Viticulture,* 2005, 56, 139-147.

Mukhtar, H; Ahmad, N. Tea polyphenols: prevention of cancer and optimizing health. *The American Journal of Clinical Nutrition,* 2000, 71, S1698-702.

Murase, T; Kume, N; Hase, T; Shibuya, Y; Nishizawa, Y; Tokimitsu, I; Kita, T. Gallates Inhibit Cytokine-Induced Nuclear Translocation of NF-κB and Expression of Leukocyte Adhesion Molecules in Vascular Endothelial Cells. *Arteriosclerosis, Thrombosis, and Vascular Biology,* 1999, 19, 1412-1420.

Nakazato, T; Ito, K; Ikeda, Y; Kizaki, M. Green tea component, catechin, induces apoptosis of human malignant B cells via production of reactive oxygen species. *Clinical Cancer Research*, 2005, 11, 6040-6049.

Niho, N; Shibutani, M; Tamura, T; Toyoda, K; Uneyama, C; Takahashi, N; Hirose, M. Subchronic toxicity study of gallic acid by oral administration in F344 rats. *Food and Chemical Toxicology*, 2001, 39, 1063-1070.

Nishikawa, T; Nakajima, T; Moriguchi, M; Jo, M; Sekoguchi, S; Ishii, M. A green tea polyphenol, epigalocatechin-3-gallate, induces apoptosis of human hepatocellular carcinoma, possibly through inhibition of Bcl-2 family proteins. *Journal of Hepatology*, 2006, 44, 1074-1082.

Ohigashi, H. Food Factors: Proceedings of the 2nd International Conference on Food Factors. IOS Press, 2000.

Okabe, S; Ochiai, Y; Aida, M; Park, K; Kim, SJ; Nomura, T; Suganuma, M; Fujiki, H. Mechanistic aspects of green tea as a cancer preventive: effect of components on human stomach cancer cell lines. *Japanese Journal of Cancer Research,* 1999, 90, 733-739.

Park, D; Jeon, JH; Shin, S; Joo, SS; Kang, DH; Moon, SH; Jang, MJ; Cho, YM; Kim, JW; Ji, HJ; Ahn, B; Oh, KW; Kim, YB. Green tea extract increases cyclophosphamide-induced teratogenesis by modulating the expression of cytochrome P-450 mRNA. *Reproductive toxicology*, 2009, 27, 79-84.

Pereira, DM; Valentalo, P; Pereira, JA; Andrade, PB. Phenols: from chemistry to biology. *Molecules*, 2009, 14, 2202-2211.

Philips, BJ; Coyle, CH; Morrisroe, SN; Chancellor, MB; Yoshimura, N. Induction of apoptosis in human bladder cancer cells by green tea catechins. *Biomedical Research*, 2009, 30, 207-215.

Potenza, MA; Marasciulo, FL; Tarquinio, M; Tiravanti, E; Colantuono, G; Federici, A; Kim, JA; Quon, MJ; Montagnani, M. EGCG, a green tea polyphenol, improves endothelial function and insulin sensitivity, reduces blood pressure, and protects against myocardial I/R injury in SHR. *American Journal of Physiology Endocrinology and Metabolism*, 2007, 292, 1378-1387.

Potter, DK; Fuller, HL. Metabolic fate of dietary tannins in chickens. *Journal of Nutrition,* 1968, 96, 187-191.

Punithavathi, VR; Prince, PSM; Kumar, R; Selvakumari, J. Antihyperglycaemic, antilipid peroxidative and antioxidant effects of gallic acid on streptozotocin induced diabetic Wistar rats. *Endocrine Pharmacology*, 2011, 650, 465-471.

Qi, XL; Xiu, J; Shan, KR; Xiao, Y; Gu, R; Liu, RY; Guan, ZZ. Oxidative stress induced by beta-amyloid peptide (1-42) is involved in the altered composition of cellar membrane lipids and the decreased expression of nicotinic receptors in human SH-SY5Y neuroblastoma cells. *Neurochemistry International*, 2005, 46, 613-621.

Qiao, Y; Cao, J; Xie, L; Shi, X. Cell growth inhibition and gene expression regulation by (-)-epigallocatechin-3-gallate in human cervical cancer cells. *Archives of Pharmacal Research*, 2009, 32, 1309-1315.

Rezai-Zadeh, K; Arendash, GW; Hou, H; Fernandez, F; Jensen, M; Runfeldt, M; Shytle, RD; Tan, J. Green tea epigallocatechin-3-gallate (EGCG) reduces beta-amyloid mediated cognitive impairment and modulates tau pathology in Alzheimer transgenic mice. *Brain Research*, 2008, 1214, 177-187.

Rosengren, A; Dotevall, A; Wilhelmsen, L; Thelle, D; Johansson, S. Coffee and incidence of diabetes in Swedish women: a prospective 18-year follow-up study. *Journal of Internal Medicine*, 2004, 255, 89-95.

Saeki, K; You, A; Isemura, M; Abe, I; Seki, T; Noguchi, H. Apoptosis inducing activity of lipid derivatives of gallic acid. *Biological Pharmaceutical Bulletin,* 2000, 23, 1391-1394.

Saroja, M; Balasenthil, S; Nagini, S. Tissue lipid peroxidation and glutathione dependant enzyme status in patients with oral squamous cell carcinoma. *Cell Biochemistry and Function,* 1999, 17, 213-216.

Sartippour, MR; Shao, ZM; Heber, D; Beatty, P; Zhang, L; Liu, C. Green tea inhibits vascular endothelial growth factor (VEGF) induction in human breast cancer cells. *Journal of Nutrition,* 2002, 132, 2307-2311.

Scalbert, A; Williamson, G. Dietary intake and bioavailability of polyphenols. *Journal of Nutrition,* 2000, 130, 2073S-2085S.

Schroeder, EK; Kelsey, NA; Doyle, J; Breed, E; Bouchard, RJ; Loucks, FA; Harbison, RA; Linseman, DA. Green tea epigallocatechin 3-gallate accumulates in mitochondria and displays a selective antiapoptotic effect against inducers of mitochondrial oxidative stress in neurons. *Antioxidants and Redox Signalling,* 2009, 11, 469-480.

Shahrzad, S; Bitsch, I. Determination of gallic acid and its metabolites in human plasma and urine by HPLC. *Journal of Chromatography B,* 1998, 705, 87-95.

Shahrzad, S; Bitsch, I. Determination of some pharmacologically active phenolic acids in juices by high-performance liquid chromatography. *Journal of Chromatography,* 1996, 16, 223–231.

Shankar, S; Suthakar, G; Srivastava, RK. Epigallocatechin-3-gallate inhibits cell cycle and induces apoptosis in pancreatic cancer. *Frontiers in Biosciences,* 2007, 12, 5039-5051.

Singh, BN; Shankar, S; Srivastava, RK. catechin, epigallocatechin-3-gallate (EGCG): Mechanisms, perspectives and clinical applications. *Biochemical Pharmacology,* 2011, 82, 1807-1821.

Singh, J; Rai, GK; Upadhyay, AK; Kumar, R; Singh, KP. Antioxidant phytochemicals in tomato (*Lycopersicon esculentum*) *The Indian Journal of Agricultural Sciences,* 2004, 74, 3-5.

Son, S; Lewis, BA. Free radical scavenging and antioxidative activity of caffeic acid amide and ester analogues: structure activity relationship. *Journal Agricultural Food Chemistry,* 2002, 50, 468-472.

Srividhya, R; Jyothilakshmi, V; Arulmathi, K; Senthilkumaran, V; Kalaiselvi, P. Attenuation of senescence-induced oxidative exacerbations in aged rat brain by (_)-epigallocatechin-3-gallate. *International Journal of Developmental Neuroscience,* 2008,2 6, 217-23.

Staff, IMM. Using epigallocatechin gallate (EGCG) to modulate Dyrk1A and APP and evaluate its impact on cognitive performance in patients with Down syndrome (DS). 7, 2013.

Stull, ND; Polan, DP; Iacovitti L. Antioxidant compounds protect dopamine neurons from death due to oxidative stress *in vitro*. *Brain Research*, 2002, 931, 181-185.

Sutherland, BA; Rahman, RM; Appleton, I. Mechanisms of action of green tea catechins, with a focus on ischemia-induced neurodegeneration. The *Journal of Nutritional Biochemistry*, 2006, 17, 291-306.

Sutherland, BA; Shaw, OM; Clarkson, AN; Jackson, DN; Sammut, IA; Appleton, I. Neuroprotective effects of (-)-epigallocatechin gallate following hypoxia-ischemia-induced brain damage: novel mechanisms of action. *The FASEB Journal*, 2005, 19, 258-260.

Swezey, RR; Aldridge, DE; LeValley, SE; Crowell, JA; Hara, Y; Green, CE. Absorption, Tissue Distribution and Elimination of 4-(3H)-Epigallocatechin Gallate in Beagle Dogs. *Toxicology*, 2003, 22, 187-193.

Takagaki, A; Nanjo, F. Metabolism of (-)-epigallocatechin gallate by rat intestinal flora. *Journal of Agricultural Food Chemistry*, 2010, 27, 58, 1313-13121.

Tsuneki, H; Ishizuka, M; Terasawa, M; Wu, JB; Sasaoka, T; Kimura, I. Effect of green tea on blood glucose levels and serum proteomic patterns in diabetic (db/db) mice and on glucose metabolism in healthy humans. *BMC Pharmacol*, 2004, 4, 18.

Ullmann, U; Haller, J; Decourt, JP; Girault, N; Girault, J; Richard-Caudron, AS; Pineau, B; Weber, P. A single ascending dose study of epigallocatechin gallate in healthy volunteers. *Journal of International Medicinal Research*, 2003, 31, 88-101.

Van Dam, RM; Feskens, EJ. Coffee consumption and risk of type 2 diabetes mellitus. *Lancet,* 2002, 360, 1477-1478.

Watanabe, A; Oshima, Y. Metabolism of gallic acid and tea catechin by rabbit. *Agricultural and Biological Chemistry*, 1965, 29, 90-93.

Weetall, HH. Enzymatic synthesis of gallic acid esters. *European Patent,* 137601, 1985.

Wei, IH; Wu, YC; Wen, CY; Shieh, JY. Green tea polyphenol (_)-epigallocatechin gallate attenuates the neuronal NADPH-d/nNOS expression in the nodose ganglion of acute hypoxic rats. *Brain Research*, 2004, 999, 73-80.

Weinreb, O; Mandel, S; Youdim, MB. Gene and protein expression profiles of anti- and pro-apoptotic actions of dopamine, R-apomorphine, green tea polyphenol epigallocatechine-3-gallate, and melatonin. *Annals of New York Academy of Sciences,* 2003, 993, 351-361.

Weinbreb, O; Amit, T; Mandel, S; Youdim, MBH. Neuroprotective molecular mechanisms of (-)-epigallocatechin-3-gallate: a reflective outcome of its antioxidant, iron chelating and neuritogenic properties. *Genes and Nutrition*, 2009, 4, 283-296.

Williamson, MP; McCormick, TG; Nance, CL; Shearer, WT. Epigallocatechin gallate, the main polyphenol in green tea, binds to the T-cell receptor, CD4: Potential for HIV-1 therapy. *The Journal of Allergy and Clinical Immunology*, 2006, 118, 1369–74.

Wolfram, S; Raederstorff, D; Preller, M; Wang, Y; Teixeira, SR; Riegger, C; Weber, P. Epigallocatechin gallate supplementation alleviates diabetes in rodents. *Journal of Nutrition*, 2006, 136, 2512-2518.

Yamaguchi, K; Honda, M; Ikigai, H; Hara, Y; Shimamura, T. Inhibitory effects of (-)-epigallocatechin gallate on the life cycle of human immunodeficiency virus type 1 (HIV-1). *Antiviral Research*, 2002, 53, 19–34.

Yang, CS; Kim, S; Yang, GY; Lee, MJ; Liao, J; Chung, JY; Ho, CT. Inhibition of carcinogenesis by tea: bioavailability of tea polyphenols and mechanisms of actions. *Proceedings of the Society for Experimental Biology and Medicine*, 1999, 220, 213-217.

Yu, GP; Hsieh, CC; Wang, LY; Yu, SZ; Li, XL; Jin, TH. Green-tea consumption and risk of stomach cancer: a population-based case-control study in Shanghai, China. *Cancer Causes Control*, 1995, 6, 532–538.

Yun, HJ; Yoo, WH; Han, MK; Lee, YR; Kim, JS; Lee, SI. Epigallocatechin-3-gallate suppresses TNF-alpha -induced production of MMP-1 and -3 in rheumatoid arthritis synovial fibroblasts. *Rheumatology International*, 2008, 29, 23-29.

Zhang, G; Matsumoto, S; Hyon, SH; Qualley, SA; Upshaw, L; Strong, DM; Reems, JA. Polyphenol, an extract of green tea, increases culture recovery rates of isolated islets from non-human primate pancreata and marginal grade human pancreata. *Cell Transplant*, 2004, 13, 145-152.

Zhang, Z; Liao, L; Moore, J; Wu, T; Wang, Z. Antioxidant phenolic compounds from walnut kernels. *Food Chemry,* 2009, 113, 160-165.

Zong, L; Inoue, M; Nose, M; Kojima, K; Sakaguchi, N; Isuzugawa, K; Takeda, T; Ogihara, Y. Metabolic fate of gallic acid orally administered to rats. *Biol. Pharm. Bull*, 1999, 22, 326–329.

Index

G

H

J

K

L

M

N

O

P

T